NEW YORK

D. Van Nostrand Company, Inc., 250 Fourth Avenue, New York 3

TORONTO

D. Van Nostrand Company (Canada), Ltd., 25 Hollinger Rd., Toronto

LONDON

Macmillan & Company, Ltd., St. Martin's Street, London, W.C. 2

PRINTED IN THE UNITED STATES OF AMERICA

Speech and Hearing
in Communication

THE BELL TELEPHONE LABORATORIES SERIES

PROBABILITY AND ITS ENGINEERING USES. *By* THORNTON C. FRY.

ELEMENTARY DIFFERENTIAL EQUATIONS. *By* THORNTON C. FRY. Second Edition.

TRANSMISSION CIRCUITS FOR TELEPHONIC COMMUNICATION. METHODS OF ANALYSIS AND DESIGN. *By* K. S. JOHNSON.

TRANSMISSION NETWORKS AND WAVE FILTERS. *By* T. E. SHEA.

ECONOMIC CONTROL OF QUALITY OF MANUFACTURED PRODUCT. *By* W. A. SHEWHART.

ELECTROMECHANICAL TRANSDUCERS AND WAVE FILTERS. *By* WARREN P. MASON. Second Edition.

RHOMBIC ANTENNA DESIGN. *By* A. E. HARPER.

POISSON'S EXPONENTIAL BINOMIAL LIMIT. *By* E. C. MOLINA.

ELECTROMAGNETIC WAVES. *By* S. A. SCHELKUNOFF.

NETWORK ANALYSIS AND FEEDBACK AMPLIFIER DESIGN. *By* HENDRICK W. BODE.

SERVOMECHANISMS. *By* LeROY A. MacCOLL.

QUARTZ CRYSTALS FOR ELECTRICAL CIRCUITS. *By* R. A. HEISING.

CAPACITORS—THEIR USE IN ELECTRONIC CIRCUITS. *By* M. BROTHERTON.

FOURIER INTEGRALS FOR PRACTICAL APPLICATIONS. *By* GEORGE A. CAMPBELL AND RONALD M. FOSTER.

VISIBLE SPEECH. *By* RALPH K. POTTER, GEORGE A. KOPP, AND HARRIET C. GREEN

APPLIED MATHEMATICS FOR ENGINEERS AND SCIENTISTS. *By* S. A. SCHELKUNOFF.

EARTH CONDUCTION EFFECTS IN TRANSMISSION SYSTEMS. *By* ERLING D. SUNDE.

RADAR SYSTEMS AND COMPONENTS. *By* MEMBERS OF THE STAFF OF THE BELL TELEPHONE LABORATORIES; Introduction by M. J. KELLY.

THEORY AND DESIGN OF ELECTRON BEAMS. *By* J. R. PIERCE.

PIEZOELECTRIC CRYSTALS AND THEIR APPLICATION TO ULTRASONICS. *By* WARREN P. MASON.

MICROWAVE ELECTRONICS. *By* JOHN C. SLATER.

PRINCIPLES AND APPLICATIONS OF WAVEGUIDE TRANSMISSION. *By* GEORGE C. SOUTHWORTH.

TRAVELING-WAVE TUBES. *By* J. R. PIERCE.

ELECTRONS AND HOLES IN SEMICONDUCTORS. *By* WILLIAM SHOCKLEY.

FERROMAGNETISM. *By* RICHARD M. BOZORTH.

THE DESIGN OF SWITCHING CIRCUITS. *By* WILLIAM KEISTER, ALASTAIR E. RITCHIE, AND SETH H. WASHBURN.

SPEECH AND HEARING IN COMMUNICATION. *By* HARVEY FLETCHER. Second Edition.

Speech and Hearing in Communication

By

HARVEY FLETCHER, PH.D.

Formerly Acoustical Research Director,
Bell Telephone Laboratories, Inc.

D. VAN NOSTRAND COMPANY, INC.

TORONTO   NEW YORK   LONDON

PREFACE

About 35 years ago the Research Laboratories of the Bell Telephone System started a comprehensive research program on speech and hearing, and its relation to the design of telephone systems. It was apparent that great advantages would come if one could describe accurately every part of the system, namely (1) the talker, (2) the microphone, (3) the electrical transmission line, (4) the telephone receiver (head phone or terminating loud-speaker), and (5) the listener.

The attack was first launched most vigorously on the constitution of speech issuing from the mouth of a typical talker to establish a reasonable description of speech; then one can find to what extent small imperfections and variations of the speech sounds affect the ability of the listener to recognize what the talker said. The work included a study of both normal and abnormal organs of speech and hearing.

As the work progressed it became apparent that better and more precise instruments must be developed than were available, and a considerable part of the effort has been devoted to the matter of securing devices which would convert sound waves into electrical form and reconvert them again to sound with the least possible distortion. Out of this have come unexpected rewards to the telephone and phonograph arts, for as these devices were perfected they found very immediate application to the great advantage of those industries.

One of the most difficult phases of the investigation has been that relating to the degree of precision with which the mind can differentiate and interpret sounds that are very nearly alike. This does not lend itself so readily to analysis and measurement as does the purely mechanical operation of the ear itself. The approach to this problem has been through the use of essentially perfect reproduction systems which could be deteriorated step by step until their faults became noticeable to the observer. This set a limit to the degree of perfection which could ever be demanded in the apparatus. When the deterioration was carried somewhat further, an estimate could be obtained of the degree of dissatisfaction presented by certain measured imperfections, and hence a practical basis of choice of a reasonably perfect system could be established.

Then after 15 years of such research work, a report was made to the public in the form of my book "Speech and Hearing" (published in 1929). Since its publication there has been a wealth of new information bearing upon this problem. Some of this information has come from the Bell Telephone Laboratories, but many other laboratories have made noteworthy contributions.

This present book deals with all of this information, and presents the subject, "Speech and Hearing in Communication", as an integrated whole. Chapters 15, 16, 17, and 18 summarize about thirty years of work with the Bell Telephone Laboratories by various groups on the perception of speech sounds by listeners having normal hearing. They present it in the form of a method of calculating the articulation score expected by any talker-listener pair using any kind of system, which may be immersed in any kind of noise. In chapter 19 this is extended to the case of deafened listeners, and it is shown what the fundamental criteria must be for designing a hearing aid to be used by a deafened person having any kind and degree of deafness.

The last chapter deals with compensation cases due to injured hearing. The principles developed in the book are applied to this problem. A simple method is evolved for obtaining the effective hearing loss. It takes into account the hearing loss in both ears. This effective hearing loss is then related to the percent compensation that such a deafened person should receive compared to that which should be received by a totally deafened person.

Particular attention should be called to the material in chapter 14 which deals with the dynamics of the middle and inner ear. This is much more mathematical than any of the other chapters. It develops equations from which one can determine the movements of the various parts of the hearing mechanism when a sound is impressed upon the ear drum. It shows that the results obtained from these equations agree with the splendid experimental work of Békésy so that one can say with considerable assurance that the dynamical behavior of the hearing mechanism is now well known.

CONTENTS

INTRODUCTION

The processes of speaking and hearing are very intimately related, so much so that I have often said that we speak with our ears. We can listen without speaking but cannot speak without listening. People who are born without hearing learn to talk only with the greatest difficulty, and none of them has yet succeeded in producing what most of us would call normal speech.

There are many aspects to the perception of speech, but the principal ones may be divided into five groups. First and foremost is the process that enables one to recognize the speech sounds which one hears, which will be called the interpretation aspect. Second, one can perceive whether the speech sound which comes to the ear is loud or soft—the loudness aspect. Third, one can perceive whether the pitch of each speech sound is high or low—the pitch aspect. Fourth, one can perceive the quality of the speech, whether it is harsh or pleasing, rich or drab, animated or dull—the quality aspect. Fifth, one can perceive whether the speech sounds are spoken very rapidly and excitedly or slowly and deliberately—the tempo aspect. It is the purpose of this book to discuss in detail these various aspects of the perception of speech with particular emphasis on the interpretation aspect and to determine how these aspects are changed as the three elements of a communication system; namely, the speaker, the listener, and the transmission system are changed. To discuss this in a quantitative way, one must have a knowledge of the processes of speaking and hearing and of the physical characteristics of the speech sounds as they are propagated through a transmission system.

Nearly everyone is familiar with the general principles of how we speak and hear. By means of the speech organs, vibrations are set up which are transmitted through the air to the ear of the listener. Here the speech waves cause the eardrum to vibrate, and it, in turn, passes the vibrations through the chain of small bones of the middle ear to the oval window of the inner ear. By means of a marvelous mechanism the vibrational energy is here transformed into nerve impulses which are sent to the brain.

Although there are a great many languages spoken in different parts of the earth, and each language has a system of speech sounds of its own, there is a great similarity among these fundamental speech sounds. Also the mechanism of producing particular speech sounds in the various languages is somewhat different, but the general mechanism is similar for all people.

CHAPTER 1

THE SPEECH SOUNDS OF ENGLISH

Different classifications of the spoken sounds of English may be made, depending upon the purpose one has in mind. The International Phonetic Association uses a basis alphabet of sixty different letters[1] and also numerous modifiers which serve to distinguish several hundred sounds. This provides greater resolving power but also entails greater complexity than ordinarily is necessary for purposes of research in communication engineering. Upon considering the manner of formation of the speech sounds and studying their physical characteristics, and particularly the average listener's auditory ability to discriminate among them, thirty-nine speech sounds which can be readily distinguished by an average English-speaking person were chosen by the Bell Laboratories for experimental articulation studies. These are the same sounds as were selected by the Simplified Spelling Board except that the sounds in the word ton and the word nation were considered sufficiently similar to be designated by a single letter "o", and similarly the sounds in the words part, not and father were designated by a single letter "a". These speech sound elements are divided into six classes: pure vowels, diphthongs, transitionals, semi-vowels, fricative consonants and stop consonants. The two classes of consonants are further divided into the groups designated voiced and unvoiced. The complete list is shown in Fig. 1. The table in Figure 1 involves a further simplification in the matter of the diacritical marks used to denote the pronunciation of particular letter symbols. The usual systems, e.g., as used in dictionaries, permit finer distinctions than those generally needed here. It will be noted that only horizontal lines above or below and vertical lines above the letters are used to indicate pronunciation. This simplification makes it much easier to write these sounds, a practical point in research on articulation.

In Fig. 1 at the top the pure vowels, the diphthongs and the transitionals are shown in a diagram which helps to illustrate the manner in which these sounds are formed. Starting with the sounds ū, the lips are rounded and there is formed a large resonating chamber in the front part of the mouth, and a smaller and less important one in the throat cavity. Passing down the left side of the triangle in the diagram from ū to a, the

---

[1] Kantner and West, *Phonetics*, New York, 1941.

mouth is gradually opened with the tongue lowered to form the successive vowels. In all these vowels the throat resonance plays a minor part. Going up the right side of the triangle from a to ē, the tongue is gradually

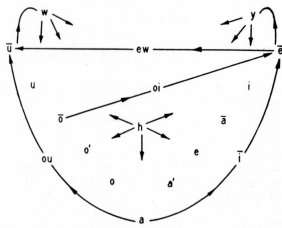

1. Pure Vowels—11
   Long —ū (tool), ō (tone), ó (talk), a (far), ā (tape), ē (team)
   Short—u (took), o (ton), á (tap), e (ten), i (tip)
2. Diphthongs—4
   ī, ou, oi, ew
3. Transitionals—3
   w, y, h
4. Semi-vowels—5
   l, r, m, n, ng
5. Fricative Consonants—8

Voiced	Unvoiced	Formation of Air Outlet
v	f	lip to teeth
z	s	teeth to teeth
th (then)	th (thin)	tongue to teeth
zh (azure)	sh	tongue to hard palate

6. Stop Consonants—8

Voiced	Unvoiced	Formation of the Stop
b	p	lip against lip
d	t	tongue against teeth
j	ch	tongue against hard palate
g	k	tongue against soft palate

FIG. 1.—CLASSIFICATION OF THE SPEECH SOUNDS.

raised to the front part of the mouth, thus forming two resonance chambers, both of which produce marked effects upon the frequency spectra of the sounds. In all these vowel sounds there are minor reso-

Key Work	Webster	Bell Labs	Int. Phonetic Ass'n
t oo l	o͞o	ū	u
t o ne	ō	ō	o or ou
t a lk	ä	ó	ɔ
t a r	à	a	a
t a pe	ā	ā	e or ei
t ea m	ē	ē	i
t oo k	oo	ᴜ	ᴜ
t o n	u	o	ʌ
t a p	a	á	æ
t e n	e	e	ɛ
t i p	i	i	I
t i me	ī	ī	aI
t ow n	ou	ou	aᴜ
t oi l	oi	oi	ɔI
f e w	ū	ew	ju
w oo	w	w	w
y ou	y	y	j
h ow	h	h	h
l ate	l	l	l
r ate	r	r	r
m ate	m	m	m
n ate	n	n	n
si ng	ng	ng	ŋ
v oice	v	v	v
f un	f	f	f
z ero	z	z	z
s it	s	s	s
th en	th	th	ð
th in	th	th	θ
a z ure	zh	zh	ʒ
sh ip	sh	sh	ʃ
b at	b	b	b
p at	p	p	p
d en	d	d	d
t en	t	t	t
j udge	j	j	dʒ
ch ur ch	ch	ch	tʃ
g oat	g	g	g
c oat	k	k	k

FIG. 2.—PHONETIC SYMBOLS FOR SPEECH SOUNDS.

nances above those corresponding to the mouth and throat cavities, but they seem to be characteristics of the quality of the voice rather than characteristics of the vowel sounds. Recent work by Dunn[2] shows that a third resonance should be present, and its frequency should be dependent upon the coupling between the throat and mouth cavities.

[2] *The Calculation of Vowel Resonances and an Electrical Vocal Track,* Journal of the Acoustical Society, Nov., 1950.

The designations for these same speech sounds as used by Webster's dictionary and by the International Phonetic Association are given in Fig. 2 (phonetic symbols for speech sounds).

It is very difficult to define differences between vowels and consonants which are adequate in all cases. In general, however, pure vowels are characterized by continuous, rather regular wave trains formed in the throat and passing through opened passages. Sounds at the lower end of the consonant list, on the other hand, represented by the unvoiced stop consonants, are characterized by transient irregular wave trains of short duration, formed mostly by the mouth and released suddenly by opening the lips. Between these two extremes is the graduated series of diphthongs, transitionals, semivowels, voiced fricatives, unvoiced fricatives, and voiced stop consonants.

The diphthongs ī, ou, oi, and ew are combinations of two of the pure vowels. If the mouth is formed to say a and then changed without interrupting the sound to the position for sounding ē, the acoustic result is signified in writing by the letter ī. Similarly, as illustrated in Fig. 1, the diphthong ou is a combination of a and ū, the diphthong oi, the combination of ō and ē, and the diphthong ew, the combination of ē and ū.

The three sounds, w, y, and h, are called transitionals since they represent a particular way of beginning the vowel sounds. If the mouth is adjusted to, say, ū and then suddenly changed so as to form any other vowel in the diagram, the result obtained is denoted in writing by placing w before the vowel. Similarly, we obtain the effect designated by y if the position of the vowel suddenly changes from ē to any other vowel. The diphthong ew and the sound represented by yū are similar but for yū the transition from the ē to the ū is much more rapid than when the diphthong is formed. An infinite variety of diphthongs and transitionals can be formed by varying both the temporal rate of change and the geometry of the vocal cavities necessary to form the two vowels. The selection given in Fig. 1 merely singles out those of sharp distinction (as judged by the ear) and of frequent occurrence in our language. When a vowel starts a syllable, it is formed by suddenly opening the glottis and thus permitting the air which has been held in the lungs to escape through the mouth formed for the proper vowel. If the glottis is originally open, the vowel is started by the sudden contraction of the lungs. Under these conditions the effect would be represented in writing by placing h before the vowel.

The sounds l, r, m, n, and ng are classified as semivowels since for these sounds the passage from the vocal cords to the outside is partially blocked. In the case of l and r the sound is allowed to flow around the tongue, which is placed in a particular position in the mouth. For the sounds m, n, and ng the usual path through the mouth is interrupted so that the sound and the air accompanying it flow through the nasal cavities. For this reason they are sometimes called nasalized stop consonants.

The fricative consonants are characterized by the rushing sound of the breath through the characteristic air outlet, which usually is of very small dimensions. The manner in which these sounds are formed is described in Fig. 1. In producing the sound f, the outlet is formed by holding the lower lip to the upper teeth. If while the f sound is being thus produced a tone from the vocal cords is also sounded, the speech sound v results. Similarly other unvoiced and voiced fricative sounds are produced by proper adjustments of the air outlet as shown in the figure. The stop and fricative consonants are classified in a similar way, both groups comprising voiced and unvoiced pairs. Thus, b and p are both characterized by a stop formed with one lip against the other lip, d and t with the tongue against the teeth, j and ch with the tongue against the hard palate, and g and k with the tongue against the soft palate.

A further scheme of classification employed by phoneticians defines *continuants* and *stops*. *Continuants* are sounds in which the air stream has continuous egress during the production of the sound. *Stops* are sounds in which the articulatory mechanism momentarily blocks the exit of the air. The voiced stops are *b*, *d* and *g*; their voiceless analogues are *p*, *t* and *k*. The other sounds, possibly with a few marginal exceptions, are the continuants, voiced and unvoiced. The voiced continuants include the pure vowels and the diphthongs, the principal sounds to carry the pitch in singing. In all voiced continuants two resonating cavities, the mouth and the throat, partake in the sound formation. Consequently the three frequency regions (formants) mentioned above are accentuated in the spectrum of the sound. It is largely the characteristics of these regions of resonance, particularly their postion in the frequency scale and their sharpness of resonance, that distinguish one vowel sound from another when they are sustained, as in singing. In speaking, however, the way these sounds are started and ended has much to do with the listener's ability to recognize them. The continuants, even the voiced vowels, are auditory acoustic entities only as combinations of the terminal (starting and ending) portions with the relatively sustained central portion. In any of the voiced sounds it is the modulation of the cord tone that distinguishes the speech sound rather than the characteristic of the vocal cords. The latter determines largely the type of voice (quality aspect) and helps to identify the person who is speaking but has little to do with those characteristics of the speech sounds which determine their auditory recognition.

CHAPTER 2

THE SPEAKING MECHANISM

In Chapter 1 there was a general discussion of voice production while describing the English speech sounds. In this chapter the detailed mechanism of voice production will be discussed.

All normal speech sounds are accompanied by a net outward flow of air. This will be referred to as the "direct current or d-c flow." With most speech sounds the prime mover, the lungs, furnishes this air stream which flows through the trachea, glottis, pharynx, mouth, and nose to the external air. The air stream flows through the glottis, the passage between the vocal cords. With the unvoiced consonants (p or f, for example) the d-c stream, which is of short duration, is supplied by the reservoir capacity of the mouth functioning as a pressure tank. The air stream flows through constricted passages formed by the teeth or lips. In either case, of course, the d-c flow does not by itself create sound waves. To produce audible sound, the air stream must be modulated at a temporal rate higher than that of the lowest audible frequency, i.e., higher than, say, 20 cycles per second. In fact, with speech sounds the lowest audible components are more nearly of the order of 80 cps. Superposed on its d-c flow the air stream must acquire alternating current (a-c) components, ranging in frequency, roughly, from 80 cps to 8000 cps. It is a function of the speech organs to introduce these a-c components.

The division of speech sounds into voiced and unvoiced refers to the circumstance that in the former group the vibration of the vocal cords is the first step in generating the a-c components of the air stream. With groups 1, 2, 3, and 4 of Fig. 1 this is the main cause. With the voiced consonants of groups 5 and 6, the vocal cord vibrations are an essential contributor, but also an essential part of the a-c generation is due to the passage of the air stream through highly constricted slit-like openings and over sharp edges, as between the lower lip and upper teeth, or between the tongue and the upper teeth. With the unvoiced consonants (groups 5 and 6 of Fig. 1) there is no vibration, or at any rate no significant a-c contribution from vocal cord vibrations. The a-c components are generated entirely by the forcing of the air stream through constrictions and other sharp edges. The configurations assumed by the tongue, the teeth,

6

the lips, the soft palate, and the hard palate are the principal elements to determine the a-c components of unvoiced sounds.

For the voiced sounds in groups 1, 2, 3, and 4, the vibration of the vocal cords transforms the d-c lung stream into a pulsating stream, which is the sum of a d-c stream with a-c components superposed on the d-c stream. Only the a-c components enter into the production of the sound waves outside, i.e., in the air external to the person speaking. The externally radiated sound is determined by the a-c components of the air stream coming out of the mouth openings and the nostrils, rather than by the a-c components of the glottis. The transition from the latter to the former involves a number of the speech mechanism. First, there are the several vocal cavities: oral, throat or pharynx, and nasal cavities. The oral cavities play the most important part. The size and shape of the oral cavity can be controlled between wide limits by movement of the tongue and lower jaw. These movements also affect the throat cavities. The nasal cavities are essentially fixed. These cavities have a profound effect upon the spectrum of the sound radiated because of their pronounced resonating actions which reinforce those a-c components of the glottis stream which lie in certain frequency regions (formants).

It may be noted here that the sound radiated is affected not only by the geometry, i.e., sizes and shapes of the several cavities and orifices, but also by the acoustic properties of their surfaces. The tongue, the cheeks, the hard and soft palates are major instances. The acoustic properties in question mainly relate to the damping or energy dissipation caused by these surfaces which absorb acoustic energy from the air of the resonating cavities.

There is some contribution to the speech sound radiated from elements other than those ordinarily designated as speech organs. Thus, the neck and the chest radiate appreciably; the more so (in relation to the total sound), the lower the frequency. The neck vibration is well known and directly utilized to actuate a throat microphone. The chest is perhaps more usually associated with singing than with speech. That it appreciably contributes to the speech spectrum at the low frequencies is suggested by the change heard in the voice of a bather when the water is only knee-deep in one case and neck-high in the other. However, by far the greatest portion of speech sound radiated comes from the oral and nasal orifices, predominantly the former.

First, we consider in a qualitative and highly idealized manner the acoustic elements at work in the production of speech sounds.

For the first four groups of speech sounds listed in Fig. 1 the situation is relatively the simplest, as indicated by the schematic of Fig. 3. The muscular contraction of the lungs tends to force a steady direct-current or d-c air stream through the larynx to the external air.

For the vowels and semi-vowels of groups 1, 2, 3, and 4 (Fig. 1) the vibration of the vocal cords partially interrupts or modulates this air stream, superposing an a-c spectrum upon it. The fundamental frequency of the rather complex vibrations executed by the vocal cords is the fundamental frequency of the particular speech sound being phonated. For the unvoiced sounds of groups 5 and 6, which involve no vibration of the vocal cords, the d-c to a-c conversion depends on forcing the air

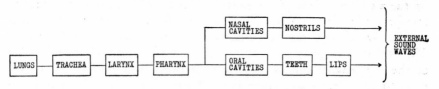

FIG. 3.—BLOCK DIAGRAM OF VOICE MECHANISM.

stream through narrow orifices and past sharp edges. Various configurations of tongue, teeth, and lip positions provide such passages. The air stream does not always originate directly in the lungs. It may employ the reservoir of air in the mouth driven outward by muscular contraction of the cheeks, as in the sound p. The resultant sound spectrum for these sounds is, in general, a rather continuous "noise" spectrum as distinguished from the discrete "line" spectrum of groups 1, 2, 3, and 4. For the voiced sounds of groups 5 and 6, both mechanisms mentioned are operative in the creation of the a-c spectrum out of the available d-c pneumatic source.

At the World's Fair in 1939 a device called the voder was used for synthesizing speech. A diagram of this device with its relation to the organs of speech is shown in Fig. 4.[1]

"Corresponding to the vocal cords which produce the buzzer-like sound there is an electrical oscillator labeled 'buzzer' that produces a steady buzzer-sounding tone. The fundamental frequency of this buzzer tone can be varied to correspond to the change of pitch of the human voice. Corresponding to the constrictions in the vocal passages from which are made the unvoiced sounds, the voder contains an electrical 'random noise' source which by itself produces a continuous hissing sound."

"The third and final step in speech production is that of selecting from the many vibration rates produced by these energy sources those needed to form the spectrum of the phonetic element desired at the

[1] Dudley, Riesz and Watkins, *A Synthetic Speaker*, Bell Telephone Laboratories Monograph B-1148, 1939.

moment. This process is carried out in the vocal system of man by adjusting the resonances and couplings of air cavities through movements of the lips, tongue, jaw, etc. In the case of the electrical mechanism this objective is attained by means of selective networks in the form of simple electrical filters the outputs of which are controlled by ten potentiometers manipulated by the fingers. In synthesizing speech sounds these finger controls are supplemented by a foot control for changing the fundamental frequency of the electrical oscillator (voice pitch change) and a wrist bar for switching between voiced and unvoiced energy sources."

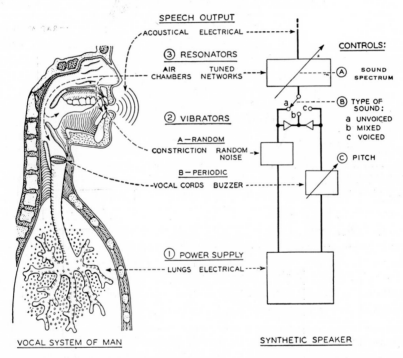

FIG. 4.—FUNCTIONAL COMPARISON OF SYNTHETIC SPEAKER WITH THE HUMAN VOCAL SYSTEM.

The keyboard operating this device is shown in Fig. 5. This illustrates the fundamental mechanism involved in speech production.

The periodic spectrum, created in the glottis by virtue of the vibration of the vocal cords, contains the fundamental and a long series of higher harmonics. Theoretically there is no definite upper limit to the order of the harmonics present. Practically in speech sounds harmonics up to the 30th or so are found to be present with significant amplitudes. The aerial resonators of the voice, constituted by the cavities and orifices of the pharynx, mouth, and nose, respond selectively, i.e., they respond much more to those harmonics whose frequencies are in the vicinity of the resonance frequencies of the resonators. This usually results in two (sometimes three, seldom one) frequency regions of prominence in the speech sound as observed in the outside air. The frequency location of

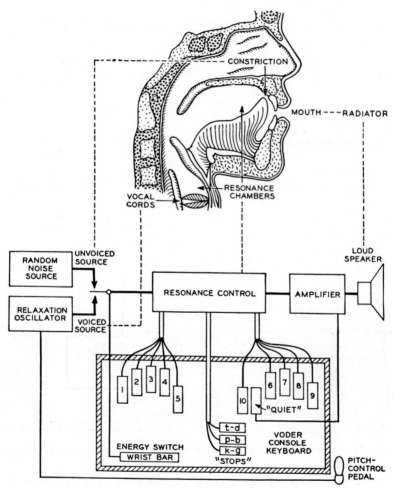

FIG. 5.—ESSENTIAL PARTS OF THE VODER.

these regions of accentuated intensity, known as formants, is an important characteristic lending individuality to the various periodic sounds.

The recent work of Potter and his co-workers[2] at the Bell Telephone Laboratories with the sound spectrograph illustrates very beautifully

[2] Potter, Kopp and Green, *Visible Speech*, D. Van Nostrand Company, Inc., New York, 1947.

what is taking place in the resonant cavities as we speak the various speech sounds. In Fig. 6 is shown a schematic of the sound spectrograph. "With the switch 'S' thrown left, one may talk into the microphone and record on a loop of magnetic tape a short sample of speech such as the

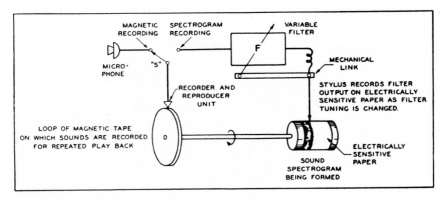

FIG. 6.—SCHEMATIC DIAGRAM OF THE SOUND SPECTROGRAPH.

words, 'Speech we may see.' Then the switch 'S' is thrown right, and the magnetic tape record is reproduced over and over again. The repeated speech sample goes to the input of the variable filter 'F'. Adjusted first to some starting frequency such as 50 cycles per second, its tuning

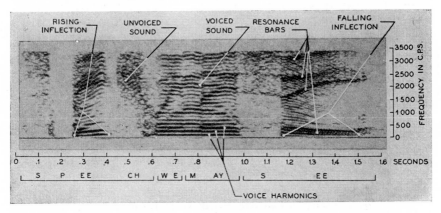

FIG. 7.—SOUND SPECTROGRAM OF THE WORDS "SPEECH WE MAY SEE" USING A NARROW-BAND ANALYZING FILTER TO PORTRAY HARMONIC STRUCTURE.

would be shifted say 15 cycles at a time for each repetition of the words. The filter output is connected to a stylus resting upon electrically sensitive paper wrapped around a drum as shown at the right. The simple oscillations separated out from the complex wave are rectified and recorded side by side as both the filter tuning and stylus position shift together over the frequency range. The darkness of the trace increases as the intensity of the oscillations increases. Hence, the record is one of varying shade rather than an oscillating lines such as is recorded in the familiar oscillogram."

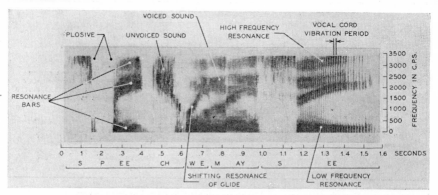

F̶ig. 8.—Sound Spectrogram of the Words "Speech we may see" Using a Wide-Band Analyzing Filter (300 Cycles) to Emphasize Vocal Resonances.

"When the filter 'F' has a bandwidth of approximately 45 cycles per second, a pattern such as is illustrated by Fig. 7 is obtained. The parts of the pattern are rather fully identified. These patterns contain details of speech sounds that are of interest in studies of speech defects, in speech rehabilitation, and in phonetic research."

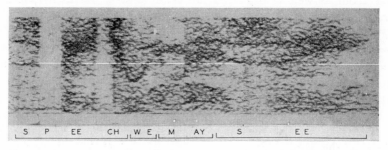

Fig. 9.—Sound Spectrogram of the Words "Speech we may see" Spoken in a Whisper, Using a Narrow-Band Filter (45 Cycles).

"When the filter 'F' has a bandwidth of about 300 cycles, as shown in Fig. 8, much of the finer detail is not portrayed. However, there remains in broad outline a picture of the intensity-frequency-time distribution, where frequency and time are shown vertically and horizontally, respectively, and intensity is shown by the shade of darkness. Patterns of this type are the ones of special interest in visual hearing."

"When the words, 'Speech we may see,' were whispered, the records shown in Fig. 9 and in Fig. 10 were obtained. Although the appearance of these two spectrograms is different, Fig. 9 for the narrow-band filter contains less information important to the recognition of the word sounds than does Fig. 10 for the much wider-band filter. The latter shows more clearly how the speech energy is distributed. It is interesting to note that, neglecting the detailed form of vertical striations, Fig. 10 shows a

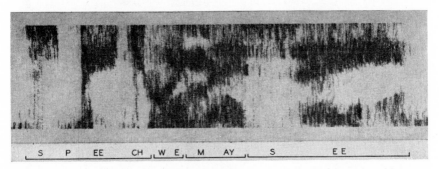

FIG. 10.—SOUND SPECTROGRAM OF THE WORDS "SPEECH WE MAY SEE" SPOKEN IN A WHISPER, USING A WIDE-BAND FILTER (300 CYCLES).

general energy distribution somewhat similar to that which appears in the patterns of Fig. 8."

"Intelligibility tests made with whispered and voiced speech reveal that when the former is loud enough to be heard easily, it may be understood about as well as the latter, although voicing makes speech more pleasant to listen to and helps to identify the speaker."

"A natural inference appears to be that the movements of the articulators, the tongue, lips, jaw, etc., play a prominent role in producing the intelligible characteristics of speech sounds. An important conclusion is that the effects of these movements may be portrayed adequately for purposes of reading, by wide-band filters."

The bars running across these spectrograms show the changing resonant frequencies of the mouth and throat and other minor resonant cavities as the words, "Speech we may see," are spoken. It was found that a band width of 300 cycles per second used in the analyzing mechanism was about the best to show how the speech organs are moving as the sounds are produced. For example, in Fig. 11 the top spectrogram shows the sounds in the sentence, "I can see it," pronounced separately. In the lower figure is a spectrogram of this same sentence spoken as in conversation. In the former for the vowels the bars representing the resonant frequencies in the mouth and throat are horizontal, showing the speech organs were held constant in position. But for the

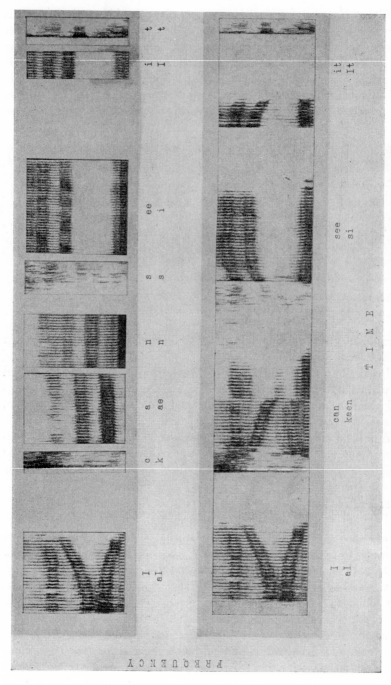

FIG. 11.—SPECTROGRAMS SHOWING CHANGING RESONANT FREQUENCIES OF THE MOUTH AND THROAT.

diphthong ī the mouth and throat cavities were changed from the position for a to the position ē. However, when the sentence is spoken as in conversation, the vowels are modified in the manner shown. The bars for ă in "can" show the effect of moving the mouth and throat cavities from positions corresponding to k to positions corresponding to ă. Similarly, the effect upon the other vowels is indicated by the changing position of these bars. Notice how clearly the stops k and t are indicated by the blank spaces.

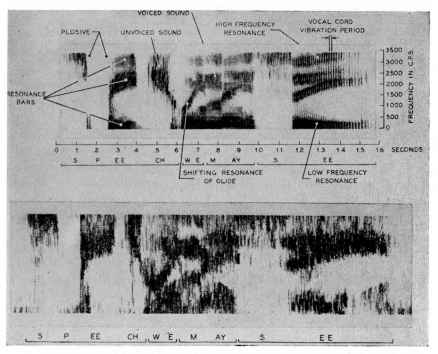

Fig. 12.—Voiced Speech Versus Whispered Speech. Sound Spectrograms of the Words "Speech we may see" Using a Wide-Band Analyzing Filter (300 Cycles).

These aerial resonators also play a part in shaping the envelope of the spectrum radiated in the case of the aperiodic sounds. Here again certain frequency regions are preferentially radiated, but the effect is less important than with the periodic sounds. The aperiodic sounds owe much more of their individuality to differences between the apertures through which the air stream is forced.

The above grouping of sounds as periodic, aperiodic, and periodic aperiodic was made with a view of the sounds of normal, say, conversational, speech. In whispered speech all sounds are aperiodic; there is no vocal cord vibration periodicity. Those sounds which normally are voiced, e.g., the vowels, still are selectively reinforced by the aerial resonators, much the same as in normal speech. This is illustrated in Fig. 12 by the spectrograms. But these resonators now are actuated by the aperiodic spectrum generated in the air stream in the process of passing through the constrictions of the (non-vibrating) glottis and pharynx. In reality there is no such thing as pure d-c flow of finite amplitude when there are severe constrictions, such as the glottis relative to the cross-sectional area of the trachea. Superposed on the d-c stream is a weak but quite appreciable aperiodic spectrum which is the breath sound one hears even though no attempt is made to produce any speech sound. In whispering what would normally be voiced sounds, the aerial resonators respond selectively to those portions of the aperiodic spectrum which correspond to the formant regions of the normally voiced sound. With unvoiced sounds there is no essential difference, other than intensity, between the normal and the whispered modes of production.

Allowing for their reduced intensity, the recognizability of whispered sounds is practically perfect, but they carry very little identification of the person speaking. This latter is largely a property of voiced sounds, residing in the vibrations of the vocal cords. The excellent recognizability of whispered sounds is due not only to the similarity of the formant regions (as compared with corresponding sounds of normal speech) but more importantly, to the similarity in the manner of starting and stopping these sounds. This is an essential characteristic of speech sounds. Broadly, we may think of the voice organs' function as twofold. On the one hand, they produce the audiofrequency spectra, comprising roughly the range from 80 cps to 8000 cps. On the other hand, these spectra are not sustained, steady state phenomena. Primarily they vary at temporal rates corresponding to the initiation and termination of the speech sound, and to the transition from one sound to another in the syllable composed of more than one sound. This is the second function of the speech organs, accomplished by rapid, more or less continuous readjustments of the organs.

Experience with persons who have had their larynx removed by a surgical operation has emphasized the fact that the differentiation of the speech sounds is practically all accomplished by the mouth and lip positions and that the sounds from the vocal cords act only as a carrier for these variations. Such an operation leaves no connection between the lungs and the mouth. It is performed in an emergency to prevent the patient from suffocating. After such an operation the patient breathes through a small opening in the neck. Because of this by-passing of the larynx the patient can make no vocal sound. However, an attachment can be made to this opening like that shown in Fig. 13 so that the patient can blow a whistle somewhat similar to that used in toy balloons and the resulting sound is directed into the mouth. With this device, which is called an artificial larynx, the patient can learn to talk again. The artificial larynx shown in Fig. 13 was developed at the Bell Telephone Laboratories in 1926. Hundreds of persons have successfully used devices of this sort. More recently, however, speech teachers have learned how to teach such patients to use the gutural sound created by belches of air from the stomach for speech modulation.

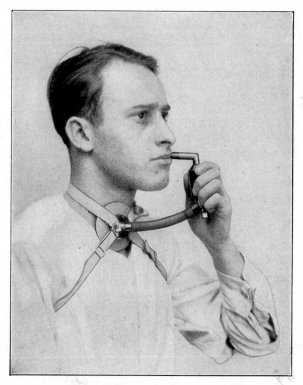

FIG. 13.—THE ARTIFICIAL LARYNX.

Good intelligible speech called oesophogeal speech can be created this way. So many laryngectomy patients now learn to speak this way that the use of the artificial larynx is rapidly decreasing.

Experimental measurement of the motion of the vocal cords is not easy, but it has been accomplished by high-speed photography. The diagram in Fig. 14 shows the arrangement for taking the pictures.[3] A photograph of the apparatus is shown in Fig. 15. The pictures are taken

[3] D. W. Farnsworth, *High-Speed Motion Picture of the Human Vocal Cords*, Bell Laboratories Record, V. 18, p. 203, March, 1940.

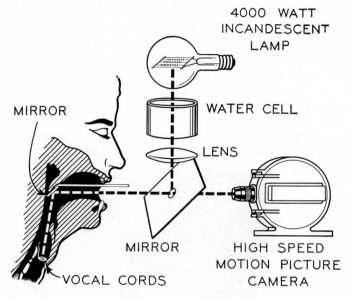

FIG. 14.—EXPERIMENTAL ARRANGEMENT FOR TAKING HIGH-SPEED MOVIES OF VOCAL CORDS.

at the rate of 400 per second. When projected by the usual motion-picture rate of 16 frames per second, one second of taking time is spread over 250 seconds of projecting time. In other words, for a voice fundamental of 200 cps one complete cycle occupying 1/200 second in taking time can be seen during 1.2 seconds so that form of vibration is easily

FIG. 15.—APPARATUS USED IN MAKING THE MOVIES OF THE VOCAL CORDS.

seen. Or, on the film there are about 20 equally spaced views of the position of the vocal cords during each cycle.

A schematic of the anatomy of the larynx is shown in Fig. 16. The larynx, a cartilaginous structure within which are the vocal cords, is indicated by the arrow. A part of the larynx is the prominence at the front of the throat known as the "Adam's apple"—the thyroid cartilage, shaped like two sides of a triangular box with the apex at the front. The epiglottis, a palmleaf-like structure, attaches to the upper part of the thyroid cartilage. It is very flexible and may be either upright, behind the base of the tongue, or folded down to cover the top of the larynx.

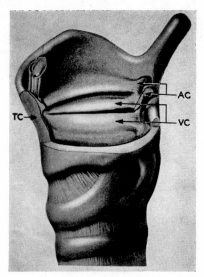

FIG. 16.—SCHEMATIC OF THE STRUCTURE OF THE LARYNX.[4]

The rear wall of the larynx is formed by the cricoid and the two arytenoid cartilages. The vocal cords (VC) have a common point of attachment to the thyroid cartilage (TC) at the front and each is attached to a process of one arytenoid (AC) at the rear. At its lower end the larynx opens into the trachea or windpipe, at its upper end it opens into the pharynx or throat; toward the infraglottal and supraglottal regions, respectively. The cords are actually thick folds or bands, rather than fine strings; some writers prefer the terms, vocal folds or vocal lips.

In normal respiration the vocal cords are widely separated at the rear end, forming a large triangular opening. In the production of a voiced sound the cords are drawn close together but not entirely closed. When the lungs are compressed to exhale, the current of air forced past

[4] Wegel, *Theory of Larynx*, Bell Telephone Journal, January, 1930.

the narrow cord opening sets them into vibration. The transition from breathing to phonation is shown in Fig. 17. These are stills taken from the high-speed movie mentioned above. The vibration of the cords causes an a-c variation of the glottis opening (often called the glottal chink or slit, or simply the glottis), resulting in an a-c spectrum superposed upon the d-c air flow. This a-c spectrum, initiating the sound wave radiated to the external air, consists of a fundamental and numerous harmonically related overtones (harmonics). In the external sound wave

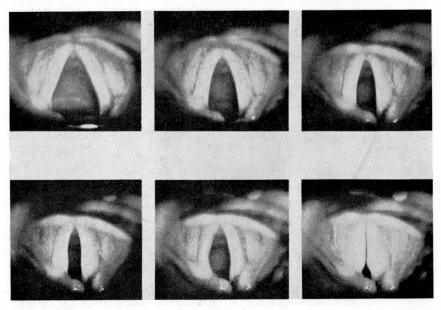

FIG. 17.—FROM BREATHING TO VOICING.

as many as 40 may have significant amplitudes. Pitch is determined by the frequency of the fundamental. The harmonics are selectively reinforced in varying ways by the air cavities of the vocal tract. It is this ability of the cavities selectively to reinforce various groups of harmonics (formants) at will that enables one to produce various speech sounds.

For the pictures, the pitch and intensity of the voicing have been varied, but, because of the necessity of maintaining the wide-open mouth position, only the vowel sound ae (intermediate between hat and fair) was used. It gives a particularly favorable view of the larynx. The pitch range covered was from about 120 to 350 cps, and the intensities varied from the softest possible voicing to that corresponding to a shout. The motion of the cords appears to be rather complex at low pitch, becoming less so as the tone is raised, until at extremely high pitches only the edges of the cords nearest the glottis are seen to vibrate, resulting in small a-c amplitudes in the width of the opening. Vibration also tends to be confined more largely toward the front end of the cords. This confined motion is known as the falsetto mechanism. Fig. 18 illustrates the changes in going from a low to a high pitch.

At very low pitch (for the particular voice used) the cords appear to be completely relaxed, as may be seen in Fig. 19, which shows one cycle of the cord motion at roughly 120 cps. The anatomical situation cor-

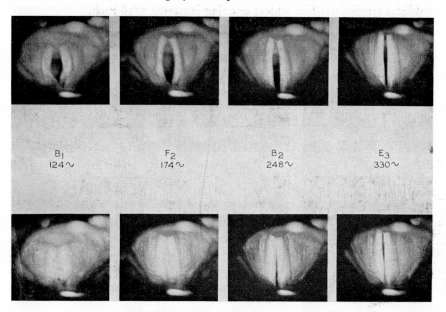

B_1
124 ∿

F_2
174 ∿

B_2
248 ∿

E_3
330 ∿

FIG. 18.—OPEN AND CLOSED POSITIONS OF VOCAL CORDS
FOR PITCHES 124, 174, 248 AND 330 CPS.

responds to small tension, both in the thyro-arytenoid muscles under-lying the vocal cords throughout their length and in the muscles which act on the cords by moving the cartilages to which they attach. As the tension in the various muscles increases, two things take place: the cords become firmer due to contraction of the underlying thyro-arytenoid, and they are stretched to a greater length by the action of the other muscles. At low pitch, and starting from the closed portion of the cycle, the cords begin to open from underneath (the infraglottal end, toward the lungs), the opening progressing upward with an outward unfolding of the cords. The lower portion is also first to close. In other words, there is a vertical variation in the phase of the cord motion. Horizontally, the opening along the length of the cords may also have a phase displacement. When the cords close, a wave-like motion or ripple is seen to pass over the top surface from the glottis toward the walls of the larynx, as the edges of the cords press firmly together.   When the voice is in this (relatively low) pitch range, the cords may be tightly closed for as long as half of the cycle. Of the six positions shown in Fig. 19, the two substantially closed con-figurations are to be understood to cover a much larger fraction of the time than would be the case in sinusoidal motion.   The length of the cords when vibrating at about 120 cps is from 1/2 to 5/8 inch (for the subjects studied).   The widest opening is nearly 3/16 inch.

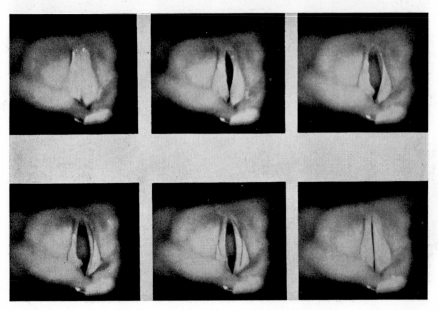

FIG. 19.—ONE CYCLE OF CORD MOVEMENT AT 120 CPS.

As the pitch is raised the motion becomes somewhat simpler.   When the folds become firmer due to muscular tension, they move more nearly as a unit, so that the opening from below upwards is less and less apparent. The fraction of the cycle time they remain closed becomes smaller until, in the falsetto, complete closure is usually not attained at all.   The length of the cords increases to about 3/4 inch, and the width of maximum opening decreases to about 3/32 inch at 240 cps.   All these dimensions are only illustrative, varying as they do with the intensity of the sound and from subject to subject.

The chief variation evident as the intensity is changed, while the pitch is held constant, is that the cords close very feebly or not at all at very low intensities, while at high intensities they close firmly and may remain closed for an appreciable time even when vibrating at a high frequency. From a study of pictures made with trained and untrained voices, the following conclusions were made. No significant differences were found in the production of a falsetto or a low-intensity sound. Two important differences were found in the production of high-intensity sound. First, the closure time in each cycle is definitely greater for the trained voice than for the untrained one. This leads to the building up of a greater pressure back of the glottis so that when it finally opens a

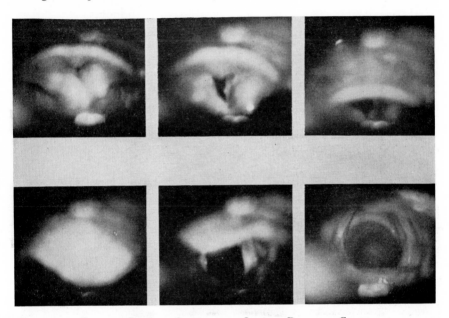

FIG. 20.—PICTURES SHOWING THE LARYNX DURING A COUGH.

greater intensity of sound results. This is a well-known principle in acoustics and is used in designing sirens which have high efficiency. It is arranged so that the time the air stream is cut off is long compared to the time it is permitted to flow. A second difference is that the amplitude of the vocal cord vibration is less for the trained voice than for the untrained one. For both these reasons a trained voice can produce a given intensity of sound with a considerably less volume of air passing through the larynx than for an untrained voice. This control ability explains why the trained voice can cover a much wider intensity range (and pitch range) than the untrained one.

An interesting set of pictures showing the production of a cough appears in Fig. 20. Here not only the vocal cords but the entire larynx is in movement.   At the beginning of the cough the walls of the larynx are greatly constricted, closing over the vocal cords.   The air is forced out of the lungs, and sudden expansion takes place.   The vocal cords are forced apart to a greater extent than ever occurs in normal breathing, and the epiglottis is blown about by the current of air.   The cough photographed was made as in an effort to expel a foreign body headed for the trachea.

CHAPTER 3

CHARACTERISTICS OF SPEECH WAVES

Speech sounds radiating from the mouth are transmitted through the air by means of pressure waves, successions of condensations, and rarefactions of the air. The magnitudes of the pressure changes making up these vibrations are exceedingly small, and the wave form is complicated as the cavities of the mouth and the throat are continually varying in size, and the stream of air is being constantly interrupted. The physical characteristics of these waves which carry typical speech sounds will be discussed in this chapter.

As an example of the type of disturbance created in the air, consider the sentence, "Joe took father's shoe bench out." This nonsensical sentence is chosen because it and its mate, "She was waiting at my lawn," contain all the fundamental sounds in the English language that contribute appreciably toward the loudness of speech. As the sound wave produced by speaking this sentence travels along, each particle of air over which it passes executes a vibration whose character is shown in Fig. 21. The vertical position gives the distance that the air particle is from its undisturbed position, and the horizontal position gives the time, the marks being hundreth-second intervals. Consider that this speech wave is transmitted down a tube 1500 feet long containing air. If the walls are smooth, there will be very little attenuation as the wave progresses. So if a snapshot photograph were taken at the instant the word "out" left the mouth, then the picture would look like that shown in Fig. 21, with this difference, that the horizontal positions would represent distances along the direction in which the wave is traveling, each marked unit representing approximately ten feet, instead of .01 second. This means that the disturbance carrying the sound j in the word "Joe" is about 1500 feet from the mouth by the time the sentence is finished. So if we stretched the picture in the figure lengthwise until it was drawn out to 1500 feet, then the particles at any instant located at the various distances would be displaced from their positions of equilibrium in accordance with the vertical distances in the picture. However, these displacements are along the direction the wave is traveling rather than at right angles to it. To make this clear, let us look at ten feet of the wave carrying the sound ū as in "shoe." See Fig. 22.

The middle row of bars represents the layers of air particles which are one inch apart before the wave passes. The bottom row of bars represents the positions of these same particles when the sound ū is being transmitted. The horizontal displacements are very much magnified. When the speech waves leave the mouth, the amplitude of vibration of the air particles for a typical speech sound is one thousandth of an inch or 1 mil.

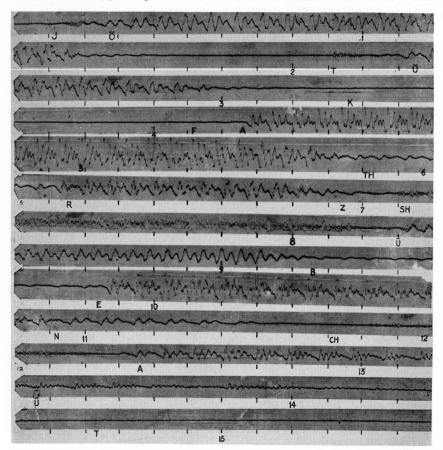

FIG. 21.—OSCILLOGRAM: "JOE TOOK FATHER'S SHOE BENCH OUT" SPOKEN.

Therefore, the scale in Fig. 21 is magnified about 5000 times for the displacements. When they reach in unconfined air ten feet from the mouth, the amplitude is reduced 60 times or to 1/60 of a mil. The amplitude can be reduced by another factor of 200 before it reaches the threshold of hearing for a listener in a quiet place. At this threshold level, then, the amplitudes are of the order of 1/10 millionth of an inch. This is for a component having a frequency of 100 cps. For the component frequencies around 1000 cps the amplitudes are about 1/10 this or approximately equal to the diameter of an air molecule. For the component frequencies between 2000 and 4000 cps the amplitude at threshold level is of the order of 1/10 the diameter of an air molecule.

FIG. 22.—CHART SHOWING DISPLACEMENT OF AIR PARTICLES AS THE SOUND WAVES "SH" AND "ū" PASS THROUGH THE AIR.

It is obvious that at such levels the random motion of the molecules at ordinary temperatures will produce statistically sound vibrations of this same order of magnitude. It is probably this thermal noise that limits the acuity of hearing in very acute ears.

It will be noticed that because of the different particles being displaced different amounts they are pushed closely together at some positions and farther apart at others. In other words, condensations and rarefactions are produced. The distance from one condensation to the next is called the wave length. By making a proper adjustment in the system for recording these sound waves, the amount of condensation and rarefaction can be recorded. You will remember that the amplitude of the vibrations on the sound sh was much smaller than that for ū, but the pressure changes are about the same for the two sounds. It will be seen that for the sound ū the wave length is about 4 feet and for the sound sh about 3 inches.

The sound wave being propagated down the tube with hard smooth walls is called a plane wave because the wave front is in a plane. When the sound is radiated from a point the waves become spherical, but they become more nearly plane as the distance from the source increases. It is well known in Acoustics that the following relations hold for plane waves in air.

Let c = velocity of propagation of the sound wave

P = atmospheric air pressure

ρ_0 = density of air at pressure P

f = frequency of vibration of the air particle

λ = wave length

J = sound power going through each square centimeter perpendicular to direction of propagation. It is called sound intensity.

t = time

y = displacement of air particle from position of equilibrium
A = maximum displacement amplitude
v = velocity of air particles due to sound wave
p = excess pressure over P and is called sound pressure
ρ = excess density over ρ_0 due to sound wave
x = distance along the direction of propagation that the sound wave has traveled.

Then the following relations hold:

$$c = \lambda f, \tag{3-1}$$

$$y = A \cos 2\pi f \left(t - \frac{x}{c} \right), \tag{3-2}$$

$$v = 2\pi f A \sin 2\pi f \left(t - \frac{x}{c} \right), \tag{3-3}$$

$$\rho = \rho_0 \frac{v}{c}, \tag{3-4}$$

$$p = \rho_0 c v, \tag{3-5}$$

$$c = \sqrt{\frac{1.41\,P}{\rho_0}}, \tag{3-6}$$

$$J = \frac{p^2}{\rho_0 c}. \tag{3-7}$$

The r.m.s. amplitude is equal to the maximum amplitude divided by the $\sqrt{2}$. The case treated is for a single frequency component.

In general, for a speech wave such as is portrayed in Fig. 21 there are an infinite number of components necessary to represent all the variations shown. However, over small periods of time only a small number is necessary, e.g., from time .04 second to .08 second can be fairly well represented by three sinusoidal components. But, in general, the amplitude at any time t is given by

$$y = \sum_{k=1}^{k=n} A_k \cos 2\pi f_k \left(t - \frac{x}{c} \right) \tag{3-2A}$$

where n is the number of components during the small interval of time considered. To represent accurately the amplitude of the entire sentence would, in general, require an infinite number of terms. However, more information about what is taking place is found by considering small intervals of time where successive waves are about the same form. Then a comparatively few components will represent the wave form.

When there are several components the relation between the r.m.s. values of y and v become a little complicated because the phases and frequencies must be considered.   But equations (3–4), (3–5), and (3–7) still hold when the values are interpreted as r.m.s. values.

The record shown in Fig. 21 was made by using an instrument called an oscillograph.   Briefly stated, this instrument works as follows: Speech waves are picked up by a microphone which converts them into similar electric waves.   These waves, in turn, cause a tiny ribbon to vibrate in front of a slit.   Light falls through this slit upon a fast moving film and is photographed.   The trace shown in Fig. 21 is the result after the film has been developed.

The oscillograms of speech sounds shown in this book were taken with an instrument developed by Crandall and Sacia[1] in 1925.   They did an excellent job so that these oscillograms are still the best samples of typical speech waves available.   The pick-up microphone used was the condenser type developed by Wente and used ever since that time for acoustical measurements.   Its electrical response is proportional to the pressure amplitude rather than particle displacement, so most oscillograms are given as pressure amplitudes versus time rather than as particle displacement versus time as shown in Fig. 21.   To obtain the latter type of oscillogram, the electrical circuit must be arranged to give a response inversely proportional to the frequency.

It is seen from the above equations that the sound pressure p may be given in terms of a number of components as

$$p = \sum_{k=1}^{k=n} P_k \sin 2\pi f_k \left(t - \frac{x}{c} \right) \qquad (3\text{--}8)$$

where the maximum amplitude P_k of each component is given by

$$P_k = 2\pi \rho_0 c A_k f_k \qquad (3\text{--}9)$$

where A_k is maximum particle displacement for component having frequency f_k.

The quantity $2\pi f_k \dfrac{x}{c}$ is called the phase of vibration between the components.   At a fixed distance from the source x/c is constant, so the phase between the component vibrations is seen to be proportional to the frequency.   If the trace on the moving film of the oscillograph is to represent the sound pressure p, then two conditions must be fulfilled. For a pick-up microphone at a fixed distance x the trace will be a true picture of the sound pressure provided (1) that the amplitude of the oscillograph ribbon is proportional to P_k at each frequency and (2) that the phase is proportional to the frequency f_k.   In Fig. 23 the curves indicate how close these conditions were fulfilled in the Crandall-Sacia instrument.

[1] I. B. Crandall, *Sounds of Speech*, Bell Technical Journal, October, 1925.

In this instrument a key was pressed by the speaker just before the sound was spoken, which released a shutter placed before a rotating film drum on which the record from the oscillograph vibrator was traced. With the size of the drum and the speed at which it was rotated, each one-hundredth of a second corresponded to 2 inches or more on the time scale. The apparatus was arranged so that the helical trace made on

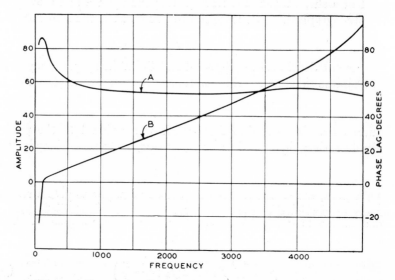

Fig. 23.—Over-all Frequency Characteristics of Amplitude and Phase of the Recording System. Curve A: Oscillograph Amplitude per Unit of Pressure on Transmitter Diaphragm. Curve B: Phase Lag of Oscillographic Amplitude Behind Pressure on Diaphragm.

the record was 200 inches in length for one second of time. As is indicated from the records obtained, special care was taken with the optical system to insure fine definition, and in the development of the films to obtain the proper contrast.

Typical Speech Waves

The wave forms of the words "farmers," "seems," "poor," and "alters" taken by this method are shown in Figs. 24, 25, 26, and 27. These serve to illustrate the complicated structure of speech waves, and the effects of starting and stopping the sound. It will be seen in Fig. 24, which gives the oscillogram of the word "farmers," that the first letter sound "f" is characterized by very high frequencies. After these high frequencies the "a" sound is produced by about five complete waves having fundamental frequencies corresponding approximately to 120 cycles per second. The "a" sound is followed by about twenty complete waves of the "r" sound having this same fundamental frequency, followed by about nine complete waves of the "m" sound also with the same frequency. As the "er" sound was reached, the pitch of the voice was slightly raised to a pitch corresponding to a fundamental frequency of

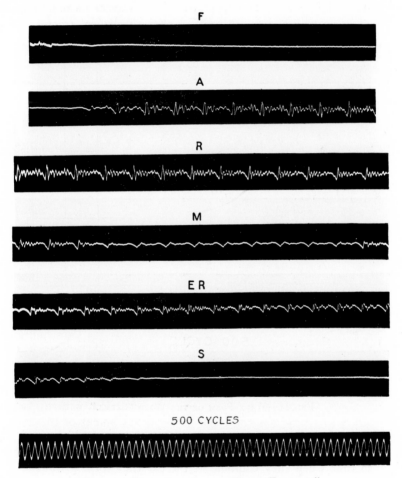

FIG. 24.—WAVE FORM OF THE WORD "FARMERS."

about 130 cycles per second. This was followed by the "s" sound, again characterized by very high frequencies.

Charts for all the speech sounds both for male and female voices were obtained by means of this apparatus. In Figs. 28–39 complete charts are given for twelve of these records, the ones selected by Crandall as being typical. In Figs. 40, 41, and 42 are shown the records taken by the same voice for all the long vowels, the short vowels, and the semi-vowels. Only the typical part of the wave is given for each case. These pictures show the forms of the waves as they emerge from the mouth. In a room with reflecting walls, the sound which finally reaches the ear of a person three or four feet away from the speaker is a combination of the original wave and several reflected waves. The amplitudes

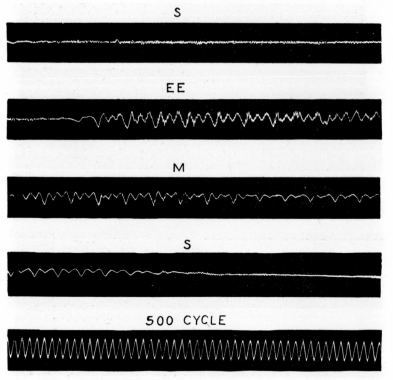

FIG. 25.—WAVE FORM OF THE WORD "SEEMS."

and phases of the components in the reflected waves which reach the ear are very different from those of the original and also from each other, so that when they combine at the ear they form a wave with a shape entirely different from that of the original wave emerging from the mouth. If the phases only of the components are changed and the relative amplitudes remain the same, the ear usually recognizes no change; in other words, the ear does not ordinarily recognize phase differences. To illustrate this change in wave form with phase shift, two graphs representing the vowel sound "ah" are shown in Fig. 43. The amplitudes of the component frequencies were experimentally determined, and the graphs were then calculated. The top wave form represents the wave picture when the component frequencies have no phase displacements.

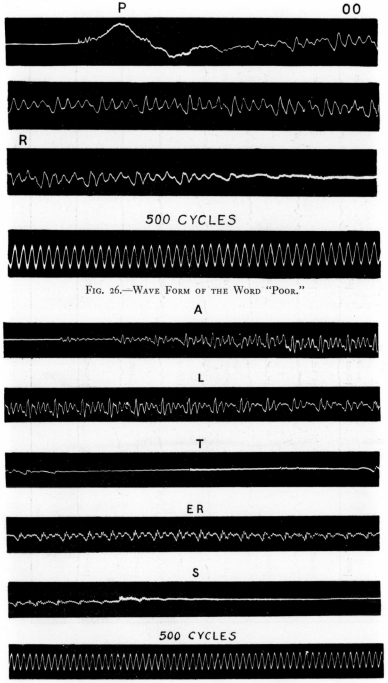

FIG. 26.—WAVE FORM OF THE WORD "POOR."

FIG. 27.—WAVE FORM OF THE WORD "ALTERS."

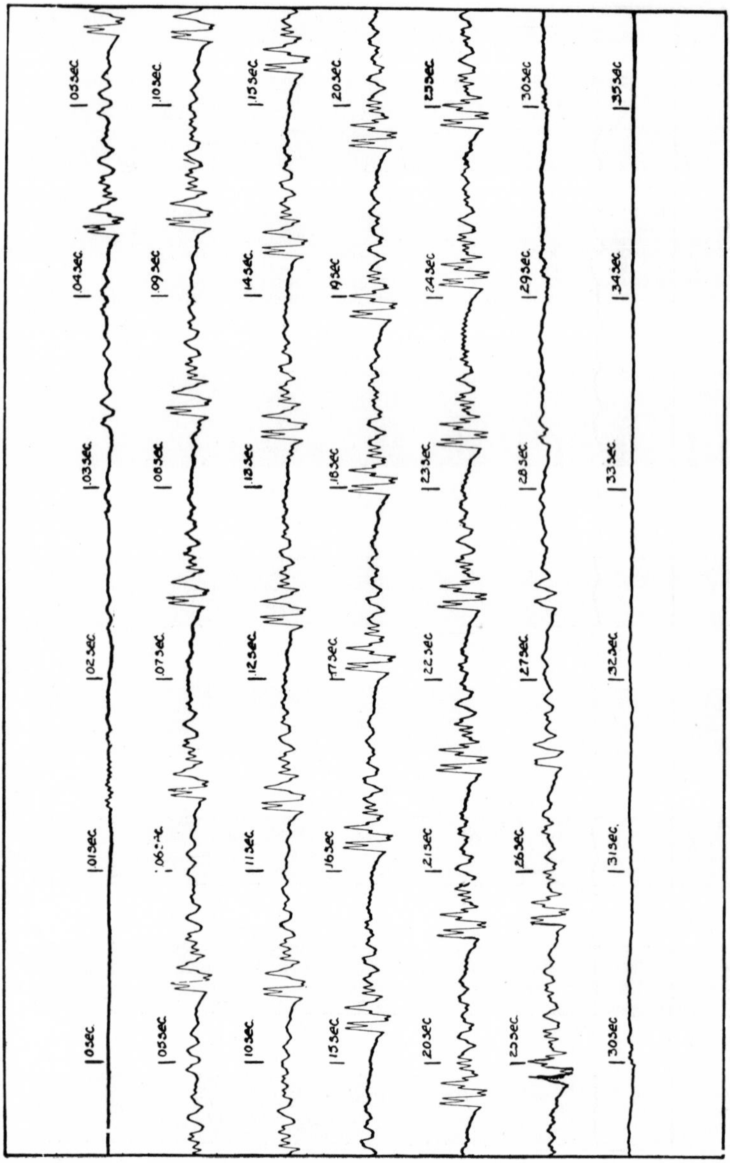

FIG. 28.—"A" AS IN "FATHER." SPOKEN BY M.A.—MALE, LOW-PITCHED.

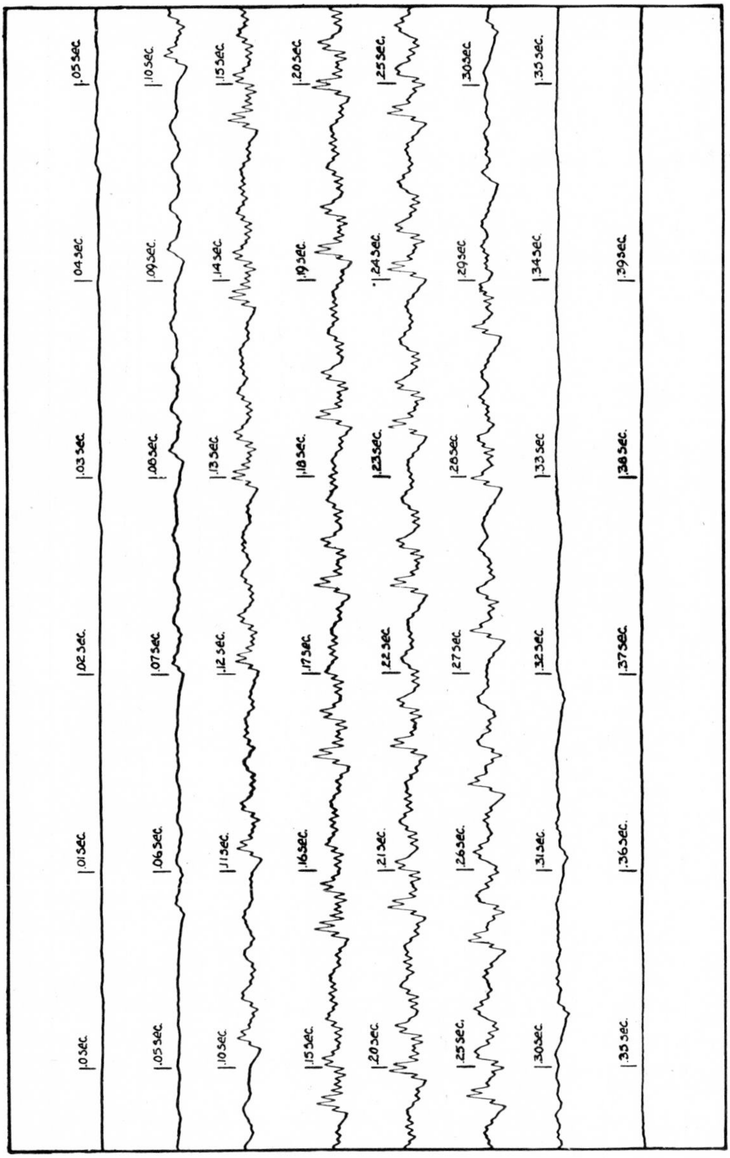

Fig. 29.—"U" as in "Put." Spoken by M.A.—Male, Low-Pitched.

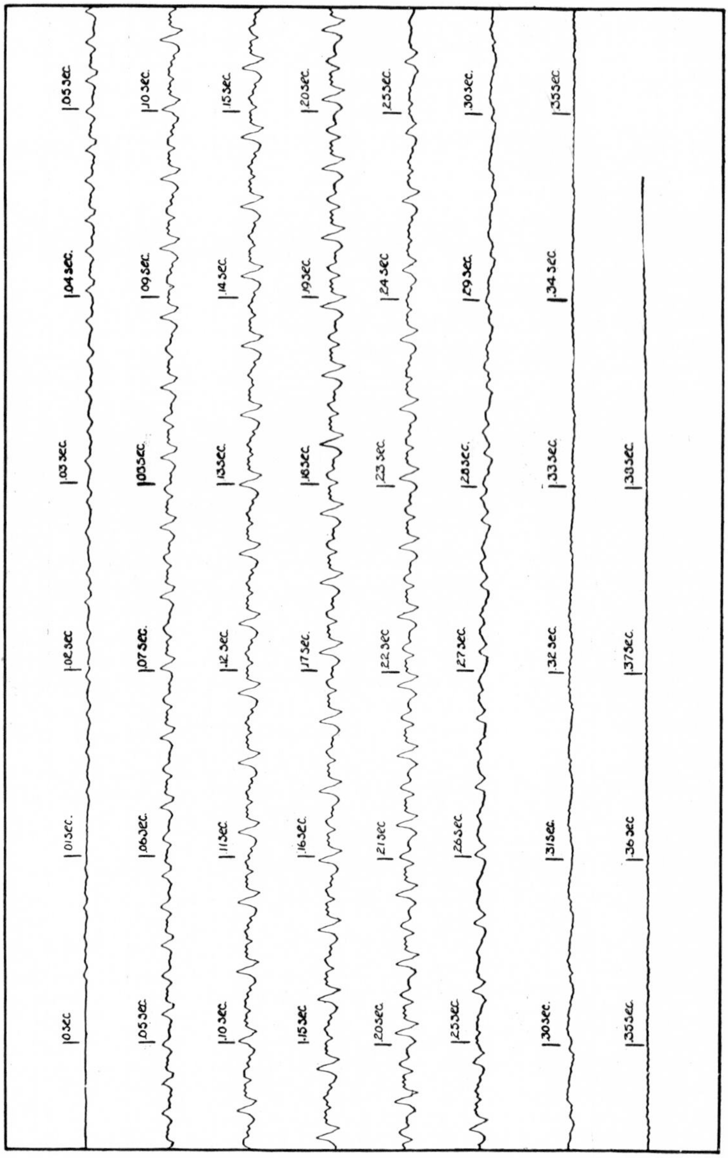

Fig. 30.—"O" as in "Ton." Spoken by F.D.—Female, High-Pitched.

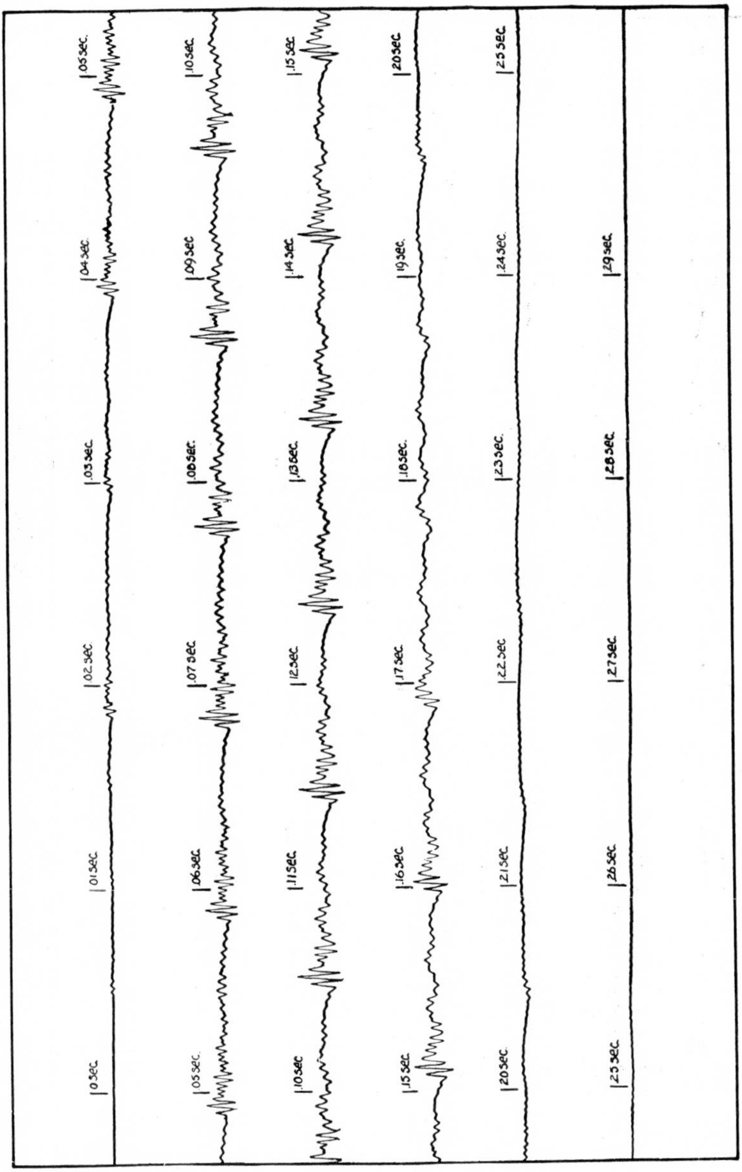

Fig. 31.—"T" as in "Tip." Spoken by M.A.—Male, Low-Pitched.

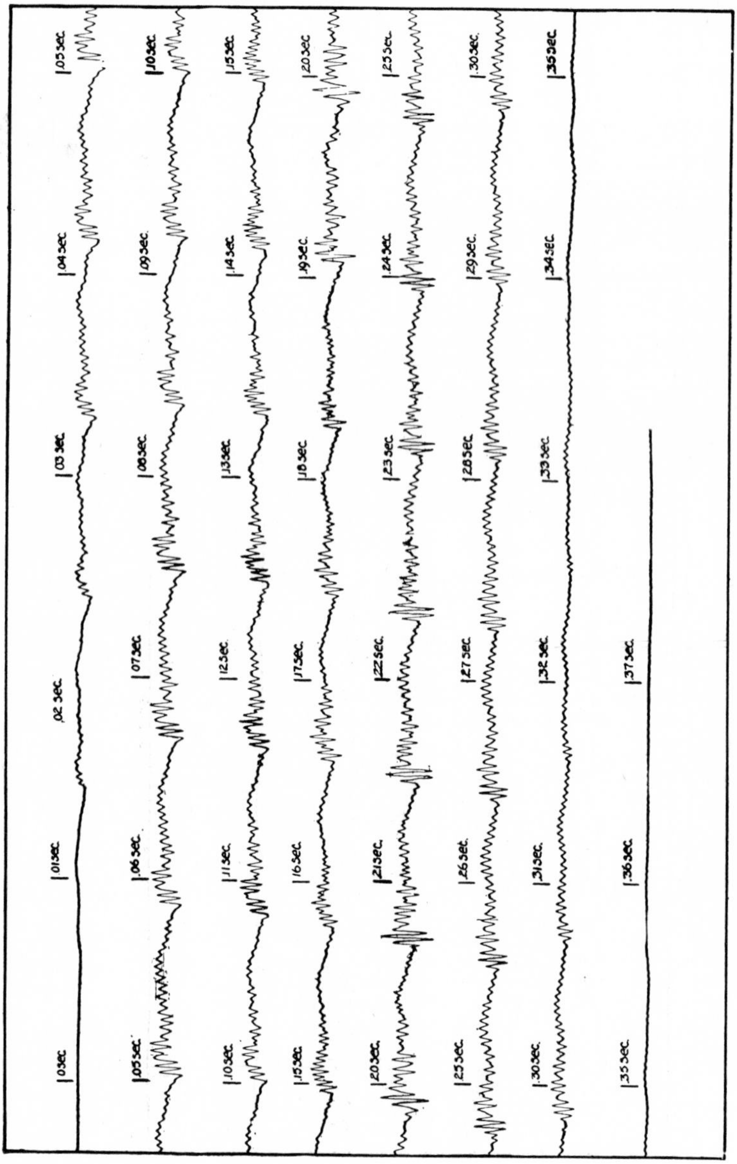

FIG. 32.—"LEE." SPOKEN BY M.B.

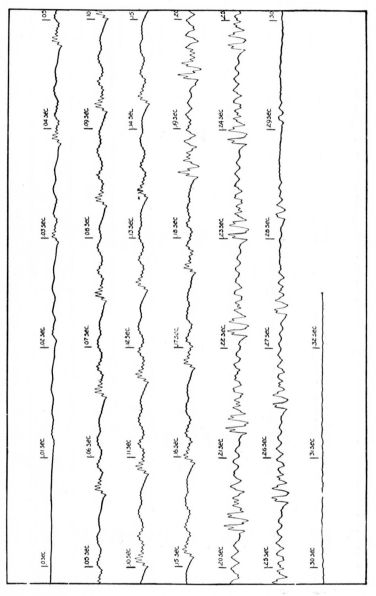

Fig. 33.—"La." Spoken by M.B.

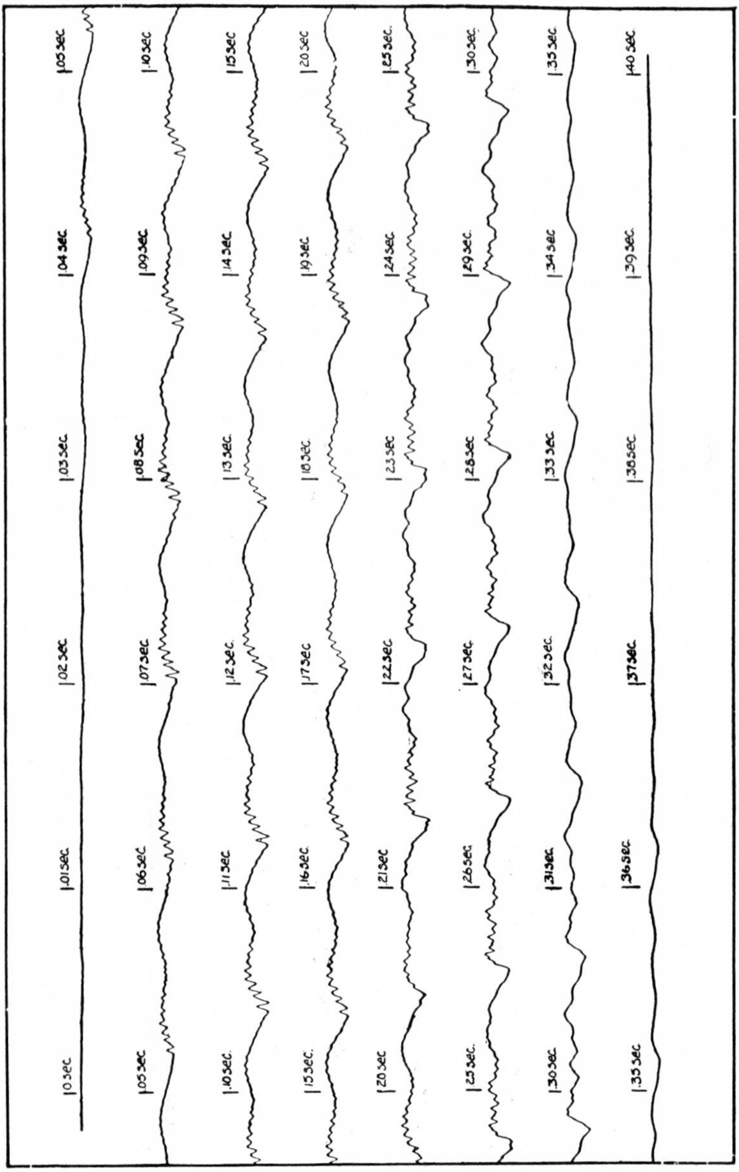

FIG. 34.—"Moo." SPOKEN BY M.B.

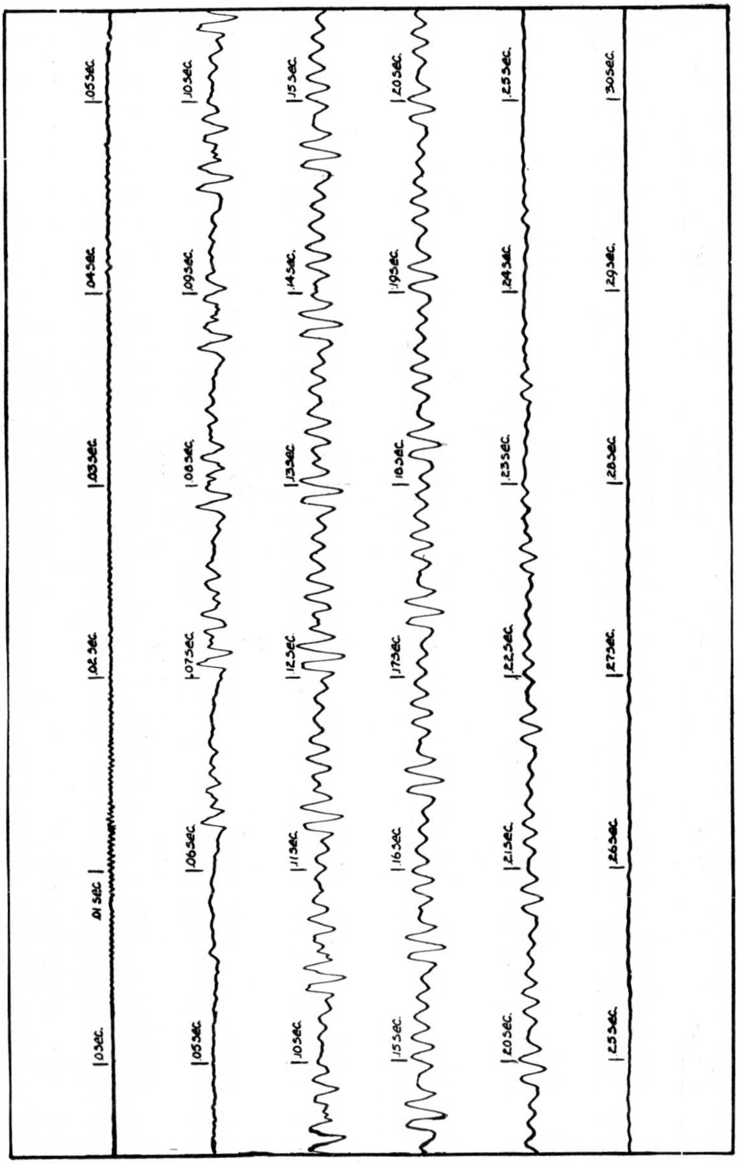

FIG. 35.—"TA," SPOKEN BY M.B.

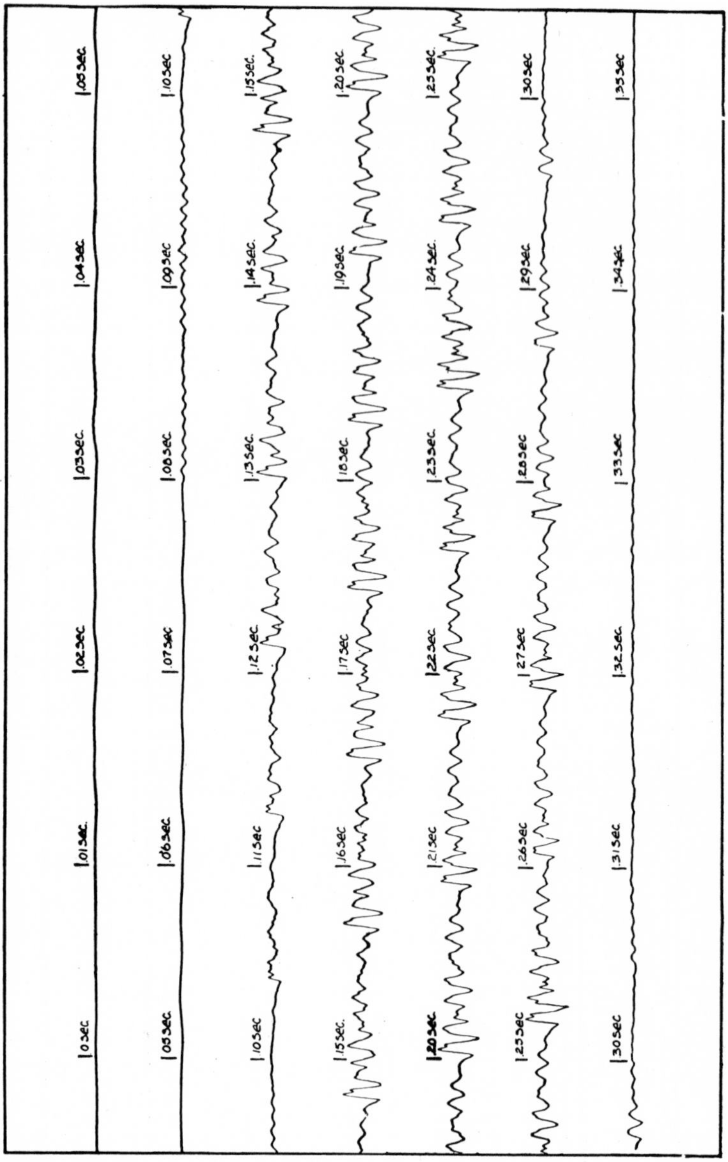

FIG. 36.—"GA," SPOKEN BY M.B.

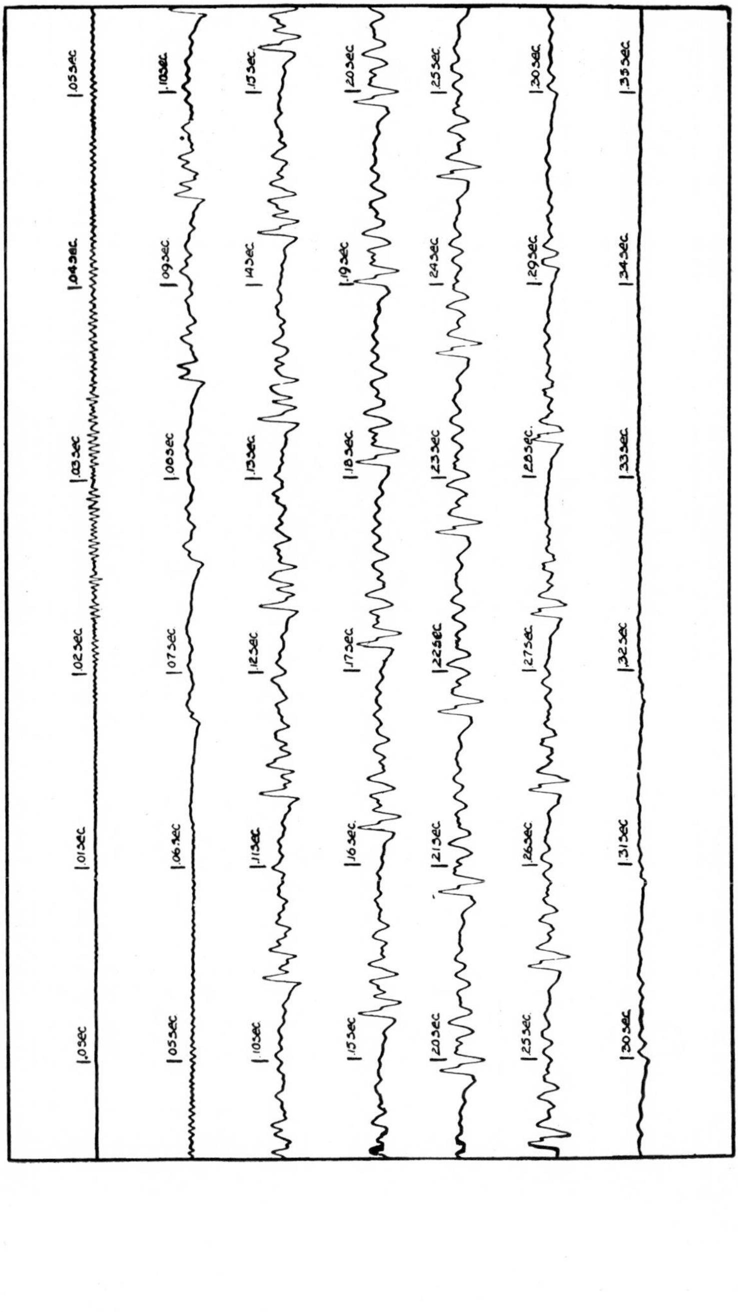

FIG. 37.—"CHA." SPOKEN BY M.A.

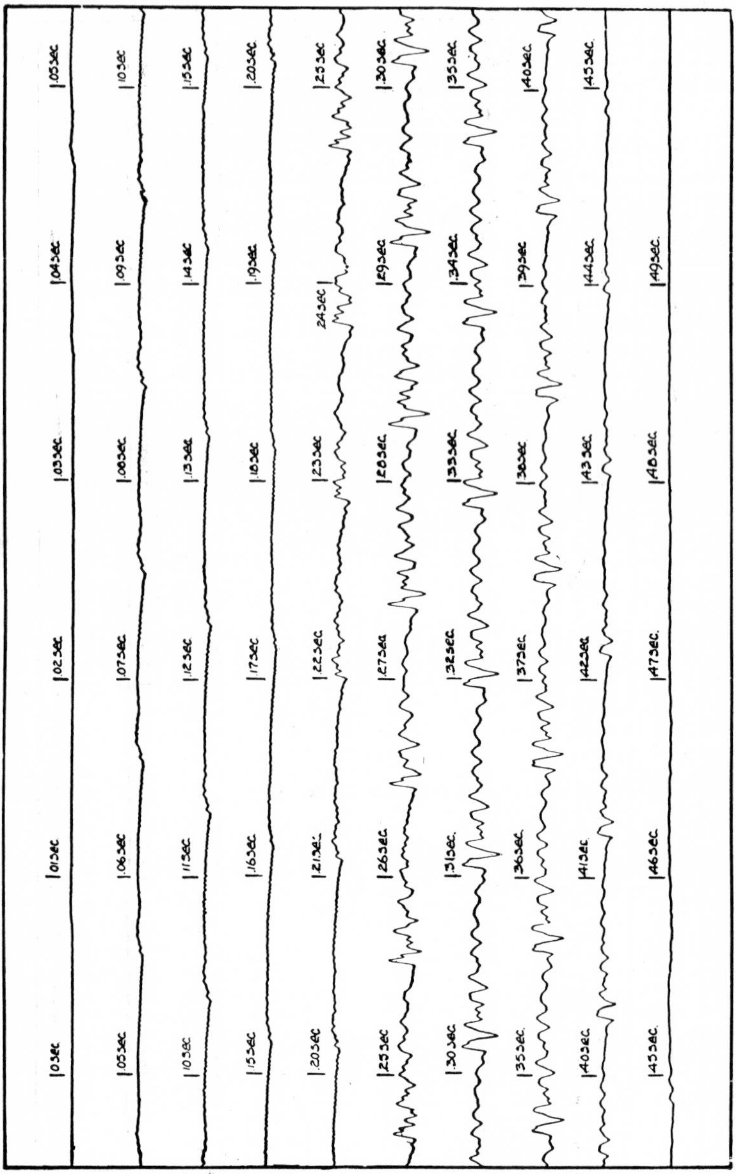

FIG. 38.—"ZA." SPOKEN BY M.B.

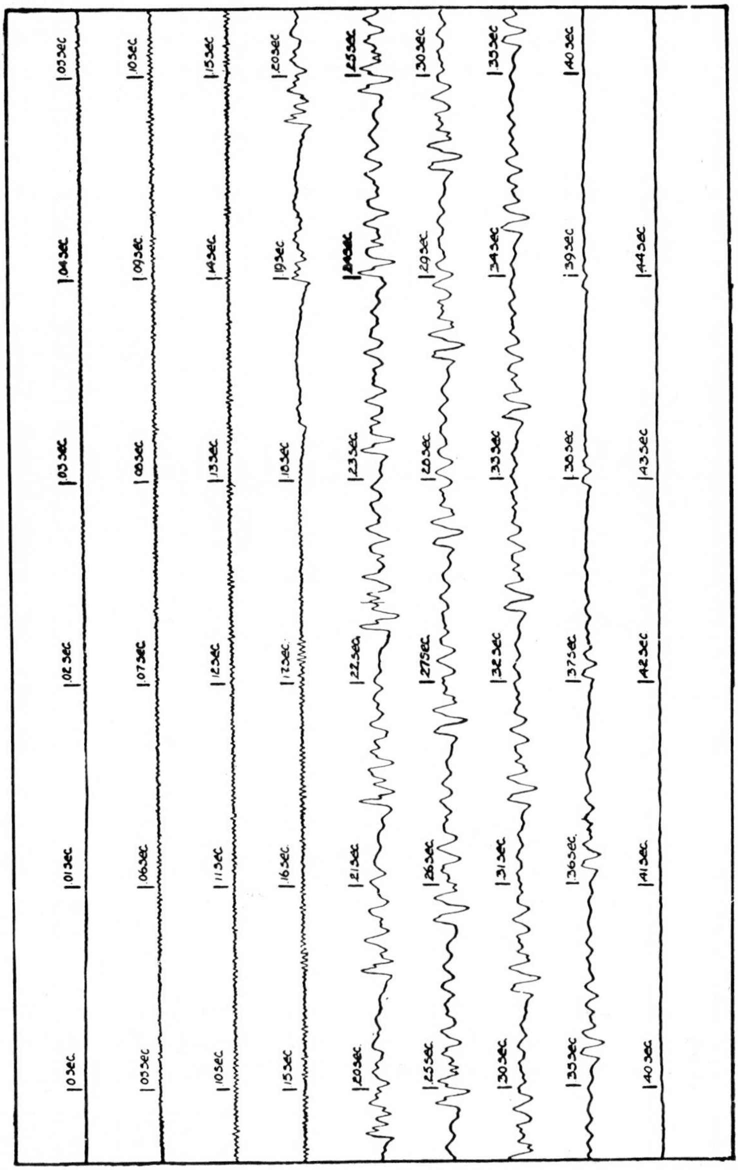

Fig. 39.—"Sa." Spoken by M.B.

The component frequencies of the bottom wave form have the same amplitudes as the first ones, but the phase displacements are proportional to the square root of the frequency. As stated, if the phase displacement is proportional to the frequency of the component, the wave picture does not change. The two wave forms are quite different although the acoustic spectra obtained from them would be the same, and the ear under most circumstances would identify them as the same sound "ah."

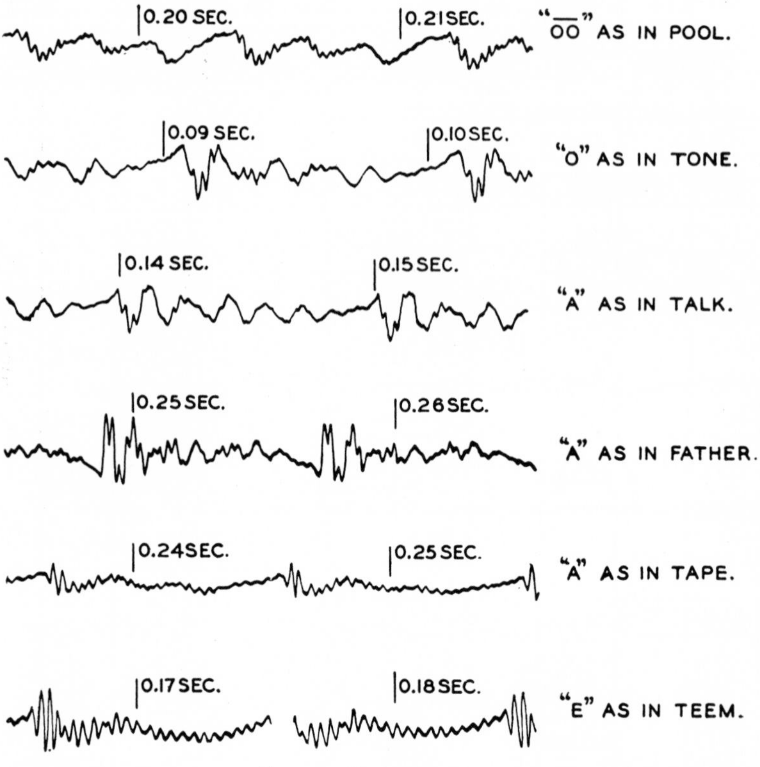

Fig. 40.—Long Vowels.

In Fig. 44 the graphs of four vowel sounds are shown. The first two correspond to "a" as in "father" but pronounced at different pitches, the first by a man and the second by a woman. The wave pictures of these sounds are quite different yet the ear will identify both of them as the vowel "a" more than 99 percent of the time. The first and third pictures and the second and fourth pictures look much more alike yet they are never confused by the ear. It is true that the ear recognizes some similarity between the first and third wave forms; they are both male voices and have the same pitch. Although the form of the speech

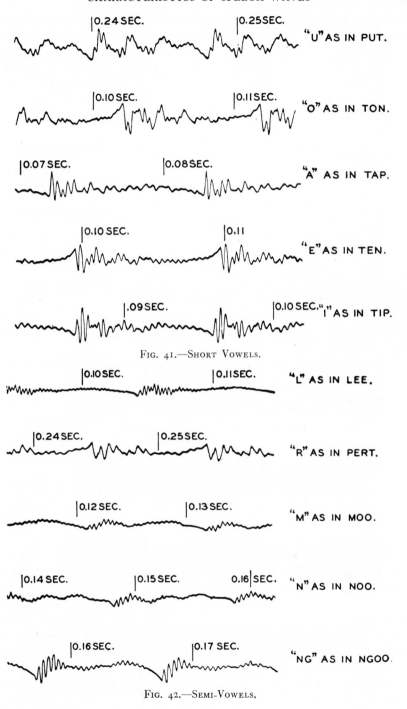

FIG. 41.—SHORT VOWELS.

FIG. 42.—SEMI-VOWELS.

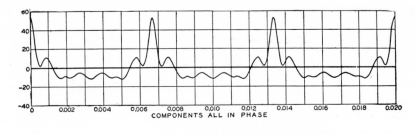

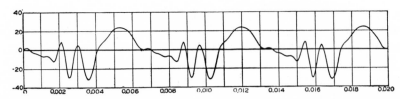

FIG. 43.—TOP WAVE FORM. ALL COMPONENTS IN PHASE. BOTTOM WAVE FORM—PHASE PROPORTIONAL TO THE SQUARE ROOT OF THE FREQUENCY OF THE COMPONENT.

wave as an oscillograph must contain the information which the ear uses to identify the speech sound, it is seen that the form may change radically without losing this pertinent information for determining the recognition aspect of perception.

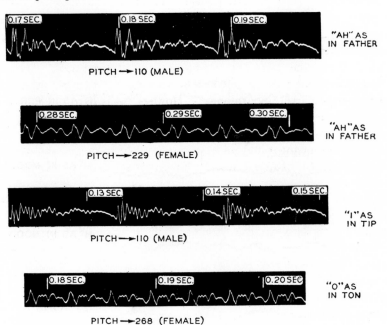

FIG. 44.—WAVE FORMS WHICH SOUND ALIKE BUT LOOK VERY DIFFERENT.

Theories of Vowel Production

The question, therefore, arises as to what characteristics of a speech sound differentiate it from another speech sound. It is evident from the preceding paragraphs that neither the fundamental frequency nor the wave form are the principal determinants of the recognition aspect of perception. Two theories of vowel production have been advanced, namely, the harmonic or steady state theory and the inharmonic or transient theory. In spite of the fact that Helmholtz[2] showed that these two theories were different only in the point of view and the method of representing the same mechanism of vowel production, we still have advocates of the two theories.

The harmonic theory was first advocated by Wheatstone in 1837. According to this theory, the vocal cords generate a complex wave having a fundamental and a large number of harmonics. The component frequencies are all exact multiples of the fundamental. As described previously when these waves pass through the throat, the mouth, and the nasal cavities, those frequencies near the resonant frequencies of these cavities are radiated into the air very much magnified, the amount depending upon the damping constant of the cavity. These reinforced frequency regions determine the vowel quality.

According to the inharmonic theory of Willis (1829) and Herman and Scripture, the vocal cords act only as an agent for exciting the transient frequencies which are characteristic of the vocal cavities. A puff of air from the glottis sets the air in these cavities into vibration. This vibration soon diminishes until it is started anew by a second puff. According to this theory, the puffs do not necessarily follow each other periodically and hence the name "inharmonic." However, it is hard to see how the physical mechanism in the throat can produce anything but fairly regular puffs since these are controlled by the elastic properties of the vocal cords and the two resonant columns of air on either side of them. An examination of the records of speech sounds shows that this is true. The different waves succeed each other quite regularly for small intervals of time. On the other hand, this examination also supports the view that these regular puffs do excite the transients of the mouth and throat cavities, for the amplitudes are large at the beginning of the wave and gradually die away toward the end. This is shown on most of the records but particularly on the three records in Figs. 28, 31, and 32. When the pitch is high, the natural vibrations do not have time to die down before another pulse sets them going again. This is illustrated in the second and fourth pictures of Fig. 44.

[2] Helmholtz, *Sensation of Tone.*

It is evident then that in this theory, as well as in the previous one, the vowel quality is dependent upon the natural frequencies and damping of the vocal cavities.

The difference in the two theories is not, as some suppose, a difference in the conception of what is going on while the vowel sounds are being produced, but in the method of representing or describing the motions in definite physical terms. The second point of view enables one to visualize in a more direct way what is taking place and consequently is of greater value to the phonetician interested in the mechanism of speech production. It probably enables one better to grasp the fundamental characteristic differences between the vowels.

The first point of view is probably more useful to the engineer who is interested in designing telephone systems to transmit speech properly. The separation of the speech into its component frequencies makes it possible to see quickly which frequencies must be transmitted by the system to carry completely all the characteristics of speech. A numerical example may help to make this clear. Let the force which is acting on the resonant cavity of the mouth due to the vibration of the vocal cords be designated by F_k for the kth component, and let f_0 be the resonant frequency of the mouth chamber, and let f_k be the frequency of the impressed force which is the frequency of each component of the sound coming out of the mouth, and Δ be the damping constant in nepers per second. Then if the system may be considered as a singly resonant one, it can be shown that the relative sound pressures for the different components are given by

$$\frac{P_k}{P_1} = \frac{F_k}{F_1} \sqrt{\frac{\left(\dfrac{\Delta}{\pi f_1}\right)^2 + \left[1 - \left(\dfrac{f_0}{f_1}\right)^2\right]^2}{\left(\dfrac{\Delta}{\pi f_k}\right)^2 + \left[R - \dfrac{1}{R}\left(\dfrac{f_0}{f_R}\right)^2\right]^2}} \qquad (3\text{-}10)$$

where P_k is the pressure amplitude of the kth component and P_1 the pressure amplitude of the fundamental. The force F_k varies from one speech sound to another and with different speakers, but for purposes of illustration let it be assumed that

$$\frac{F_1}{F_R} = R^{3/2}.$$

This assumption seems to give results which correspond roughly to the experimental results, as for example, that shown in the lower chart of Fig. 46. Typical values for sound "a" in father are $\Delta = 500$ nepers per second and $f = 900$ cps. In Fig. 45 are shown the calculated relative pressure amplitudes for two cases (1) when $f_1 = 125$ cps; (2) when $f_1 = 250$ cps. Such a representation is called acoustic line spectra.

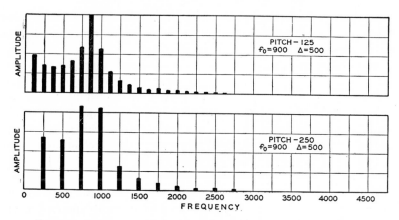

FIG. 45.—CALCULATION OF THE LINE SPECTRA OF VOWELS HAVING A
PITCH DIFFERENCE OF ONE OCTAVE.

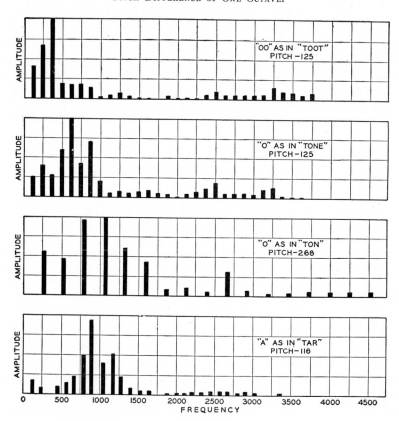

FIG. 46.—LINE SPECTRA OF ū, ō, ŏ, a.

The acoustic spectra of eight of the eleven vowel sounds are shown in Figs. 46 and 47. These spectra were obtained from typical wave pictures taken with the high quality oscillograph. Only the steady-state part of the wave was analyzed.[3]

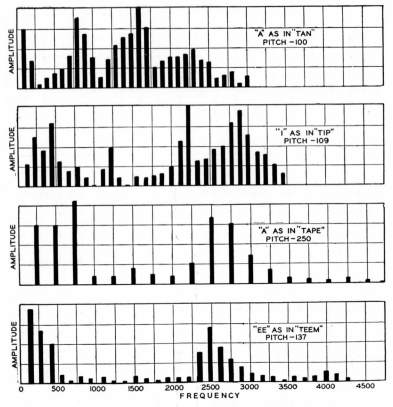

FIG. 47.—LINE SPECTRA OF ă, i, ā, AND ē.

Maxima similar to those in the two calculated cases are plainly evident in these charts. Those spectra shown in Fig. 46 have one principal region of resonance with indications of one or more regions of less importance while those in Fig. 47 have two principal regions of resonance with other smaller ones. It is well to emphasize here the fact that these charts represent the results obtained with typical voices. When the records of several speakers are analyzed, quite different acoustic spectra are obtained, but, in general, the regions of maximum amplitude are approximately the same.

[3] These acoustic spectra were computed by W. Koenig of the American Telephone and Telegraph Company.

In order to show the effect of pitch upon the acoustic spectra of vowel sounds, an analysis was made of vowels intoned at pitches corresponding to the notes of the major chord, namely, at frequencies 128, 160, 192, and 256 cps.   The resulting spectra for ē and ā are shown in Figs. 48 and 49. It will be noticed that for the sound ē the frequency regions 300 and 2300 cps and for the sound ā the regions 500 and 1900 cps are magnified.

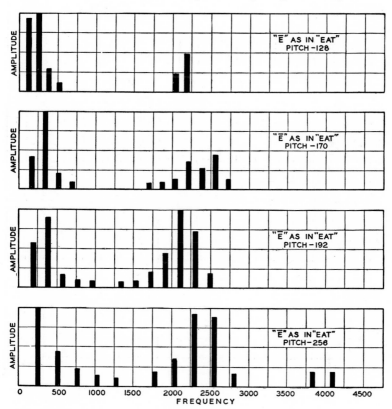

FIG. 48.—LINE SPECTRA OF ē WHEN PRONOUNCED AT FOUR DIFFERENT PITCHES.

With these concepts in mind we return now to the sentence, "Joe took father's shoe bench out."   As these waves strike the ear, the listener does not sense the separate successive condensations but only the rate at which they are hitting the ear.   As this rate is increased or lowered, a listener perceives an increasing or lowering of the pitch of the tone.

If we analyze the wave when the sentence, "Joe took father's shoe bench out," is spoken, the variations in pitch of the speech sounds can be determined from the vibration rate.   Such an analysis is shown in Fig. 50. The frequency is represented on the vertical axis.   The duration of the sounds in fractions of a second is represented on the horizontal axis. It will be seen that the pitch rises and falls as the various sounds are spoken. This representation of the pitch variation is called the fundamental melodic stream. It is the melody in the same sense as this term is used in music, although it is evident that the pitch changes do not take place in musical intervals as would be the case if the sentence were sung.

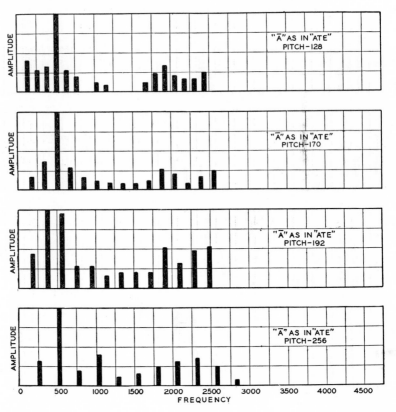

FIG. 49.—LINE SPECTRA OF ā WHEN PRONOUNCED AT FOUR DIFFERENT PITCHES.

To show the contrast a graph was made when the sentence was intoned on the musical intervals do, re, me, fa, me, re, do. An analysis of the graph gave the result also shown in Fig. 50. In the case of the sung sentence the pitch changes are around definite intervals on the musical scale while for the spoken sentence the pitch varies irregularly, depending upon the emphasis given. The pitch of the fricative and stop consonants is ignored in the musical score, and since these consonants form no part of the music, they are generally slid over, making it difficult for a listener to understand the meaning of the words. Some teachers of music object

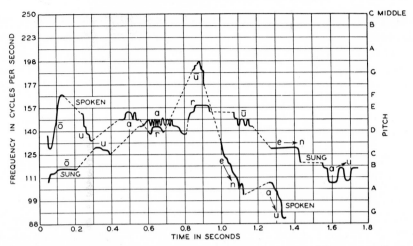

FIG. 50.—MELODIC CURVES. "JOE TOOK FATHER'S SHOE BENCH OUT" SPOKEN AND SUNG.

to this statement of the situation, but I think most people will agree that a singer's principal aim is to produce beautiful vowel quality and to manipulate the melodic stream so as to produce emotional effects. To do this, it is necessary in singing to lengthen the vowels and to shorten

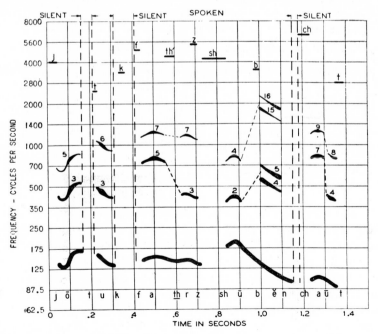

FIG. 51.—MELODIC CURVES. "JOE TOOK FATHER'S SHOE BENCH OUT" SPOKEN.

and give less emphasis to the stop and fricative consonants. It is for this reason that it is more difficult to understand song than speech.

There are two secondary melodic streams of speech represented by the second and third curves from the bottom of Fig. 51 which are due to the resonances imposed upon the speech sound by the throat and mouth cavities. The numbers on these curves give the number of the harmonic which is reinforced. These two secondary melodic streams are not sensed as changes in pitch but rather as changes in the vowel quality. Then there

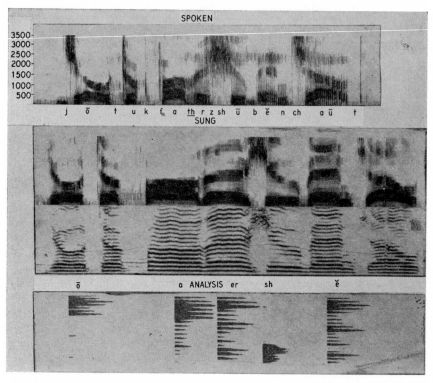

FIG. 52.—SENTENCE, "JOE TOOK FATHER'S SHOE BENCH OUT," SPOKEN AND SUNG, AND ANALYSIS.

is a fourth stream, or it would probably be better to say, a fourth series of interrupted sounds which are very high in pitch and are the sounds which enable us to identify the fricative consonants. The secondary melodic streams produced while speaking the same sentence are approximately the same for different persons, even for a man and a woman, while the fundamental melodic stream is usually quite different. This latter stream is not used in identifying words, but it is used sometimes to give different meanings to the same words.

The analysis of this sentence was made about twenty years ago. The spectrograph described in Chaper 2 will make a somewhat similar analysis and automatically plot the results in three or four minutes time. In Fig. 52 is shown the spectorgram of this sentence taken with this instrument. The top chart of this figure is for the case when the sentence is spoken and a 300-cycle filter is used in the spectrograph. It will be remembered that the vertical axis represents "frequency" and the horizontal axis, "time," and the relative blackness is a function of the intensity of the component frequencies. The two and sometimes three broad bars represent the formant frequency of the vowels and are called, as mentioned above, the two secondary melodic streams.

The second chart from the top gives a similar spectrogram for the sung sentence. It will be noticed that the bars representing the sung vowel remain horizontal and are much longer than for the same spoken vowels.

In the third chart the sentence was sung, but a narrow band filter was used in the spectrograph. With such a narrow band pass filter the components (harmonics) are shown by the horizontal lines, and it is seen that the melody is carried by each component. For the tenth harmonic the variation in frequency is ten times that for the fundamental, but the variation in the logarithm of the frequency is the same for all the components. This latter physical quantity corresponds more nearly to the pitch aspect of perception. This aspect of pitch will be discussed more in detail in a later section. The relative blackness gives only a rough notion of the relative intensities of the components because in the recording circuit there is an automatic gain control which reduces a large range of intensities to a very small one. However, the spectrograph has a feature for showing the relative intensity of these harmonics over a small interval of time, the position of this interval being placed anywhere along the time axis. It is called the slicer as it takes a sample slice at any position. Such a slice at five positions is shown at the bottom of Fig. 52. The horizontal peak for each component is proportional to the relative intensity level of the components in decibels. For example, in the lowest chart is shown the analysis for the sounds ō, a, er, and ah and ĕ. The vertical scale gives a mirror image of the frequency scale shown on the top chart. The horizontal extent of the lines represent the relative intensity level in db of the various components. In other words, the slicer portrays the line spectra of the speech sounds. It will be seen that for ō, a, er, and ĕ the line spectra are defined, but for sh the sound energy is scattered over the frequency region indicated.

The characteristic formant frequencies are indicated for ō as about 500 and 1100 cps; for er as 600, 1500, and 2800 cps; for a as about 600 and 1300 cps; and for ĕ as about 550, 1800, and 300 cps.

General Characteristics of Speech

The pitch of the voice when speaking the vowels varies with different individuals, corresponding to about 90 cycles per second for a very deep-voiced man and to about 300 cycles per second for a shrill-voiced woman. The average pitch used by a woman is near middle C or 256 cycles per second and that by a man is about one octave lower. The oscillograph records show that there is usually, although not always, a rise in pitch as the sound progresses. Speaking concerning the general characteristics as deduced from these records, Crandall[4] says:

"Consider now the general properties of the spoken vowel sound as deduced from these records. First there is a period of rapid growth in amplitude lasting about .04 second during which all components are quickly produced and rise nearly to a maximum amplitude; second, the middle period, the characteristics of which have been noted, lasting about .165 second, followed by the period of gradual decay lasting about 0.09 second, bringing the total length to approximately 0.295 second. There is a tendency to short duration among the 'short' vowels (e.g., short O, e, i) and a tendency to longer records among the broader sounds, as might be expected."

"The behavior of the fundamental frequency (or 'cord tone') during the course of the record will follow normal or individual characteristics as has been described."

"The low frequency characteristic appears early, usually before the fourth cycle (for men) or before the seventh (for women) and normally is in harmonic relation with the fundamental. In the eleven pure vowel sounds this point was examined at 264 locations in 88 records with the result that the harmonic relation obtained in at least 214 cases. Furthermore, the normal behavior of the amplitude of the low frequency characteristic suggests the decay of a transient oscillation during each fundamental cycle—this effect being noticeable in at least 64 of the 88 pure vowel records. This transient effect was also noticeable in 13 of the 16 records of ar and er, where the harmonic effect was not so noticeable.[5] The appearance of the transient effect depends to some extent on the relative frequencies of the fundamental and the characteristic; where the fundamental period is short (as often in the case of the women's records) there is not sufficient time for decay of the characteristic tone before it receives a new impetus in the next cycle of the fundamental."

"As noted above, all the records contain high frequency vibrations which are of such amplitude that they suggest characteristic frequencies.

[4] Bell Technical Journal, October, 1925.

[5] These are very apt to be diphtongal in character which may account for this lack of harmonic effect.

A general mean of these frequencies would be in the neighborhood of 3200 cycles, and in the case of two records by speaker FC (Group I and Group XIII) the frequency rises to about 5000 cycles. Recalling the usual classification of the vowel sounds into two groups—(1) those of 'single' resonance, placed on the left leg of the triangle, and (2) those of 'double' resonance placed on the right leg of the triangle—there are some differences in the behavior of the high frequency components which can be related to these broad classes. In the sounds of the first class the high frequency component is usually small in amplitude, more subject to individual bias in its frequency, and may or may not build up in amplitude as early as the low frequency characteristic. In the sounds of the second class the high frequency characteristic is usually prominent from the start and builds up very rapidly; while there is less variation in its frequency with the individual speaker. In sounds of the first class there is no decided suggestion of a transient in the high frequency while in sounds of the second class the transient effect is pronounced."

"With these considerations in mind there is presented in Table I a summary of the data obtained from this preliminary examination of the vowel records. The mean duration time, and its subdivisions, are shown in the second column for each pure vowel sound, with mean duration only for the sounds ar (Group VII) and er (Group X). The fundamental and characteristic frequencies of each sound are shown in the three columns headed 'Mean High Characteristic Frequency' respectively. Each mean is taken from four records. The two columns headed 'Scattered Low Frequency' and 'Scattered High Frequency' contain mean values of additional components, occurring in one or more records, in certain frequency ranges, the number of records in which such components are noted being shown in parentheses following the mean. The table illustrates and emphasizes many points which have been brought out in the preceding discussion, particularly the closeness with which the high frequency characteristics are defined in the vowels of the second or 'doubly-resonant' class."

Potter and Steinberg have obtained spectrographs of all the speech sounds. In Fig. 53 they are given for the cases of every consonant-vowel combination. Each of the consonants listed in a horizontal line across the top of this chart was pronounced and followed by each of the vowels in the vertical column. In the first vertical row, the steady intoned vowel without beginning or ending consonant is shown. The influence of the various consonants is clearly shown.

An analysis of the format frequencies from intoned vowels was made. After considering these data, the data of Crandall and Sacia, and some of the earlier observers, it was concluded that the characteristic formant frequencies for the vowels and semi-vowels are those in Fig. 54. However, as more data become available it is apparent there are considerable variations from these values by different speakers and also by the same speaker at different times.

There is usually a third and sometimes a fourth format frequency in the high range, but the variations from speaker to speaker and from word

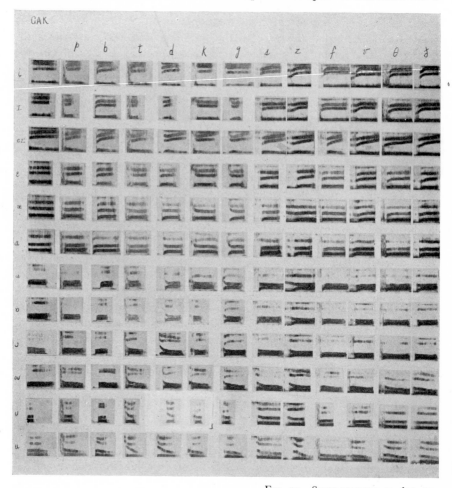

FIG. 53.—SPECTROGRAMS OF ALL OF

to word are so great that these higher components are considered to be characteristic of the speaker rather than of the vowel.

The recent work of Potter and Steinberg indicates that all the format frequencies are slightly higher for a woman's voice and considerably higher for a child's voice. They suggest that it is probably some relation between their format frequencies rather than the absolute values that are characteristic of the vowels. In any case it is known that the manner of starting and stopping a vowel gives more information that may be used to recognize it than is given by the formant frequencies.

Sixteen consonant sounds were studied by Crandall and he summarizes his results in Table 2 with the following comments:

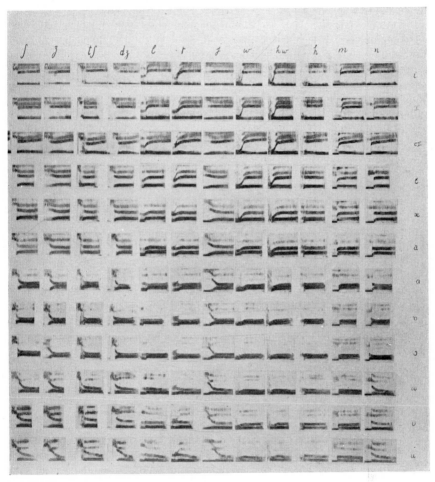

THE VOWEL AND CONSONANT SOUNDS.

b versus p

"Both Paget and Miller have noted the essential impulsive quality of these sounds, and have produced them by sudden closing and opening of the mouth of a resonator. Paget considers p to be the essential impulsive quality of these sounds, and have produced them by sudden closing

TABLE I

STATISTICAL DATE FROM 104 RECORDS OF VOWEL SOUNDS

Sound	Duration				Mean Fundamental Frequency		Mean Low Characteristic Frequency		Scattered Low Frequency		Mean High Characteristic Frequency		Scattered High Frequency	
	Start	Middle	Decay	Total	Male	Female	Male	Female	Male	Female	Male	Female	Male	Female
I oo (pool)	.061	.164	.126	.351	140	270	411	581	750 (1)	1200 (1)	.....	.....	3700 (4)	4412 (4)
II u (put)	.057	.115	.077	.249	138	250	457	691	988 (4)	1100 (3)	.....	.....	3637 (4)	4250 (4)
III o (tone)	.053	.139	.133	.325	116	237	520	729	830 (3)	1112 (4)	.....	.....	3475 (4)	3700 (4)
IV a (talk)	.034	.191	.065	.290	112	243	722	801	950 (2)	1150 (2)	.....	.....	3612 (4)	4075 (4)
V o (ton)	.046	.179	.061	.280	118	253	654	854	1100 (4)	1188 (4)	.....	.....	3212 (4)	3353 (3)
VI a (father)	.029	.199	.078	.306	113	234	955	1036	1150 (2)	1425 (2)	.....	.....	3683 (4)	4200 (3)
VII ar (part)	.....	.....	.....	.345	110	231	630	701	917 (3)	1012 (4)	1965	2162	3800 (2)	4150 (1)
									Note 1	Note 1	Note 1	Note 1		
VIII a (tap)	.038	.180	.076	.294	123	232	796	960	.....	.....	1900	2165	3150 (3)	3175 (2)
IX e (ten)	.034	.119	.066	.219	121	247	612	775	.....	.....	1800	2000	2925 (4)	2925 (4)
											Note 2	Note 2	Note 2	
X er (pert)	.....	.....	.....	.331	131	239	570	712	.....	.....	1688	2188	3050 (2)	3500 (1)
XI a (tape)	.042	.172	.091	.305	125	235	494	614	.....	.....	3000	2800	.....	.....
XII i (tip)	.036	.126	.049	.211	137	253	450	523	.....	.....	2950	2962	.....	.....
XIII e (team)	.036	.189	.116	.341	136	252	296	332	.....	.....	2987	3266	.....	4800 (1)
Means or "Normals"	.042	.161	.085	.288 (11) / .296 (13)	125	244								

NOTE 1—Both of these sets of frequencies must be characteristic of *ar*.

NOTE 2—The high frequency characteristics are less definitely located, for short *e*, than for any other doubly resonant vowel sound.
The two sets of frequencies given above define a band of frequencies centered about 2400 cycles within which the characteristic high frequency must be contained.

and opening of the mouth of a resonator.   Paget considers p to be the
more suddenly released, i.e., to have the steeper wave-front.   From the
records this is not evident; following the voicing period, the b would seem
to be more suddenly produced, as judged by the growth in amplitude of
the 'a' sound following.''

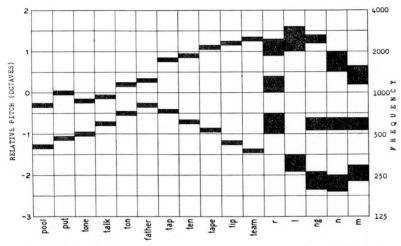

FIG. 54.—CHARACTERISTIC RESONANCE POSITIONS FOR THE SPOKEN VOWELS.

d VERSUS t

"For these (see Table 2) we note a high-frequency characteristic of
about 4000 cps.   Paget observed an upper resonance 5 to 8 semi-tones
higher than that of the associated vowel, and a low resonance of about
362 cps.   We note in the records a low frequency of the order of 500
cps, in the case of d.   Paget notes a 'greater amplitude in t due to higher
air pressure' and the records show a greater amplitude for the high
frequency in the case of t, except right at the transition point, where d
shows the high frequency of large amplitude.   No conclusion can be
given as to relative steepness of wave-front, d versus t, because in both
cases we note for speaker MB a steeper wave-front than for MA.   The
difference between d and t may depend entirely on the voicing and on
the complicated phenomena at the transition point.''

g VERSUS k

"k shows the characteristic transients (1500, 4000; Table 2, notes
4 and 5) to much more pronounced degree than g.   From the records
it would seem that g, in addition to the voicing, disclosed a steeper
wave-front, the four transitional cycles required for k emphasizing
this point.   No other generalizations seem warranted, on account of the

TABLE 2

SIX STOP CONSONANTS; TRANSITIONAL th AND th

Plate No.	Sound	Speaker	Duration	Consonant Characteristics				Transitional Characteristics				Vowel Fundamental	
				Near Start		Mid Portion to End		Low Frequency	High Frequency (Note 6)	No. of Cycles	First Cycle Short	Near Start	Near End
				Voicing (Fundamental and Harmonics)	High Frequency	Voicing	High Frequency						
129	ba	MA	.12	90,180	none	90,180	none	700	2700	1	......	100	115
130	ba	MB	.19	100,200	none	92,184	none	700	3100	1	yes	116	107
131	pa	MA	.02	unvoiced	none	unvoiced	2800 (Note 2)	1000	3600	1	yes	100	111
132	pa	MB	.04	(one 60-cycle vibration)	none	(one 60-cycle vibration)	3800	900	3600	1	yes	119	114
133	da	MA	.13	90,180	none	79,158	3800 (Note 3)	500	2800	3	yes	103	115
134	da	MB	.10	98,196	none	98,196	3600	600	3200	2	......	112	109
135	ta	MA	.07	unvoiced	none	(one 100-cycle vibration)	4300 (Note 3)	......	3200	4	yes	104	112
136	ta	MB	.06	unvoiced	none	unvoiced	3600	900	3000	2	yes	120	113
137	ga	MA	.12	100,200,300	none	84,252	1600, 2800 (Note 4)	550	3000	3	......	101	111
138	ga	MB	.10	100,200,300	none	95,190	1400, 4000	600	3600	2	......	112	112
139	ka	MA	.07	unvoiced	none	unvoiced	1500, 4000 (Note 5)	1200	3800	4	yes	109	118
140	ka	MB	.08	unvoiced	none	unvoiced	1600, 4200	1300	4000	4	yes	125	116
141	dtha	MA	.20	83,166	4000 (Note 1)	95,189	4200 (Note 1)	600	3000	2	......	104	116
142	dtha	MB	.18	100,200	2600	100,200	2700	600	2600	4	......	109	107
143	tha	MA	.02	unvoiced	none	unvoiced	none	600	3200	1	yes	110	110
144	tha	MB	.02	unvoiced	none	(one 100-cycle vibration)	none	600	3200	1	yes	113	107

NOTE 1—A trace of these at beginning of the early fundamental cycles. NOTE 2—One faint transient. NOTE 3—Transients; longer for ta than for da. NOTE 4—One transient. NOTE 5—Irregular transients. NOTE 6—Possibly due in some cases to the a sound.

complicated series of events recorded. These sounds are treated at length by Paget who observes considerable variation in their resonant ranges, depending on the associated vowel. It will be noted, however, that in these four records, particularly consonant characteristics are persistent and of large amplitude before the vowel sound begins to appear."

th versus th

"The high frequencies (2600, 3000, 3200) culminating at the transition point seem to be the key to these records. They are more persistent for *th*, while th appears to show the steeper wave-front. Paget states that 'in *th* the middle resonance is overblown, . . . louder than the corresponding resonance in th. He gives also an 'upper sibilant of 3444–5650' louder for *th* than th, and 'difficult to identify.' It was noted that in one record for *th* there is during the voicing period a faint high frequency which has been set down in Table 2 as 4000 cycles. This faint 'sibilant' (which may always be audible though it fail to be recorded) establishes a certain kinship between these two sounds and those following (the fricative consonants) which are rich in sibilant sounds."

v versus f

"v shows a pronounced voicing, and previously noted, a less prominent high-frequency component than its partner f, or any of the other fricative consonants. Comparing v versus f with *th* versus th it seems from the records that the former pair are of higher frequency (particularly f) and that for v and f the higher frequency characteristic is more pronounced; just the opposite conclusion to that reached by Paget. f may indeed differ more from v than v from *th*, thus raising difficulties of classification both physically and phonetically, which cannot be resolved on the basis of the few records available. The exceedingly fine distinction between the sounds v and *th* could be no more strikingly shown than it is in the records given, for both speakers."

j versus ch

"Some of the recorded phenomena of this pair suggest correspondences between them and the pair g and k; but the pair j and ch shows a higher frequency characteristic during the important mid-portion of its history. Of the pair, ch seems to show the steeper wave-front, that is, the more rapid transition to the vowel sound."

zh versus sh

"With this pair we pass to the field of pure sibilants, in which there is no evidence of impulsive action or steepness of wave-front. The action

TABLE 3

FRICATIVE CONSONANTS

Plate No.	Sound	Speaker	Duration	Consonant Characteristics				Transitional Characteristics				Vowel Fundamental	
				Near Start		Mid-portion to End		Low Frequency	High Frequency (Note 3)	No. of Cycles	First Cycle Short	Near Start	Near End
				Voicing (Fundamental and Harmonics)	High Frequency	Voicing	High Frequency						
145	va	MA	.20	97,195,390	3000	87,174	none	600	2700	3	......	101	116
146	va	MB	.25	112,224	3200 (trace)	100,200	none	600	3400	2	......	112	107
147	fa	MA	.15	unvoiced	3100	unvoiced	3500, 7000	500	2800	4	yes	112	121
148	fa	MB	.30	irregular	3200, 6400	unvoiced	3200, 6400	600	3600	3	yes	111	104
149	ja	MA	.22	81,243	3400	81,162	2600, 5200	450	2700	4	......	110	110
150	ja	MB	.14	trace	3300	90,179	2000, 4800	500	3100	4	......	115	111
151	cha	MA	.07	unvoiced	4800	unvoiced	2800, 4800	{500, 1500	3000	2	yes	104	111
152	cha	MB	.08	unvoiced	3600	unvoiced	3600, 6400	{500, 1600	trace	2	yes	119	115
153	zha	MA	.28	86,172,344	3000, 4000 (Note 1)	87	3000, 4000 (Note 1)	450	2900	4	......	100	111
154	zha	MB	.13	96	2600, 4200	99	3000, 4200	{500, 2000	......	4	......	114	111
155	sha	MA	.18	unvoiced	2800, 3600 (Note 2)	unvoiced	2800, 4600 (Note 2)	450	3200	3	yes	104	104
156	sha	MB	.17	unvoiced	2200, 5000	unvoiced	2600, 500	{500, 1800	2800	3	yes	117	112
157	za	MA	.24	96,384	2800, 5600 (Note 1)	89,178	5200, 7000 (Note 1)	400	3100	4	......	98	108
158	za	MB	.22	100,300	2200, 4400	100,200	2800, 5600	550	2800	5	......	111	107
159	sa	MA	.27	unvoiced	5600, 8000	unvoiced	6000, 7800	500	2900	2	yes	114	114
160	sa	MB	.19	unvoiced	4000, 6400	unvoiced	4200, 6600	650	2900	2	yes	117	108

NOTE 1—Alternating; lower frequency in first part of fundamental cycle, higher frequency in latter part of cycle.
NOTE 2—Alternating, irregularly.
NOTE 3—Possibly due to the a sound.

seems to be that in the voiced sound there is, in addition to the presence of the fundamental tone, a breaking up of the characteristic high frequency wave-train into discrete units corresponding to the fundamental tone, whereas in the unvoiced sound the high frequency characteristic is continuous, though irregular. Thus noting that the characteristic frequency is of 3000 to 4600 cycles the outstanding phenomena of zh and sh are well defined. In addition to frequencies of 2048–3249 noted by Paget, he gives a 'pronounced middle resonance of 1625–2048.' This latter observation of Paget's may correspond to the 1800–2000 frequency in the records of MB in the transition region, but this component does not seem to be prominent in the records."

Z VERSUS S

"The general properties of these sounds can be inferred from the discussion of the preceding pair (zh and sh), adding only the fact that their principal characteristic is of much higher frequency. From Table 3 we note a range of 4200–8000 cycles; Paget gives 'a characteristic upper resonance of 5790–6886.' Paget also gives 'a middle resonance of 1084–2298.' The records do not show as low a range of characteristic frequencies unless it be the frequency range 2200–2800 (see note 1, Table 3), within which fall certain vibrations occurring in the early parts of the fundamental cycles of the voiced sounds zh and z. The true s sound is, as Paget has stated, 'a relatively complex hiss' and this is true of sh as well. And to complete the record, we must observe that zh and z are even more complex, if possible, and thus not inappropriate examples of the sounds of speech with which to conclude this survey."

Thus it is seen that the sound waves produced in the air when one is speaking are very complicated. However, the ear under favorable circumstances has little difficulty in recognizing the words and sentences which are spoken. The general characteristics of such speech sounds have been described, but it is extremely difficult to define each speech sound uniquely in terms of physical quantities.

CHAPTER 4

ACOUSTICAL SPEECH POWERS

When the sentence, "Joe took father's shoe bench out," is spoken by a typical voice, the kinetic and potential energy in the resultant sound wave is about 300 or 400 ergs. If this is compared to the billion ergs per second passing though an ordinary incandescent lamp, it is seen to be a very small amount of energy. Indeed it would take 500 people talking continuously for a year to produce enough energy to heat a cup of tea. It was this smallness of the speech power that made measurements of it extremely difficult until the advent of the vacuum tube. Now, however, calibrated microphones and vacuum tube amplifiers are in every acoustical laboratory.[1]

Most such instruments are calibrated to read r.m.s. pressure. Knowing this, one can find the sound intensity by equation (3–7). The measuring instrument may be arranged to measure instantaneous pressure as illustrated by the oscillograms in Chaper 3, or they may be arranged to read instantaneous power. The oscillogram of the word "quite" in Fig. 55 illustrates the latter type.

For purposes of engineering telephone systems, it is desirable to know both the acoustic and electric power of the speech being transmitted. If the power becomes too small, it is masked by extraneous noise. If it becomes too large, parts of the transmitting apparatus become overloaded, that is, they fail to transmit the speech without distortion. Also, when the speech is transmitted along one pair of wires which is close to another pair, the cross talk between the two may become objectionable when the speech power in one or both of them becomes too great.

Since speech is so variable it is convenient to use several terms in describing the power:

The *instantaneous speech power*, J_i, is the rate that the sound energy is being radiated at any instant. It frequently rises to one hundred times the average power.

The *average speech power*, J_a, is the total speech energy radiated while a person is talking divided by the time interval during which he talks.

[1] For methods of calibrating microphones see Beranek, *Acoustic Measurements*, Chapter 4.

The *mean speech power*, J_m, is the average speech power over each one-hundredth of a second period. It is useful in showing the variations of the speech power without showing the periodic fluctuations of the wave. For example, the curve at the bottom of Fig. 1 shows J_m versus t for the word "quite."

The *syllabic speech power*, J_s, is the maximum value of J_m which is reached when a syllable is spoken. It is a good measure of the emphasis which is given the syllable by the speaker.

The *phonetic speech power*, J_p, is the maximum value of J_m for the vowel or consonant being spoken. It is useful in comparing the relative amounts of power in the various speech sounds. The phonetic power of the vowel in a syllable is usually the same as the syllabic power.

The *peak speech power*, J_{max}, is the maximum value of J_i during the interval considered. The peak factor is the ration of J_m/J_a.

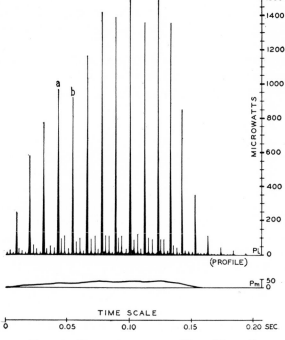

FIG. 55.—OSCILLOGRAM OF THE WORD "QUITE."

For example, in Fig. 1 the instantaneous power, J_i, varies from zero to high values for each cycle of the wave. The peak power reaches 1500 microwatts, and then slowly decreases again to zero, all in a period of 0.2 second. The phonetic power of the vowel ī is seen to be 40 microwatts.

Before giving typical values for these various speech powers, some additional terms which are convenient to use will now be defined; viz., decibel intensity level, pressure level and sensation level. If J_1 and J_2 are any two sound intensities, then the *intensity level difference*, α, between these two intensities when expressed in *decibels* is given by

$$\alpha = 10 \log \frac{J_1}{J_2} \qquad (4\text{--}1)$$

and is usually designated db difference. When J_2 is equal to the reference intensity adopted by the American Standards Association; namely, $J_2 = J_0 = 10^{-16}$ watts per square centimeter, then α becomes the *intensity level* of the sound. It is the number of db that the sound intensity at any point is above the reference intensity.

If p_1 and p_2 are two sound pressures corresponding to J_1 and J_2, then the *pressure level difference* α is equal to

$$\alpha = 10 \log \left(\frac{p_1}{p_2} \right)^2 = 20 \log \frac{p_1}{p_2}. \qquad (4\text{--}2)$$

When the pressure p_2 is equal to the reference pressure adopted by the American Standard Association; viz., $p_2 = p_0 = 0.0002$ dyne per square centimeter, than α becomes the *sound pressure level*, or the number of db above the reference pressure.

These two reference levels are chosen so that in air the intensity level and pressure level of the sound are approximately equal. The difference is usually less than 1 db. They would be exactly the same if the acoustical impedance $\rho_0 c$ were constant and equal to 40 c.g.s. units, and one were always dealing with a plane wave. The difference between these two levels in db is

$$\text{Pressure Level} - \text{Intensity Level} = 5 \log \frac{313}{273 + t} + 10 \log \frac{H}{76} \qquad (4\text{--}3)$$

where t is the temperature in degrees centigrade and H the barometer in centimeters. For most practical problems this difference can be neglected. A change in temperature from 0 to 50°C produces a change of only 0.36 db and a change in atmospheric pressure from 60 to 76 cm produces only a change of 1 db.

When J_2 or p_2 are at values corresponding to the threshold level of hearing, then α becomes the *sensation level* or number of db above the threshold level of hearing.

An instrument calibrated to read pressure level in db is called a sound level meter.

Keeping in mind the kinematic nature of speech, let us now consider some statistical averages. If ten different persons spoke the sentence discussed above, there would be a considerable range of differences in the frequencies and intensities used to transmit it through the air. To get a typical cross section of American speech would require at least 100 such sentences pronounced by at least 5 men and 5 women. This would involve the analysis of 18,000 fundamental sounds besides the transitions between them. Also, as was seen from the oscillograms given above, the wave form changes even where it is ideally supposed to be constant so that three or four sample waves from each steady state condition

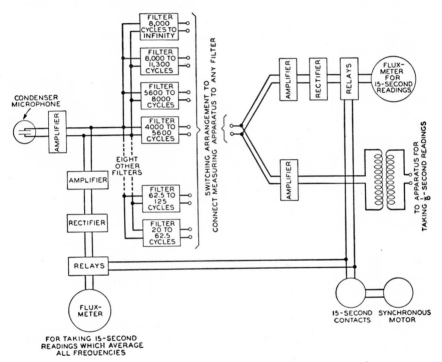

Fig. 56.—Schematic of Electrical Circuit for Measuring the Average Power-Frequency Distribution of Sounds.

should be analyzed to find the components in each sound. Thus, we have the problem of recording and analyzing about 70,000 such waves. To analyze such a wave by the usual academic methods, namely, to plot the wave to a definite scale and then analyze it into its components by means of a Henrici or similar analyzer, would require at least two or three hours. So such a job for analyzing only the steady-state part of speech would require about 210,000 hours, or 100 years working seven hours a day for 300 days per year. In other words, such a method of attacking the problem is altogether too slow. To find the average intensities and frequencies involved in conversational speech, much more powerful methods for obtaining statistical averages were adopted.

The apparatus developed by Sivian, Dunn, and White for getting such statistical data will now be described.

The speech to be analyzed is picked up by a condenser microphone and sent into a vacuum tube circuit. This circuit is arranged so that any one of 14 band pass filters can be inserted. After passing through

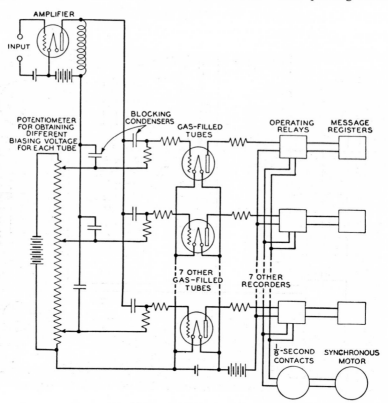

FIG. 57.—SCHEMATIC OF ELECTRICAL CIRCUIT FOR MEASURING THE PEAK
POWER-FREQUENCY DISTRIBUTION OF SOUNDS.

the filter, the electrical speech wave is then sent through a rectifier and finally into a meter. A schematic [2] of the circuit is shown in Fig. 56. Two kinds of meters are used. The first is a flux meter as shown in Fig. 56 for integrating the speech energy over any desired interval. When the rectifier is designed to give a value which is proportional to the average

[2] H. K. Dunn, *A New Analyzer of Speech and Music*, Bell Laboratories Record, November, 1930, and Sivian, Dunn and White, *Absolute Amplitudes and Spectra of Certain Musical Instruments and Orchestras*, Journal Acoustical Society of America, Jan. 1931.

voltage, then the deflection of the needle of the flux meter will be proportional to the average pressure times the time. In other words, this device will read the average pressure during any desired time interval. In this way it is possible to find the average pressure in any one of the 14 bands. If the rectifier is adjusted so that the reading is proportional to the square of the impressed voltage, then the reading will correspond to the average power. Knowing the calibration[3] of the transmitter and also its distance from the mouth of the speaker, it is possible to calculate approximately the average speech power as shown below.

FIG. 58.—PHOTOGRAPH OF THE LEVEL ANALYZER.

The other type of meter shown in Fig. 57 consists of a series of parallel circuits, each containing an argon filled three-electrode tube connected in such a way that in adjacent circuits the tube breaks down and allows the passage of current for voltage levels which are 6 db (decibels) apart. Ten such circuits then cover a range of 54 db. In each of these circuits a relay and counter are connected so that for each tube discharge the counter operates. In this way the number of times that the tube breaks down is

[3] *Speech and Hearing*, p. 305, and also L. J. Sivian, *Absolute Calibration of Condenser Transmitters*, Bell System Technical Journal, Jan. 1931.

automatically registered.   The speech wave coming from the rectifier is sent into this meter where the peak values are measured; that is, the number of times the pressure exceeds a value fixed by each of these circuits will be registered automatically by the corresponding counter.   The apparatus is arranged so that every other 8th second interval is measured, the intervening interval being required for resetting the apparatus.   In Fig. 58 an observer is shown reading the message registers after a test has been taken.   The breakdown tubes are seen at the left and the filters at the right mounted on relay racks.

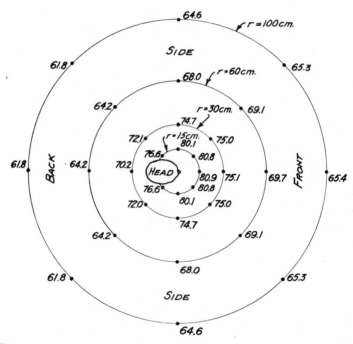

FIG. 59.—RELATIVE SPEECH INTENSITY LEVELS AROUND THE HEAD OF THE SPEAKER—WHOLE SPEECH.

It is thus seen that with this apparatus 1000 observations may be recorded on a four minute conversation, the final results being read directly from the series of counters.   With this apparatus the average r.m.s. pressure at a given distance in front of the mouth was obtained for five women and six men using a sufficiently long sample of speech to be typical.   This sound pressure can be converted by equation (3–7) into sound intensity.   However, because of the diffraction of the head and body this intensity varies for different positions around the head.

Think of a sphere about the head of a typical speaker with the lips as the center and with any convenient radius, for example, 30 cm.   Now, while our speaker is reading a typical speech, measurements of sound pressure are made at different positions all over the surface of this sphere. These sound pressure measurements are converted to sound intensities. In this way the sound power through each square centimeter of the sphere is determined. These are added together to obtain the total speech power used by the talker. For, example, in Fig. 59 are shown the intensity levels on the horizontal plane through the lips. The numbers give the intensity levels in db at azimuth intervals of 45° and on circles having radii of 15, 30, 60, and 100 cm. The shadowing effect of the head is

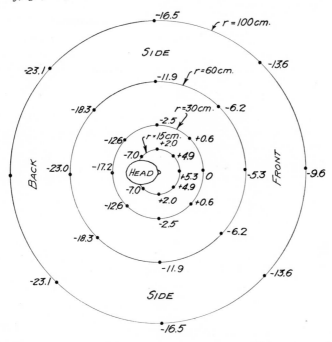

Fig. 60.—Relative Speech Intensity Levels around the Head of the Speaker. Band of Speech 2800 cps to 4000 cps.

clearly shown. For example, on the 30 cm circle the level drops from 75.1 to 70.2 db as one goes from 30 cm directly in front of the lips to 30 cm directly back through the head from the lips. The total speech power determined in this way for this talker was 27 microwatts.

The shadowing effect of the head for speech is more pronounced for the high frequencies. For example, when only the band of frequencies from 2800 to 4000 cps are considered the results shown in Fig. 60 were obtained. It will be seen that as one goes around on the 30 cm circle the sound level drops 17.2 db from the front position to the back position. It will be noticed than in Fig. 59 that the variations on any circle in front of the head is very small while in Fig. 60 they are much larger, as much as 6 db.   All of these data are useful for determining proper microphone placement for speech pick-up.

Variations similar to these were found as the elevation angle increases above the horizontal plane.   However, as the elevation angle goes below the horizontal in the front hemisphere, the intensity levels increase slightly rather than decrease.   This is probably due to two causes, (1) reflections from the body and (2) direct radiation from the chest.[4]

It is convenient to rate power of speech used by a talker in terms of the intensity level produced at one meter distance from the lips and directly in front of the talker.   It is called the talker's level.   Since the intensity of the speech sounds are varying at this point, the long time average intensity is taken, and this is converted to intensity level.   The data similar to those in Figs. 59 and 60 enable one to establish a relation between the talker's level β_t and the total speech power J_t which is radiated by the talker.   Although the talking levels used by different talkers vary greatly, the distribution of the relative levels about the head is very nearly the same.   This is so because the heads and bodies of different persons are approximately the same size so that diffraction pattern is approximately the same.   Then

$$J_t = 8 \times 10^{\frac{\beta_t - 60}{10}} \text{ microwatts.} \tag{4-4}$$

This corresponds to $\beta_t = 65.4$ when $J_t = 27.5$.   For example, a talker's level of 60 db corresponds to a total speech power of 8 microwatts and a talker's level of 70 db corresponds to 80 microwatts.   If one assumes that the intensity level is the same all over a front hemisphere with radius 100 cm and equal to 65.4 db, which is the measured value directly in front of the speaker, and that none goes into the back hemisphere, then the total power is 22 microwatts.   When this is compared to the integrated value of 27 microwatts, it is seen that this assumption is a very good one.

As stated above, Dunn and White made measurements of the total speech power used by each of six men and five women.   The average for the men was 34 microwatts and for the women, 18 microwatts, corresponding to talker's levels of 66.2 and 63.4 db.   The values of speech powers ranged from 10 to 90 microwatts for the six men and from 8 to 55 for the five women, covering a talker level range from 60 to 70.5.   The corresponding *average speech power* is 32 microwatts and *average intensity level* is 66 db.   If the silent intervals are excluded, the experimental data indicated that these levels will be increased 3 db.

[4] For further details for the distribution of speech pressures around the head, see Dunn and Farnsworth, Journal Acoustical Society America, January, 1939.

When one talks as loudly as possible, the talker level can be raised to about 86 db, and when talking as softly as possible, it can be lowered to 46 db, so from a soft whisper to a loud shout there is a range of about 60 db.

Measurements of the talker levels of a large number of persons, each one talking into the telephone in a conversational manner, were made and the results obtained are shown in Table 4. It is seen that 7% of the

TABLE 4

DISTRIBUTION OF TALKER LEVELS FOR PERSONS USING THE TELEPHONE

Percent of Talkers	Talker Level Range
7	Below 54 db
9	54 to 57 db
14	57 to 60 db
18	60 to 63 db
22	63 to 66 db
17	66 to 69 db
9	69 to 72 db
4	72 to 75 db
0	Above 75 db

people talk so softly that they produce talker levels below 54 db corresponding to a total speech power of 2 microwatts. About 40% of the people have talker levels within 3 db of the average 66 db, and no person had a talker level greater than 75 db.

Now let us focus our attention upon the level variations produced by a typical talker. As the conversation proceeds the speech power varies from zero to peak values which frequently are 100 times the average power. Measurements taken with the Level Analyzer (Fig. 55) indicated the variations of these peak powers were as depicted in Table 5. The

TABLE 5

PEAK POWERS IN CONVERSATIONAL SPEECH

Peak Level Range Above Average	Percent of Time Intervals	Peak Level Range Below Average	Percent of Time Intervals
Above 21 db	0.1	0 to 3 db	5.5
From 18 to 21 db	1.7	3 to 6 db	4.5
15 to 18	5.1	6 to 9	4.0
12 to 15	10.5	Below 9 db	12.0
9 to 12	17.0		
6 to 9	18.6		
3 to 6	12.7		
0 to 3	8.3		

peak level in each successive 1/8 second interval is compared to the average level over a long period. For example, it is seen that for 17% of these short 1/8 second intervals the peak level is 9 to 12 db above the average, and for 4.5% of these intervals the peak level is 3 to 6 db below the average. The most frequently occurring value of the peak level is 10 db above the average. The measurements indicated that the average powers in these successive 1/8 second time intervals was about 10 db below the values tabulated in Table 5. This means then that the

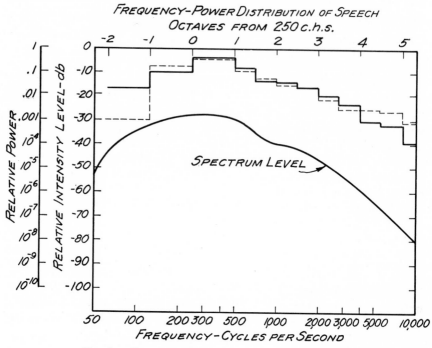

Fig. 61.—Frequency-Power Distribution of Speech.

most frequently occurring average level is about the same as the long time average which seems reasonable. These peak levels and average levels in successive 1/8 second intervals with respect to the long time average are about the same for men as for women.

Although men's and women's voices are alike in this respect, there are other differences. As stated before the pitch of a woman's voice is about one octave higher than that of a man's. Tests with the sound level analyzer showed that the intensities of the components carried by frequencies above 3000 cps were definitely greater for women's voices than for men's. This seems to mean that the women gave greater emphasis to the sibilant sounds.

Measurements were made with this instrument of sound pressures of the speech 30 cm from the lips of the talker and in successive 1/2 octave bands of frequency, and the results are shown in Fig. 61 by the upper curve. The three lower bands were octaves; namely, 62.5 to 125 cps, 125 to 250 cps, and 250 to 500 cps. The remaining bands were half octaves. The horizontal solid bars give for men's voices the intensity level in each band as the db below the average intensity for speech as a whole. The broken bars are for women's voices. The arrow in the first bar for women's voices means that the level was below 30 db below the average for women's voices. The apparatus would not measure lower levels in this band.

On the left-hand scale these values are expressed as ratios of the power in the band to the total speech power. For example, for men's voices less than 3% of the power lies in the first band between 62.5 and 125 cps. More than 1/3 of the power lies in the octave between 250 and 500 cps. It is also seen that the last three half octaves carry considerably more power in the voices for women than for men, although in either case it is less than 1/3%.

There are two other important ways of representing the spectral distribution of the power in speech; viz., by the power distribution function curve J_f versus f, and the spectrum level curve.

The power distribution function J_f is defined by

$$J_f = \frac{J}{\Delta f} \qquad (4\text{--}5)$$

where J is the fractional power in each of the bands in Fig. 61 and Δf is the width of the band in cps. For example, the first band is an octave wide and 62.5 cps wide, while the last band is a half octave wide but is 3200 cps wide. The curve for J_f obtained in this way is shown by the curve in the lower half of Fig. 61 and by the scale at the left. From the definition of J_f

$$J_{12} = \int_{f_1}^{f_2} J_f df \qquad (4\text{--}6)$$

where J_{12} is the power in the band between f_1 and f_2. The fractions are chosen so that when the limits go from 0 to infinity $J_{12} = 1.0$. This is for speech at the 30 cm distance in front of the lips of the talker. The spectral distribution curve changes for different positions about the head, but for positions in front these changes are small. They are definitely smaller than those variations due to sampling of voices even when averages of as many as eleven voices are used. Therefore, it is safe to use this same curve for all positions in front and beyond 30 cm. In particular, it will be used for the reference one meter distance. The spectrum level at any frequency for the case when the whole speech is at an intensity level of o db is defined by

$$\text{Spectrum Level} = \text{10} \log J_f \qquad (4\text{--}7)$$

and the same bottom curve represents the spectrum level curve when the

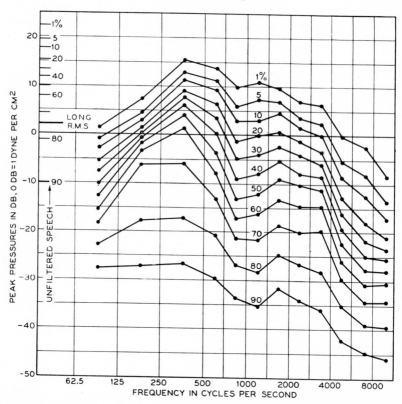

FIG. 62.—PEAK PRESSURES IN ONE-EIGHTH-SECOND INTERVALS OF CONVERSATIONAL SPEECH, AT 30 CM FROM THE MOUTH: COMPOSITE FROM THE VOICES OF 6 MEN. MEASUREMENTS WERE IN THE BANDS INDICATED BY THE DIVISIONS OF THE FREQUENCY SCALE, AND THE PERCENTAGES ARE THOSE OF INTERVALS HAVING PEAK PRESSURES GREATER THAN THE INDICATED ORDINATES.

right-hand scale of db is used. The spectrum level curve for speech at any talker level β_t is then

$$\text{Spectrum Level} = \text{10} \log J_f + \beta_t, \qquad (4\text{--}8)$$

that is, the curve is shifted upwards β_t db.

This holds strictly for the case when $\beta_t = 66$. However, this curve changes when one is speaking very loudly or very softly, but for changes

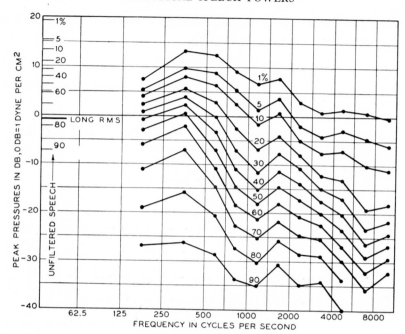

FIG. 63.—PEAK PRESSURES IN ONE-EIGHTH-SECOND INTERVALS: COMPOSITE FROM THE VOICES OF 5 WOMEN.

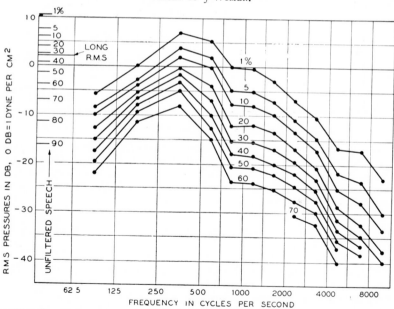

FIG. 64.—R.M.S. PRESSURE IN ONE-EIGHTH-SECOND INTERVALS—COMPOSITE OF 6 MEN VOICES.

in intensity of 5 or 6 db it may be considered to hold. But it must be remembered that to define the voice accurately, one must know the spectrum level curve and the talking level β_t.

Measurements were made to determine how the levels in any one band varied from one 1/8-second interval to another. The results are shown in Fig. 62 for the six men and in Fig. 63 for the five women. The peak pressures are plotted in db above one dyne. The dots give the measured value in each band. The straight lines connecting are just to assist the eye in following the data. The line marked 50 is the dividing line between the intervals, one-half being at lower levels than indicated by this line, and one-half being at higher levels.

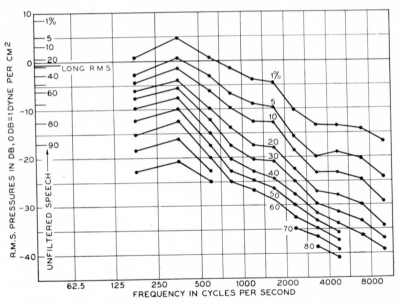

Fig. 65.—R.M.S. Pressure in One-Eighth-Second Intervals—Composite of 5 Women Voices.

Similar data are given in Figs. 64 and 65 for the r.m.s. levels instead of peak levels. From these two sets of data one can obtain the peak factor for each band and each r.m.s. level. The peak factors obtained by using the 10% of the time curve is shown in Fig. 66. Except for the low levels (high percentages above 50) the calculation for the other percent curves gives about the same results.

Power in the Fundamental Speech Sounds

In the course of conversation the fundamental vowel and consonant sounds are produced with varying degrees of power depending upon their position in the sentence and the emphasis desired. In spite of this variation some of the speech sounds are always much more powerful than others, and it is interesting to know typical values used in conversation. The phonetic and peak powers of the individual speech sounds can be obtained by means of a calibrated condenser transmitter. Sacia and Beck[5] have obtained in this way from measurements of oscillograms some

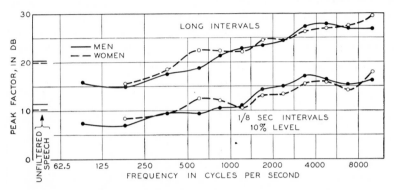

FIG. 66.—RATIOS OF PEAK TO R.M.S. PRESSURES IN SPEECH FOR DIFFERENT FREQUENCY REGIONS AND IN ONE-EIGHTH-SECOND INTERVALS AND IN LONG INTERVALS.

values for most of the speech sounds. Although sixteen people were used in obtaining these data and the sounds made in various combinations, they are still insufficient to give average values which can be said to be typical. However, the values obtained do give a good notion of the range of powers involved. These data are given in Table 6 under the columns headed "Phonetic Power" and "Peak Power." The figures are in microwatts power radiating from the mouth of the speaker.

As a check against the results obtained by this method, there is given in the last column of Table 6 a set of figures which are the average values of two other methods used for determining phonetic power. The first method uses a form of articulation test, taking advantage of the fact that as the speech level is decreased the weaker sounds will be the first to be misunderstood since the ear fails to hear their essential characteristics first. By observing the amount of attenuation necessary to reduce each speech sound to the point where it is misunderstood some arbitrary percent of the number of times uttered, it is possible to obtain approximately the relative power of each sound.

The second method reduces each sound to the level at which it may no longer be heard. This is done by using a telephone circuit, giving a very faithful reproduction of the speech sounds and into which is intro-

[5] Bell System Technical Journal, July, 1926.

TABLE 6

POWER IN MICROWATTS IN THE FUNDAMENTAL SPEECH SOUNDS

Phonetic Sound	Key Word	Phonetic Power		Peak Power		Calculations from Threshold and Articulation Measurements
		Average	Maximum	Average	Maximum	
ū	tool	23	60	235	700	38
u	took	26	100	470	890	50
ō	tone	25	80	435	1300	74
o′	talk	45	120	615	1500	87
o	ton	24	110	450	1700	83
a	top	41	120	700	1600	68
á	tap	25	90	650	1800	57
e	ten	22	90	500	1700	34
ā	tape	23	60	525	1700	35
i	tip	20	50	350	1300	22
ē	team	20	80	310	1500	16
m	me	1.8	17	110	200	2.9
n	no	2.1	18	47	70	4.1
ng	ring	.3	3.6	97	170	12
l	let	.3	9.6	130	230	18
r	err	16	30	200	600	33
v	vat	.03	2.4	25	30	1.0
f	for	.08	3.6	3	4	1.0
z	zip	.7	7.2	30	40	1.2
s	sit	.9	8.7	30	55	.9
th	thin	....	....	1	1	.3
th̲	that	....	....	9	10	2.3
zh	azure	....	....	40	55	
sh	shot	1.8	6.0	110	130	11
b	bat	....	....	7	7	1.1
p	pat	....	....	6	7	1.0
d	dot	.08	2.9	4	7	1.7
t	tap	.1	6.0	16	19	2.7
j	jot	.5	3.6	24	36	4.1
ch	chat	1.4	19	52	60	6.1
g	get	....	....	8	9	3.3
k	kit	.3	4.8	6	9	3.0

duced suitable attenuators. The number of db that each sound must be attenuated to make it inaudible, is thus a measure of its phonetic power.

Table 7 shows the results for each sound using these last two methods. The figures in the last column of Table 6 are averages from columns 2 and 3. Later it will be seen that the minimum pressure at from one to three thousand cycles is approximately 0.0006 bars. This corresponds to

8.7 × 10⁻¹⁰ microwatts per square centimeter. The area of the hemi-sphere through which the sound is passing is approximately 10 sq. cm when the lips of a speaker are one-half inch from the ear. Consequently, the power of this minimum sound is approximately 87×10^{-10} microwatts. Having, from the "average" column of Table 4, the amounts the various sounds must be attenuated to reach this minimum level, a simple calcu-

TABLE 7

RELATIVE SENSATION LEVELS PRODUCED BY AN AVERAGE SPEAKER
FOR THE FUNDAMENTAL SPEECH SOUNDS

Speech Sound	Threshold	Articulation	Average
ó (talk)	100.0	100.0	100.0
o (ton)	99.6	100.0	99.8
ō (tone)	99.6	98.9	99.3
ī (bite)	99.5	100.0	99.8
ou (bout)	99.2	100.0	99.6
á (tap)	99.2	97.2	98.2
e (ten)	98.4	93.5	95.9
a (top)	97.4	100.3	98.9
u (took)	97.1	98.1	97.6
ū (tool)	95.9	94.3	95.1
ā (tape)	93.3	98.2	95.8
i (tip)	92.6	95.5	94.0
ē (team)	89.4	96.3	92.9
r (err)	96.0	95.5	95.8
l (let)	93.5	92.6	93.1
ng (ring)	88.9	93.8	91.4
sh (shot)	88.9	93.2	91.1
ch (chat)	87.2	89.7	88.5
n (no)	86.8	86.7	86.75
m (me)	85.4	85.1	85.3
th (that)	84.2	. . . . .	84.2
t (tap)	84.1	86.4	85.3
h (hat)	83.9	81.7	82.8
k (kit)	83.8	85.3	84.6
j (jot)	83.7	89.7	86.7
f (for)	83.6	77.7	80.7
g (get)	82.9	86.9	84.9
s (sit)	82.4	78.1	80.3
z (zip)	81.6	81.6	81.6
v (vat)	81.4	80.1	80.8
p (pat)	80.6	81.4	81.0
d (dot)	78.9	87.8	83.4
b (bat)	78.8	83.7	81.3
th (thin)	78.7	71.2	75.0

lation gives the phonetic power of each at normal levels, and these are the values listed in the last column of Table 6.

After considering the different sets of data, Table 7A was constructed which gives the relative amounts of power in the different sounds, with the power in the faintest sound as a basis of comparison.

TABLE 7A

RELATIVE PHONETIC POWERS OF THE FUNDAMENTAL SPEECH SOUNDS AS PRODUCED
BY AN AVERAGE SPEAKER

ó	680	ū	310	ch	42	k	13
a	600	i	260	n	36	v	12
o	510	ē	220	j	23	th	11
á	490	r	210	zh	20	b	7
ō	470	l	100	z	16	d	7
u	460	sh	80	s	16	p	6
ā	370	ng	73	t	15	f	5
e	350	m	52	g	15	th	1

It is seen that the most powerful sound is ó (awl), and the faintest sound th (thin), the ratio of powers between these two being 680. The difference in level expressed in db corresponding to this figure is 28. From the data available the indications are that in an average room in the city the noise is such as to raise the threshold of hearing approximately 30 db. Also the sound is attenuated more than 40 db if the speaker is about 10 feet away from the listener. Consequently, under such circumstances the sound th is barely audible.

The pure vowels are the most powerful sounds and have a range of intensity of about 3 to 1. As would be expected, the open vowels ó, a, o, and á have the largest phonetic powers. The diphthongs are not given, but they have about the same power as the vowels which compose them.

The semi-vowels are next to the pure vowels in phonetic power. Of these, n is the weakest and r the strongest. It is interesting to note that the unvoiced fricatives, sh and ch, have powers comparable to the semi-vowels. Next follow the stop and fricative consonants; z, s, t, g, v, and *th* having about the same power which is about one-fifth that of the semi-vowels and then b, d, p, and f having a slightly lower power.

The syllabic power varies more with the emphasis given than with the vowel sound used. A vowel in an accented syllable has usually three or four times as much phonetic power as one in an unaccented syllable. This difference is dependent upon the speaking habits of the individual.

The peak power varies considerably with the type of voice, the values given in Table 6 being typical. For engineering purposes, it may be considered to be about five times the syllabic power. In this connection Sacia[6] says:

"I have become able to associate peak factors with vocal qualities in the following way: the voices with the higher peak factors are those which in the ordinary terminology are said to be 'resonant' or 'vibrant'; they have the greater carrying power, especially over the telephone;

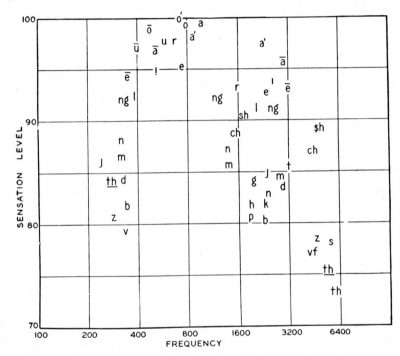

FIG. 67.—COMBINED CHARACTERISTICS OF THE FUNDAMENTAL SOUNDS OF SPEECH.

they are rich in the musical sense and are, therefore, well suited to singing, although many such voices, unfortunately, are never applied to the art."

It is seen then from Table 6 that for an accented syllable the peak power frequently rises to 700 microwatts. For the four percent of speakers who are in the class producing an average power of from four to eight times the average for the entire group, this peak value might reach as high as 5000 microwatts.

From the data given it is estimated that the average phonetic power in the faintest speech sound; viz., th (as in thin), is approximately 0.05

[6] Sacia, C. F., *Speech Power and Energy*, Bell System Technical Journal, October, 1925.

microwatt. This value, of course, is for one speaking with a typical average voice. For those speaking with softer voices, a much smaller power for this sound would be produced. The reduction, however, would not be as great as for the vowel sounds. A round figure of about 0.01 microwatt probably represents the faintest sound and of about 5000 microwatts the peak value of the loudest sound that will be encountered in conversation. This represents a range in intensity of 500,000 to 1 or 56 db. When dealing with only one speaker, the range of intensity of the speech sounds is usually between 35 and 40 db.

All of the figures given are based upon average American speakers. Although no measurements have been made upon persons who are specially trained to speak distinctly, such as actors and public speakers, it is very probable that such tests would show that the weaker sound would be given considerably more power by such trained speakers than is ordinarily used by the average speaker. Because of this fact, the range of intensities used by such speakers would be narrower than indicated by these figures. However, the greater range of emphasis used by them would tend to make the necessary intensity range even wider.

Relative Distribution of Speech Power into Frequency Bands

The frequency range necessary for the faithful transmission of speech is of considerable importance. In Chapter 3 were given the characteristic frequency regions, and in the present chapter the characteristic intensity regions for the various speech sounds are given. Fig. 67 is a plot showing these combined characteristics of most of the fundamental sounds of speech. The ordinates give the sensation level of the principal components and the abscissas the characteristic frequency regions of each speech sound. When a sound has several principal components, the position of each is indicated. Although it cannot be claimed that this chart gives more than a very rough picture of the true facts, it may serve to give a general picture of the intensities and frequencies involved in the transmission of speech.

CHAPTER 5

FREQUENCY OF OCCURRENCE OF THE DIFFERENT SPEECH SOUNDS

Words

After learning the physical characteristics of the speech sounds, it is natural to inquire how frequently they are used in conversational speech. It is evident that such knowledge will be useful in telephone engineering as well as in other fields. Godfrey Dewey[1] has made an extensive study of the frequency of occurrence of words, syllables, and fundamental vowel and consonant sounds in written material. This material was taken from representative sources such as modern newspapers, fiction, American speeches, personal correspondence, business correspondence, modern advertising, religious English, scientific English, and American magazines. As a result of this study, Dewey found the 100 most frequently occurring words to be those shown in Table 8. The numeral gives in percent the frequency of occurrence of the word.

The definite article, "the," accounts for more than 7% of all the words occurring on an average written page. Some words, such as winter, tomorrow, succeed, and railroads, which seem very familiar, occur only once in 10,000 words. The first 10 words given in this list account for more than 25% and the 100 words account for more than 50% of all the words occurring.

Syllable Combinations

Dewey's studies indicated also that the 100 most frequently occurring syllables are as shown in Table 9. The figure at the left of the phonetic syllable gives in percent the frequency of occurrence.

Fundamental Sounds

The analysis of the phonetic pronunciation of the words enables one to find the frequency of occurrence of the fundamental speech sounds. Such values obtained by Dewey are given in Table 10.

It is seen from this table that the sound i (as in tip) is the most frequently occurring phonetic sound. The sounds n, t, r, and o (as in ton), are the next four sounds in the order of their frequency of occur-

[1] Dewey, Godfrey, *Relative Frequency of English Speech Sounds*, Harvard University Press, Cambridge, Mass., 1923.

TABLE 8
Relative Frequency of Occurrence of Words

7.31	the	.58	not	.31	their	.20	time	.15	these
3.99	of	.58	at	.30	there	.20	up	.14	two
3.28	and	.57	this	.30	were	.20	do	.14	very
2.92	to	.54	are	.30	so	.20	out	.13	before
2.12	a	.52	we	.29	my	.19	can	.13	great
2.11	in	.51	his	.26	if	.19	than	.13	could
1.34	that	.50	but	.25	me	.18	only	.13	such
1.21	it	.47	they	.25	what	.18	she	.13	first
1.21	is	.46	all	.25	would	.17	made	.12	upon
1.15	I	.45	or	.24	who	.16	other	.12	every
1.03	for	.45	which	.23	when	.16	into	.12	how
.84	be	.44	will	.23	him	.16	men	.12	come
.83	was	.43	from	.22	them	.16	must	.12	us
.78	as	.41	had	.22	her	.16	people	.12	shall
.77	you	.39	has	.21	war	.16	said	.11	should
.72	with	.36	one	.21	your	.16	may	.11	then
.68	he	.33	our	.21	any	.15	man	.11	like
.64	on	.33	an	.21	more	.15	about	.11	well
.61	have	.32	been	.21	now	.15	over	.11	little
.60	by	.32	no	.20	its	.15	some	.11	say

TABLE 9
Relative Frequency of Occurrence of Syllables

7.3	the	.85	waz	.57	ol	.39	on	.28	os
4.0	av	.84	with	.56	kan	.38	men	.28	wud
3.3	in	.84	di	.54	wē	.38	érz	.28	som
3.3	ánd	.83	ti	.53	ez	.38	our	.28	what
3.2	i	.82	an	.52	bot	.34	en	.28	if
3.2	o	.78	áz	.52	hiz	.34	mī	.28	ōn
3.2	tū	.71	ō	.48	thā	.34	thár	.27	kom
2.4	ing	.70	hē	.48	nō	.33	op	.27	yu
2.1	or	.69	á	.47	wil	.33	out	.27	dā
1.6	ri	.68	ól	.47	on	.33	bin	.26	nes
1.4	it	.68	en	.46	ōā	.33	wor	.26	el
1.3	thát	.66	háv	.46	án	.32	thār	.26	si
1.3	iz	.64	bī	.45	which	.31	ev	.26	them
1.3	ī	.64	ar	.45	sō	.31	mē	.26	dis
1.2	li	.62	bi	.43	fram	.31	tu	.26	oth
1.1	fór	.61	át	.41	hád	.30	ex	.25	hū
.97	bē	.60	ór	.41	won	.29	its	.25	vér
.92	shon	.60	nat	.40	ment	.29	kán	.25	when
.91	ed	.58	tor	.39	ház	.29	dér	.24	dū
.86	yū	.57	this	.39	bul	.29	him	.24	pē

TABLE 10

RELATIVE FREQUENCY OF OCCURRENCE OF SPEECH SOUNDS

Speech Sound	Key	Relative Frequency	Speech Sound	Key	Relative Frequency
ū	tool	1.60	m	....	2.78
ō	tone	1.63	n	....	7.24
ó	talk	1.26	ng	hang	0.96
a	top	3.33	v	....	2.28
ā	tape	2.35	z	....	2.97
ē	eat	3.89	th	then	3.43
u	took	0.69	zh	azure	0.05
o	ton	5.02	f	....	1.84
á	tap	4.17	s	....	4.55
e	ten	3.44	th	thin	0.37
i	tip	7.94	sh	shell	0.82
ī	dike	1.59	b	....	1.81
ou	our	0.59	d	....	4.31
oi	oil	0.09	j	....	0.44
ew	few	0.31	g	....	0.74
w	....	2.08	p	....	2.04
y	....	0.60	t	....	7.13
h	....	1.81	ch	chalk	0.52
l	....	3.74	k	....	2.71
r	....	6.88			

rence, and they account for more than 36% of all the sounds found on a written page. It is seen from the tables given above that a comparatively small part of the more common words comprise the large part of our ordinary speech. That this is true is emphasized by the following summary taken from Dewey's book.

GENERAL SUMMARY

9 words are found to form over		of the total words
12 syllables are found to form over	25%	of the syllables
4 sounds are found to form over		of the sounds
69 words are found to form over		of the words
70 syllables are found to form over	50%	of the syllables
9 sounds are found to form over		of the sounds
732 words are found to form over		of the words
339 syllables are found to form over	75%	of the syllables
19 sounds are found to form over		of the sounds
1027 words occurring over ten times form	78.6%	of the words
1370 syllables occurring over ten times form	93.4%	of the syllables
41 + 1 sounds form	100%	of the sounds

All of the above relations are for written English. In telephone engineering we are more interested in spoken English, particularly as it is used over the telephone. French, Carter and Koenig[2] have made a similar analysis for telephone conversational speech. The material was obtained from telephone conversations over typical toll circuits terminating in New York City.

All the data were obtained as follows: During one week the observer noted only the nouns used, the next week only the verbs, etc. The results obtained from 500 conversations are given in Table 11.

TABLE 11

OCCURRENCE OF PARTS OF SPEECH

Parts of Speech	Number of Words		Ratio Total to Different
	Total	Different	
Nouns	11,660	1,029	11.3
Adjustives and Adverbs	9,880	634	15.6
Verbs	12,550	456	27.5
Auxiliary Verbs	9,450	37	255.
Pronouns*	17,900	45	398.
Prepositions and Conjunctions*	12,400	36	344.
Articles*	5,500	3	1850.
	79,390	2,240	35.4

* Derived from data on less than 500 conversations.

It is seen that bout 80,000 words were recorded, but of these less than 2300 were new words or less than three percent. Particularly, in the last three classes shown the number of new words are strikingly small. The common sounds so frequently used in telephone conversations; namely, er, wh, yeah, uh-huh, oh, all right, hello, good-by, and profane words, were left out of this count. This class constituted about 25% of all the words. These figures indicate that the conversation framework is built up by a comparatively small number of words in a great variety of patterns around the principal words which are nouns. The authors state that of the total 80,000 words there were 737 that constituted 96% of all the different words used. It is obvious that a student wishing to understand conversational English need only to memorize this rather small list of words. The list is given in the paper by these authors.

As stated by them, "The 50 most common words in telephone conversation and in written English are shown in Table 12, arranged in their order

[2] Bell Technical Journal, April, 1930.

TABLE 12

FIFTY COMMONEST WORDS IN TELEPHONE CONVERSATION
COMPARED WITH WRITTEN ENGLISH

Telephone Conversation	Written English	Telephone Conversation	Written English
1. I	the	26. GO	HIS
2. you	of	27. TELL	BUT
3. the	and	28. with	they
4. a	to	29. me	ALL
5. on	a	30. HIM	OR
6. to	in	31. ABOUT	WHICH
7. that	that	32. at	will
8. it	it	33. THINK	from
9. is	is	34. this	HAD
10. and	I	35. DAY	HAS
11. GET	for	36. THING	ONE
12. will	be	37. SAY	OUR
13. of	was	38. CAN	an
14. in	AS	39. CALL	BEEN
15. he	you	40. would	NO
16. we	with	41. THEM	THEIR
17. they	he	42. was	THERE
18. SEE	on	43. NOW	WERE
19. have	have	44. from	SO
20. for	BY	45. what	MY
21. KNOW	NOT	46. MORNING	IF
22. DON'T	at	47. an	me
23. DO	this	48. JUST	what
24. are	are	49. OVER	would
25. WANT	we	50. be	WHO

of frequency of occurrence. These words form 60% of the total in conversation and 46% in written English. There are 29 words which are common to the two lists. The personal nature of telephone conversation is shown in the two words which head the list. The most striking difference between the two is the large number of active verbs which occur in the list for conversation: 'get,' 'see,' 'know,' etc., 12 in all. None of these appears among the 50 commonest words of written English. Three nouns, 'day,' 'thing' and 'morning,' appear in the conversational list, none in the other. Only one conjunction is found in the conversational list, while five appear in the list for written English.

"When the first 100 words in telephone conversation are compared with the first 100 in written English two somewhat unexpected facts emerge. In Telephone conversation 14 out of the first 100 are words of more than one syllable; in written English there are ten. Four two-syllable words appear among the first 50 telephone words; the first 59 of written English are monosyllables. A more striking difference concerns the origin of the words. Among the first 100 telephone words there are 11 which are derived through old French from the Latin; in written English there are only two from the Latin. Six of the 11 words occur in the first 65 telephone words, while the first word of Latin origin in written English is the 70th. The telephone words of Latin origin are, in order of occurrence: 'just,' 'very,' 'order,' 'minute,' 'price,' 'car,' 'letter,' 'fine,' 'company,' 'stuff,' 'number'; in written English these words are 'people' and 'very.' The predominance of business words in this list for telephone conversation suggests the influence of trade between England and France in the Middle Ages."

The syllabic forms of the syllables ranged from a single vowel to the complicated two consonant–one vowel–two consonant type. The frequency of occurrence of the various types is given in Table 13.

TABLE 13

TYPES OF PHONETIC SYLLABLES IN TELEPHONE CONVERSATIONS
Relative Occurrence per Hundred

Type	Occurrence
V	9.7
VC	20.3
CV	21.8
CVC	33.5
VCC	2.8
CCV	00.8
CVCC	7.8
CCVC	2.8
CCVCC	0.5
	100.

It is seen that for the large mjority of syllables the forms are CV, VC, and CVC.

The words were analyzed to find the frequency of occurrence of the phonetic sounds with the results given in Table 14.

The phonetic sound is indicated by the keyword for the vowels i (pin), ī (kine), etc. The relative frequencies for vowels, initial consonants, and final consonants are in the ratio 92,522, 64,043, and 65,544. The numbers in Table 14 must be multiplied by 0.417, 0.288, and 0.295 to get the percent of times each sound occurs compared to all the sounds.

To compare with written speech as shown in Table 10, the vowel sounds in par and pot were considered as a (top); those in pair and pane as ā (tape); those in about, differ, notion, people, purr, and pun, as o (ton);

TABLE 14

RELATIVE OCCURRENCE OF SPEECH SOUNDS IN TELEPHONE CONVERSATION

Vowels		All Words (Except Articles) Initial Consonants		Final Consonants	
pin	10.27	W	9.38	t	14.30
pine	7.58	T	7.86	r	13.05
pan	6.89	*th* (then)	6.72	n	12.52
pen	6.60	Y	6.48	l	8.40
peel	6.44	D	6.21	z	6.01
pool	6.26	M	5.89	m	5.48
pot	5.21	H	5.75	d	4.44
pane	4.78	K	5.55	v	4.23
pole	4.74	S	5.46	ng	3.57
pawn	4.15	N	4.99	s	3.13
pun	4.14	B	4.64	k	2.85
pull	2.96	G (gun)	4.33	f	1.37
pout	1.69	L	4.31	th″ (with)	1.25
par	1.31	F	3.96	p	1.24
pair	1.09	R	2.78	ch	.53
purr	.80	P	2.54	b	.42
pew	.26	th (thin)	2.02	g	.38
poise	.19	SH	1.74	sh	.32
		V	1.25	j	.14
	75.36	J	.83	th′ (myth)	.04
Unaccented Vowels		CH	.55	zh (azure)	.01
		Z	.34	h	—
poss*i*ble	5.52	ZH	.02	w	—
*a*bout	5.33	NG	—	y	—
diff*er*	4.56				
receive	3.78		93.60		83.68
not*ion*	2.65	*Compounds*		*Compounds*	
want*e*d	1.83				
peop*le*	.97	PR	1.06	nt	4.40
		RW	.91	nd	2.56
	24.64	ST	.87	st	1.18
		TR	.69	ts	1.11
		FR	.62	nk	.76
		PL	.36	ld	.75
		KW	.28	rz	.57
	100.00	BL	.23	ks	.47
Total Number		SP	.19	kt	.42
of Sounds	92,522	KL	.18	rd	.37
		Others	1.01	Others	3.73
			6.40		16.32
			100.00		100.00
			64,043		65,544

those in want*e*d and pen as e (ten); those in pin, poss*i*ble and rece*i*ve, as i (tip). The frequency of occurrences for the final and initial constants were combined, and the combinations at the bottom of Table 14 were rated as single consonants. When this is done, the results are those shown in Table 15.

TABLE 15

COMPARISON OF THE FREQUENCY OF OCCURRENCE OF PHONETIC SOUNDS IN WRITTEN
AND CONVERSATIONAL SPEECH

Speech Sound	Written	Conversational	Speech Sound	Written	Conversational
u (tool)	1.6	2.0	m	2.8	3.6
ō (tone)	1.6	1.5	n	7.2	8.1
ó (talk)	1.3	1.3	ng	1.6	1.1
a (top)	3.3	2.1	v	2.3	1.8
ā (tape)	2.4	1.9	z	3.6	2.2
ē (eat)	3.9	2.1	th (then)	3.4	2.5
u (took)	0.7	1.0	zh	0.05	0.01
o (ton)	5.0	6.0	t	1.8	2.0
á (tap)	4.2	2.1	s	4.6	4.0
e (ten)	3.4	2.7	th (thin)	0.4	0.7
i (tip)	7.9	6.3	sh	0.8	0.7
ī (dike)	1.6	2.4	b	1.8	0.6
ou (our)	0.6	0.6	d	4.3	4.6
oi (oil)	0.1	0.1	j	0.5	0.3
ew (few)	0.3	0.1	g	0.8	1.5
w	2.1	3.7	p	2.1	1.7
y	0.6	2.1	t	7.1	9.8
h	1.8	2.2	ch	0.5	0.3
l	3.7	4.6	k	2.7	3.6
r	6.9	6.1			

There are some clear-cut differences, the value of 2.1% for á (tap) being the largest one, but it is remarkable that they are so nearly alike. Conversational speech is distinguished from written speech principally by the small number of words that are used repeatedly. In conversation 155 of the most frequently used words made up 80% of the total occurrence, while in written English 640 must be included to reach the 80% mark.

CHAPTER 6

NOISE

Since the presence of noise has a profound effect upon the perception of speech sounds this chapter briefly describes the methods of representing noises and gives typical levels encountered in communication. From the standpoint of interference with speech perception all sounds which are not speech are classed as noise.

Sometimes noise is defined as an unwanted sound. Usually, however, those sounds to which no definite pitch can be assigned are classed as noise. The clapping of hands, shuffling of feet, the hammering of typewriters, or the roar of the traffic in the street, are typical types of noise. In Fig. 68

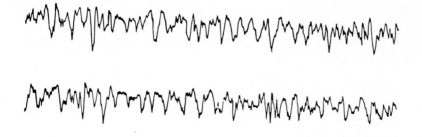

Fig. 68.—Typical Wave Form of a Street Noise and a Pure Tone of 500 Cycles.

is shown a typical oscillographic wave form of street noise. As will be seen, its principal characteristic is the great irregularity in the vibration. The wave form at the bottom is for a pure tone having a frequency of 500 cps.

When transmitting speech or music either directly to an audience in a large hall or over an electrical system, such as a radio or a telephone system, there is always an interference to the proper reception of such speech and music, due to other sounds being present. These extraneous sounds which serve only to interfere with the proper reception are designated by engineers as "noise." With such a designation, the sound may be either periodic or non-periodic as long as it is something that would be better eliminated.   In telephony noises result from a number of different sources.   Some of these noises arise from inductive effects between telephone lines and other types of electrical transmission lines; other noises are caused by electrical disturbances originating within the telephone system itself.   In addition to these, there is always, of course, a certain amount of noise, generally classed as "room noise," in places where telephones are used.

A sample spectrum of line noise current is shown in Fig. 69.   This was obtained by analyzing the current flowing in an open wire toll line which was terminated by a resistance of 700 ohms.   It is seen that the

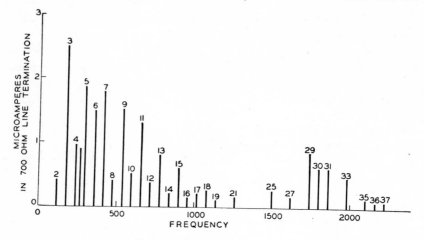

FIG. 69.—LINE NOISE SPECTRUM.

components, with one exception, are all harmonics of a 60-cycle fundamental.   Also, it will be noticed that the odd harmonics are much stronger than the even ones, which is a notable characteristic of a power generator. It is evident then that the principal part of this line noise current is due to the inductive effect of a power line carrying a 60-cycle current upon this particular telephone line.   When a subscriber's circuit is connected to such a line, a hum is heard in the telephone receiver which is called line noise.

Other types of electrical disturbances which may be picked up or which may originate in the telephone system itself produce sounds at the receiver which are more nearly true noise sounds as they have no periodic characteristics.   For example, an important source of noise in toll circuits comes from the amplifiers and is called "resistance" noise, or sometimes "white" noise.   It arises from the thermal agitation of the electrons in a resistance connected to the grid of a vacuum tube.   The voltage fluctuations V^2 on the grid of such a vacuum tube in a resistance R connected across it is known [1] to be given

$$V^2 = 1.64 \times 10^{-20} R \, \Delta f \qquad (6-1)$$

for a temperature $27°$ Centigrade, and where Δf is the band of frequencies passed by the amplifier. The fluctuating electrical power W expressed in watts in the resistance R is given by

$$W = V^2/R = 1.64 \times 10^{-20} \, \Delta f \qquad (6-2)$$

or is 1.64×10^{-20} watts per cycle. This is the same for any value of the resistance. Any signal in the resistance lower than this value will be hopelessly lost.

If the resistance is connected to a high gain amplifier and then to a telephone receiver having a flat response over this band of frequencies and which is held to the ear, then the sound power going into the ear due to this resistance noise is

$$1.64 \times 10^{-20} \, \Delta f \, E. \, G. \text{ watts}$$

where G is the power gain of the amplifier and E the efficiency of the receiver. Since the area of the ear opening is approximately $1 \ \overline{cm^2}$, this may be considered the approximate sound intensity at the ear opening. The spectrum level curve for such noise then is flat and the ordinates of it are the same for all frequencies. For this reason whenever a sound from any source has a flat spectrum level curve, it is called resistance noise or white noise.

The intensity level β corresponding to this noise power is given by

$$\beta = -38 + 10 \log \Delta f + 10 \log E + 10 \log G. \qquad (6-3)$$

The last term is the gain of the amplifier in db. For example, for a telephone receiver having an efficiency of 75% and passing a band of frequencies 8000 cycles wide the noise level at the ear is

$$\beta = 10 \log G,$$

that is, it is equal to the gain of the amplifier.

When considering a commercial telephone system, this kind of noise is never heard at the listener end due to resistance at the speaker's end, because the gain in the system as a whole is always less than zero. In order to keep this noise down to a satisfactory level, the speech power in the electrical form is never permitted to be reduced to values near the resistance noise values. It will be seen, however, that levels near zero can arise in the receiver without having any amplifier gain.

---

[1] Johnson and Llewellyn, Bell Technical Journal, 1935.

In carbon microphones an electrical [2] noise arises which is much larger than the resistance noise and is called carbon noise. It is always present when the so-called "burning" has been eliminated. If V_c is the voltage fluctuation at the terminals of the microphone, then Christensen and Pearson [2] found empirically that

$$V_c^2 = KV^{1.85}F^{1.25} \log f_1/f_2$$

where K is a constant which varies with the kind of carbon used, V is the d.c. voltage across the microphone, R is the d.c. resistance, and f_1 and f_2 are the limits of the frequency band that is passed. For a 395-B telephone microphone, $K = 1.3 \times 10^{-11}$, $R = 45$ ohms, $V = 2.5$. Then for such a microphone the noise power in it is

$$V_c^2/R = 1.5 \times 10^{-10} \log_{10} f_1/f_2 \text{ watts.} \qquad (6\text{--}4)$$

For a frequency band from 200 cps to 3000 cps this is 1.8×10^{-10} watt. If the difference $f_2 - f_1 = \Delta f$ is small compared to f_1, then this equation (6–4) becomes

$$\frac{V_c^2}{R} = 0.66 \times 10^{-10} \frac{\Delta f}{f} \text{ watts.} \qquad (6\text{--}5)$$

The watts per cycle at 1000 cps is then 0.66×10^{-10} as compared to 1.6×10^{-20} for the resistance noise, or a level difference of about 66 db. For the 395-B microphone $V_c = 9 \times 10^{-5}$. When a person speaks into this microphone, it produces speech voltages of the order of 0.1 volt, or the speech signal is about 60 db above the noise. It has been seen in Chapter III that some of the consonant sounds may be 40 db below the louder vowel sounds. Also, when the speaker is about a meter away from the microphone, the voice level is reduced about 35 db. Under such circumstances the weaker speech sounds would be below the noise level.

If such a microphone is efficiently coupled to an amplifier with power gain G, and the output end of the amplifier is connected to a telepohne receiver of efficiency E, then the intensity level β of the carbon noise in the ear is approximately

$$\beta = 58.5 + 10 \log \frac{\Delta f}{f} + 10 \log G + 10 \log E. \qquad (6\text{--}6)$$

It is seen that for a band width $\Delta f = 100$ around 1000 cps levels between 40 and 50 are produced without any gain in the amplifier. So this type of noise becomes important in deaf sets using carbon microphones. There are many other sources of electrical noise arising in telephone circuits which cannot be discussed here, but they are all classed as line noise.

[2] Christensen and Pearson, Bell System Technical Journal, pp. 197–223, 1936.

The room or booth on the receiving end of the line always has some noise present. It varies in character from the ticking of a clock in a quiet country home to the intense noise in a booth on the platform of a subway railway station. The type of room noise which is the most characteristic is that which is usually characterized as "roar" from the street. Such noises can be represented by a spectrum level curve.

In general if α_f is the ordinate in such a curve then the level α_{12} in the band of frequencies between f_1 and f_2 is given by

$$\alpha_{12} = 10 \log \int_{f_1}^{f_2} 10^{\alpha_f/10} \, df. \qquad (6\text{--}7)$$

For example, a "white" noise transmitted in a band of frequency from 100 cps to 4100 cps corresponding to the important speech range of frequencies the value of α_{12} is

$$\alpha_{12} = \alpha_f + 26, \qquad (6\text{--}8)$$

that is, the total level is 26 db above the common spectrum level.

TABLE 16

CRITICAL BAND WIDTHS IN db

f	κ	f	κ	f	κ
100 cps	19.4 db	1200 cps	18.4 db	3000 cps	21.5 db
200	17.2	1400	18.8	3500	22.3
300	17.0	1600	19.2	4000	23.1
400	17.0	1800	19.6	6000	25.7
600	17.2	2000	19.9	8000	27.7
800	17.6	2500	20.9	10000	29.2
1000	18.0				

Another important source of noise is that coming from the medium (film, disc, or magnetic tape) used in recording and reproducing sounds. At a convenient point in the output circuit the electrical spectrum level curve can be taken, i.e., the value $10 \log (P_R \Delta_f)$, where P_R is the electrical power coming into a band a frequency Δ_f cycles wide. If now β_f is the power level at this same point due to a pure tone that has been recorded at as high a level as possible without producing more than 2% harmonic distortion, then the signal to noise ratio curve is defined by

$$\beta_f - 10 \log (P_R \, \Delta_f) + \kappa \qquad (6\text{--}9)$$

where κ is an important quantity called the critical band width in db which varies with frequency as shown in Table 16.

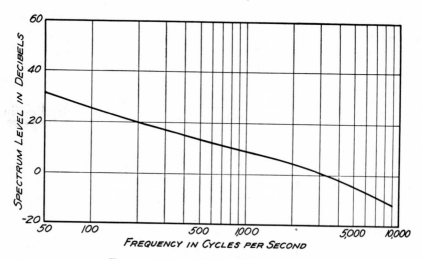

FIG. 70.—AVERAGE ROOM NOISE SPECTRUM.

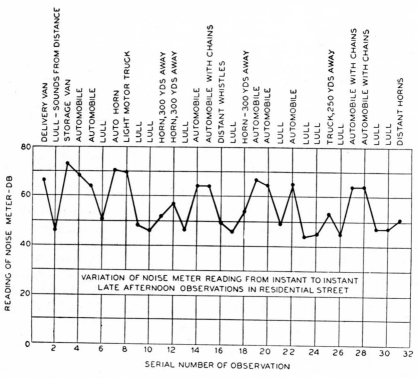

FIG. 71.—VARIATION OF NOISE LEVEL ON A RESIDENTIAL STREET.

The critical band width Δf in cps is given by

$$\kappa\Delta = 10 \log (\Delta_f)_c. \qquad (6\text{--}10)$$

For example, at 1000 cps the value of $(\Delta_f)_c = 63$ cps and at 2000 cps it is 98 cps, and at 10,000 cps it is 832 cps.

It will be seen later that due to characteristics of hearing such a band width of noise will just mask a pure tone which lies in the same band and when the two have the same intensity level at the ear. So with this concept the *signal-to-noise ratio at each frequency is the number of db that a tone which has been recorded at maximum level can be lowered in level before it is masked by the noise.*

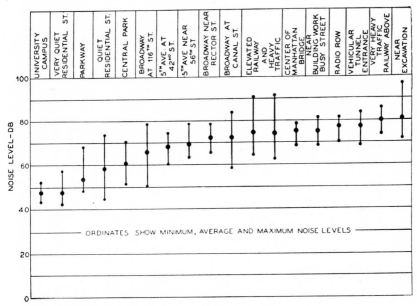

FIG. 72.—NOISE LEVELS AT VARIOUS PLACES IN N. Y. C.

In a survey of room noises made by Seacord[3] it was found that 43 db was the average sound level in residences not having radios playing. The standard deviation of levels in different residences from this figure was 5.5 db. The distribution about this average value indicated that about one-half the residences have noise levels between 39 and 47 db, and 90% are in the range between 33 and 52 db.

Hoth[4] found that the form of the noise spectrum was about the same

[3] D. F. Seacord, *Room Noise at Subscribers' Telephone Locations*, Journal Acoustical Society America, vol. 12, pp. 183–187, July, 1940.

[4] D. F. Hoth, *Room Noise Spectra at Subscribers' Telephone Locations*, Journal Acoustical Society America, vol. 12, pp. 499–504, April, 1941.

for all types of rooms.   Using his relation, we find that the spectrum
for the average room noise having a total level of 43 db is that shown in
Fig. 70.   The ordinates give the spectrum level.

This finding of Hoth is very important for engineering purposes.   For
to specify the noise in a room one need to give only the total intensity

SURVEY OF NEW YORK CITY NOISE ABATEMENT COMMISSION		NOISE LEVEL	OTHER SURVEYS	
DISTANCE FROM SOURCE	SOURCE OR DESCRIPTION OF NOISE		SOURCE OR DESCRIPTION OF NOISE	SURVEY NO
FEET		DB		
		130	THRESHOLD OF PAINFUL SOUND	4
		120		
2	HAMMER BLOWS ON STEEL PLATE-SOUND ALMOST PAINFUL (INDOOR TEST)		AIRPLANE; MOTOR 1600 RPM; 18 FT FROM PROPELLER	5
		110	AERO ENGINE UNSILENCED – 10 FT	4
		100		
35	RIVETER			
15–20	ELEVATED ELECTRIC TRAIN ON OPEN STRUCTURE	90	PNEUMATIC DRILL – 10 FT	4
			NOISIEST SPOT AT NIAGARA FALLS	2
15–75	VERY HEAVY STREET TRAFFIC WITH ELEVATED LINE	80	HEAVY TRAFFIC WITH ELEVATED LINE, CHICAGO	7
15–50	AVERAGE MOTOR TRUCK		VERY NOISY STREET NY OR CHICAGO	1
15–75	BUSY STREET TRAFFIC	70	VERY BUSY TRAFFIC LONDON	4
15–50	AVERAGE AUTOMOBILE			
3	ORDINARY CONVERSATION		AVERAGE SHOPPING ST. CHICAGO	6
15–300	RATHER QUIET RESIDENTIAL STREET, AFTERNOON	60	BUSY TRAFFIC, LONDON	4
15–50	QUIET AUTOMOBILE			
	MINIMUM NOISE LEVELS ON STREET	50	QUIET AUTOMOBILE LONDON	4
			QUIET ST BEHIND REGENT ST, LONDON	4
15–500	IN ENTIRE CITY DAY TIME { MIN AVERAGE MIN INSTANTANEOUS			
50–500	IN MID-CITY NIGHT { MIN INSTANTANEOUS	40		
50–500				
		30	QUIET ST EVENING, NO TRAFFIC SUBURBAN LONDON	4
		20	QUIET GARDEN, LONDON	4
			AVERAGE WHISPER – 4 FT	3
		10	QUIET WHISPER – 5 FT	4
			RUSTLE OF LEAVES IN GENTLE BREEZE	3
		0	THRESHOLD OF HEARING	

FIG. 73.—NOISE LEVELS OUT OF DOORS DUE TO VARIOUS NOISE SOURCES.

level as read on a sound level meter and then assume the shape of the
spectrum level curve is that given in Fig. 70.   If α db is the sound level
obtained in such a room, then $\alpha - 43$ is the amount the curve in Fig. 70
must be raised to represent the noise condition in the measured room.   It
is obvious that this rule cannot be used blindly, but it is very useful
nevertheless, and it is customary to give a single figure to represent the
noise in a room.

Surveys of street noise in various cities have been made. Some results taken in New York City by the Noise Abatement Commission are given below. In Fig. 71 is shown the type of variation of the noise level with time on the corner of one of the streets in Brooklyn, New York.

In Fig. 72 are shown the noise levels at various locations in New York City. The maximum level found in the survey was 101 db due to a riveter 35 feet away from the meter. The level at the operator's ear, which is about two feet away from the source, will then be about 126 db. The minimum was found to be 42 db on the upper campus of New York University.

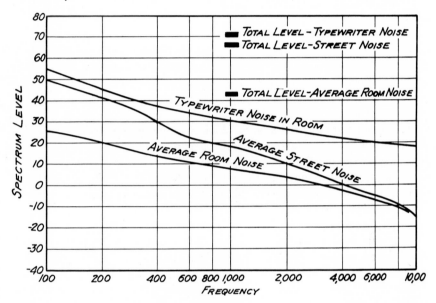

FIG. 74.—CURVES FOR TYPICAL STREET NOISE, AND TYPEWRITER NOISE IN A ROOM.

The table in Fig. 73 gives a good idea of the range of noises encountered in daily life. An interesting relation was found between the number of automobiles passing per minute and the noise level. As one would expect, the noise level rose 10 db as the traffic increased tenfold. The intensity of the noise was proportional to the number of automobiles passing a given point.

The shape of the spectrum level curve is, of course, different for these various kinds of noise, but frequently it is very similar to that given for room noise in Fig. 70.

In Fig. 74 such curves are given for typical street noise, and noise in a room where a typewriter is being operated fairly rapidly. For comparison purposes the average room noise curve from Fig. 71 is also shown.

CHAPTER 7

MECHANISM OF HEARING

Vibrations in the sound wave communicate mechanical vibrations to the eardrum which, in turn, communicates the vibration to the inner ear where the nerve endings are excited.

The ear mechanism may be divided into three general parts: the outer ear, the middle ear, and the inner ear. The outer ear consists of the external part or pinna, and the ear canal or auditory meatus. The middle ear contains three small bones or ossicles called, respectively, the hammer, the anvil, and the stirrup. The inner ear contains the cochlea, vestibule, the semicircular canals, and the endolymphatic duct and sac. In the cochlea are located nerves which give us the sense of hearing, and in the semicircular canals are located nerves which cause reactions concerned with the maintenance of equilibrium.

Fig. 75 shows a schematic diagram of the parts of the ear with the inner ear much enlarged. The pinna is used by a number of animals to aid in collecting the sound. The human pinna has almost lost this function, but a cupped hand held to the ear sometimes supplants it.

The ear canal, or auditory meatus, G, is about three centimeters long. It is closed at the inner end by the eardrum or tympanic membrane. Attached to the drum from its center and upwards by a long part called the handle is the first of the ossicles, called the hammer. The top of the hammer is connected with the anvil by a joint, and the anvil, in turn, is connected to the stirrup, the small bone that conveys the motion through the oval window to the labyrinth in the inner ear. The part of the stirrup lying in the oval window is flat and is called the foot plate. It is held in place by an annular ligament of the membrane which prevents the fluid of the inner ear from coming into the middle ear. The mastoid cells are connected to the middle ear but are not concerned with hearing.

The inner ear has a dense bony wall forming an irregular cavity, referred to as the bony labyrinth and is filled with fluid. It contains a smaller structure of the same general shape called the membranous labyrinth which contains a fluid that is separate and distinct from the rest of the fluid in the bony structure. Its walls are formed by a very soft membrane so that sound waves pass through them with little obstruction. The cavity of the inner ear is encased in solid bone and has only two small openings into the middle ear; one, at the oval window into which fits the stirrup and one, at the round window indicated at r. An elastic membrane is stretched across the round window and is sometimes referred to as the secondary eardrum. The middle ear is connected to the outside air by means of a small tube called the Eustachian tube, which opens into the upper part of the throat behind the nasal cavity.

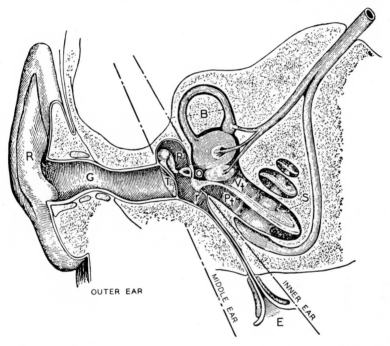

OUTER EAR

MIDDLE EAR

INNER EAR

FIG. 75.—SEMIDIAGRAMMATIC SECTION THROUGH THE RIGHT EAR (CZERMAK): G, EXTERNAL AUDITORY MEATUS; T, MEMBRANA TYMPANI; P, TYMPANIC CAVITY; O, FENESTRA OVALIS; R, FENESTRA ROTUNDA; B, SEMICIRCULAR CANAL; S, COCHLEA; VT, SCALA VESTIBULI; PT, SCALA TYMPANI; E, EUSTACHIAN TUBE; R, PINNA.

The inner ear consists of three principal parts; namely, (1) the semi-circular canals which take no part in the mechanism of hearing, but serve as an organ of balance, (2) the vestibule, the space just behind the oval window, and (3) the cochlea which is really the end organ of hearing. Cross-sections of the cochlea as it twists into a relatively long spiral of two and three-quarter turns like a snail shell are indicated at S in Fig. 75. The center of the spiral is a bone called the modiolus, which is perforated to allow space for the auditory nerve. The nerve enters the base of the cochlea and outside it unites with the nerves from the semicircular canals into two parts forming the eighth cranial nerve. The cochlea is divided along its length into three parts by the basilar membrane and

Reissner's membrane.   These form three parallel canals which are wound into the spiral.   A cross-section showing the shape of these canals is given in Fig. 76.   The oval window is at one end of the scala vestibuli and the round window at the end of the scala tympani.

As indicated in this figure, the canals are called the scala media or canal of cochlea, scala tympani, and scala vestibuli.   As stated before, the

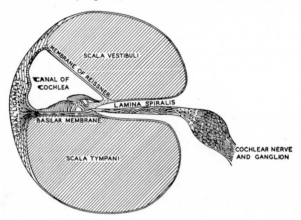

FIG. 76.—COCHLEA IN TRANSVERSE SECTION. OBSERVE ESPECIALLY THE CANAL OF THE
COCHLEA WHICH IS A PART OF THE MEMBRANOUS LABYRINTH.

membrane of Reissner is a very thin flexible membrane which will very readily pass any sound waves, so that from a dynamical consideration, the canal of cochlea and scala vestibuli may be considered as a single chamber filled with fluid.   The partition between the scala tympani and the other two chambers is composed of a bony projection called the lamina spiralis for more than half the width, the remainder being a flexible membrane called the basilar membrane.   It is seen from this figure that if any vibratory energy is communicated from one side of this partition to the other, it must vibrate the basilar membrane.   On top of the basilar membrane lies the organ of Corti, which contains the nerve terminals in the form of small hairs extending into the canal of cochlea.   Attached to the lamina spiralis and lying over the hair cells is another soft loose membrane called the tectorial membrane.   The details of this part of the inner ear are made clearer by Fig. 77, which is a greatly magnified cross-section of these two membranes.   It is seen from this figure that there are five rows of hair cells at the terminals of the so-called rods. There are about 5000 rods in each of the four outer rows and about 3500 in the inner row, making a total of about 23,500 rods.   At the end of each rod there is a hair cell from which project twelve to fifteen hair cilia into the liquid of the cochlea.   When a sound excites the sense of hearing there is a relative motion between the basilar membrane and the tectorial membrane which causes the hair cells to stimulate the nerve endings at their base. The base of the inner rod of Corti is supported on the edge of the bony projection, called the lamina spiralis. For this reason, according to some authors[1] the motion which stimulates the hair cells is a lateral one between the rods and the tectorial membrane due to the rocking motion of the former. According to Dr. Shambaugh, the stimulation is principally due to the vibration of the tectorial membrane. Helmholtz, as well as many other writers on the subject, assumed that the basilar membrane was the principal vibrator carrying the rods of Corti with it. Thus the hair cells are excited by their relative motion

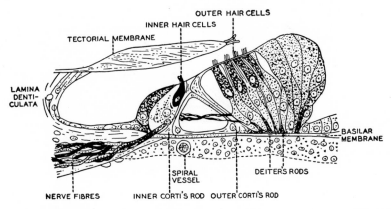

FIG. 77.—CORTI's ORGAN (after Retzius). THE TECTORIAL MEMBRANE IS SHOWN CONTRACTED IN THE PROCESS OF HARDENING THE TISSUE, AND TORN AWAY FORM THE PLATEAU OF CORTI.

to the tectorial membrane. Any of these points of view are still possible even if we assume that the ends of the hair cells are imbedded in the tectorial membrane.

Most students of hearing believe that these hair cells act like microphones. As soon as they are vibrated, electrical potentials are created which have frequencies equal to stimulating vibration frequencies and are the seat of the so-called cochlear electrical potentials which are measured in animal experimentation. This electrical potential spreads throughout the adjoining tissues. If two electrodes are placed in or near the cochlea, they will pick up this alternating potential. If they are connected to an amplifier and oscilloscope, the wave form of this cochlear current can be seen. Weaver and Bray at Princeton started research with these cochlear potentials about twenty years ago, and many others have since worked in

---

[1] Emile ter Kuile was one of the first to maintain this view, Pflüger's *Archives*, Vol. LXXIX, p. 146, 1900.

this field so that a large quantity of data are now available concerning them.

It is found that these hair cells broadcast an electrical wave through the tissues near them of the same form as the air sound wave. For example, if the electrodes embedded near the cochlea are connected through an amplifier to a loudspeaker instead of an oscilloscope, then the sound from the loudspeaker can be identified as the same as the stimulating sound. The relation obtained by Weaver between the pressure level in a cat's ear and the cochlear potential produced across a pair of electrodes placed near the inner ear is shown in Fig. 78. Up to 80 db these potentials are proportional to the sound pressure in the ear.

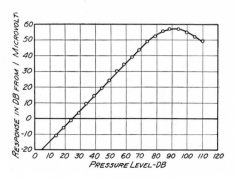

FIG. 78.—COCHLEAR POTENTIALS INDUCED BY A 1000-CYCLE STIMULATING TONE.

According to Weaver, it is these cochlear potentials which set off the nerve impulses which pass along the auditory nerve to the brain. These impulses probably start from the nerve endings. Whether it is the cochlear potentials or the vibration of the hair cell, it is known that whenever there is a cochlear potential (and hence a vibration), the nerve starts sending nervous impulses along its fiber to the brain causing the sensation of hearing. More will be said later about this mechanism.

The drum of the ear and the ossicles of the middle ear act as a sort of transformer to communicate the vibratory energy from the air, a light medium, into the liquid, a dense medium. Due to the fact that the area of the stirrup which plunges into the fluid of the inner ear is about one-twentieth of that of the eardrum and also due to the lever action of the three bones, the pressure exerted by the oval window of the middle ear upon the fluid of the inner ear would be from thirty to sixty times that exerted by the air upon the eardrum if all containing walls and basilar membrane of the inner ear were rigid. This transformer action permits the sound waves due to speech to pass more readily from the air into the liquid.[2]   It will be shown later that for frequencies below 600 cps the sound pressure back of the stapes is less than that in front of the eardrum.

The relative sizes of the parts of the inner ear may be judged from Fig. 79[3], which shows the cochlea uncoiled.   It is seen that the length of the uncoiled cochlea in this sample is about 31 millimeters.   The cross-sections of the cochlear passages on each side of the basilar membrane vary as one goes from the oval window to the helicotrema as indicated in the figure.   The area of the stapes where it fits into the oval window

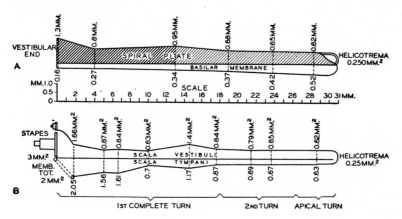

Fig. 79.—A. The Dimensions and Shape of the Human Basilar Membrane and Bony Spiral Lamina. B. Diagram of the Sectional Areas of the Cochlear Passages (drawn to scale). In each case the actual measurements and scale of measurements are given.

is seen to be about 3 square millimeters.   The opening between the two chambers at the helicotrema is about one-quarter square millimeter. These figures emphasize the fact that this important mechanism of hearing is really very small.   As mentioned above, the nerve terminals are scattered along the basilar membrane, and all the differentiations of complex sounds which are heard are made possible by the corresponding stimulation patterns produced in this membrane only one-quarter millimeter wide and about from 30 to 35 millimeters long.

[2] The specific impedance of the air is 41.5 and that of the water 144,000. The transformer ratio which will transform a maximum amount of power from one medium to the other is the square root of the ratio of impedances, or 59. However, the body of liquid in the ear is so small that it probably moves bodily back and forth and is not compressed. Consequently, the impedance at the oval window may be very different from that offered by the same area in a large body of water.

[3] The dimensions for this figure were obtained from the book by Wrightson and Keith entitled *An Inquiry into the Analytical Mechanism of the Internal Ear.*

Mechanism of Nerve Conduction

The auditory nerve is very similar to a cable trunk. It contains about 3000 medullated nerve fibers, each consisting of an "axis cylinder" surrounded by a fatty substance called the myelin. The axis of this cylinder has a diameter of about 0.001 centimeter and forms only about 9 percent of the fiber. It is thus seen that nerve fibers are constructed very much like insulated telephone wires and bound together in a strikingly similar manner to telephone cables. This analogous structure led some physiologists to the conclusion that all nervous impulses were electrical in origin and that their transmission was very similar to the electrical transmission on telephone lines. This theory, however, was found to be untenable.

Most of the earlier experiments on nerve conduction were made with motor nerves so that the mechanism of nerve conduction described here is based upon such experiments by several investigators. However, recent work of Davis and Galambos [4] shows that the action in the auditory nerves is essentially the same. A nervous impulse may be excited by heat; chemical, electrical, or mechanical stimuli; or by reflex stimuli. Touching the nerve with a red-hot iron, with an acid, or pinching it, sets up a nervous impulse. The most common method in the physiological laboratories of exciting such an impulse is to use the shock obtained from a "make-and-break" induction coil. In order to set up such an impulse, the strength of the stimulus and its rate of change must be greater than a certain minimum. It has been found that the nervous impulse which travels along the nerves is not at all analogous to an electrical current traveling along a wire. An elemental nerve fiber has no impulse at all or else it fires with its full force. In other words, in normal nerve fibers the impulse is either of normal strength or zero strength throughout its entire course and seems to be the same regardless of how it is stimulated. The minimum value for starting the full nervous impulse is different for the different nerve fibers constituting the nerve.

In describing nerve conduction, physiologists frequently say it is similar to what goes on when a gunpowder fuse is lighted. The rate of the fire traveling down the fuse and the intensity of the heat which it creates are in no way dependent upon the way the fuse was lighted at the end. From this point of view, it is seen to be a necessary condition that the loudness produced by a tone exciting the ear must be directly related to the number of fibers being excited and the rate at which the excitations occur, since each fiber always carries its maximum impulse. It would seem necessary also that the minimum stimulus to excite each fiber must differ greatly.

[4] Davis and Galambos, Journal Neurophysiology, 6, pp. 39–58, 1943.

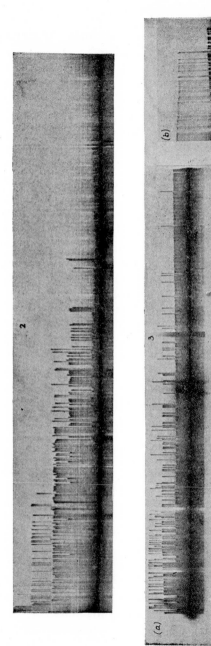

Fig. 80.—Muscle Contractions in a Frog Leg Due to Progressively Increasing the Intensity of Electric Spark Stimulating the Nerve.

This is beautifully illustrated by some experimental work of Porter and Hart.[5] The nerves controlling muscle contraction were stimulated by electric shocks. The currents producing these shocks were gradually increased. The successive contractions of the muscles did not increase gradually but in definite steps as shown in Fig. 80. This figure is a record taken from their experimental work. The height of each line is a measure of each successive contraction.

If the auditory nerves act in a similar way, then, as a tone is gradually increased in intensity from below the threshold to loud values, the excitations reaching the brain must increase in definite steps, the threshold corresponding to the first nerve fibers being excited. When all of the nerve fibers are excited and firing at their maximum rate, no further increase in loudness is possible.

After a nervous impulse has passed down the nerve, there is a "refractory" phase during which time the nerve is unable to respond or conduct. Then follows a "relative refractory" period during which the excitability, the conductivity, and the speed of propagation gradually return from zero to normal. As the condition of the nerve returns to normal, it overshoots the mark and becomes supernormal; that is, it is more sensitive, more highly conductive, and the speed or propagation is greater. This supernormal condition gradually dies away, until the nerve is once again in its normal stage. During the relative refractory phases that the nerve conducts impulses reduced in magnitude "all or none" is qualified. The length of this refractory period has been measured by several observers, and, although there is a wide disagreement, the best estimate at the present time seems to place it at about 0.001 second and the relative refractory period at about 0.003 second. According to these figures, the maximum number of nervous impulses which a single nerve fiber can send to the brain is 1000 per second. Those periodic excitations greater than 300 per second will not be transmitted as normal impulses, since each succeeding excitation will lie in the relative refractory period. Consequently, if nerves in the ear act like this, then when a pure tone having a frequency of 2000 or 3000 cycles excites the ear the number of nervous impulses being sent to the brain per second by each nerve fiber is considerably less than the exciting frequency, and depends upon the intensity.

The remarkable work of Davis and Galambos[6] has recently confirmed that this is the correct picture for single nerve fibers in the auditory nerve. By means of a micro-pipette they were able to adjust an electrode so that the electrical impulse from a single nerve fiber in a cat's ear

[5] Porter, E. L., and Hart, V. W., *Reflex Contractions of all or None Character in the Spinal Cate*, American Journal of Physiology, October, 1923.

[6] Davis and Galambos, Journal Neurophysiology, 6, pp. 39–58, 1943.

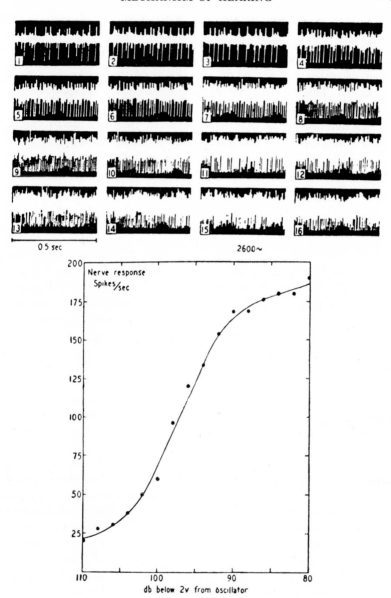

Fig. 81.—Frequency of Nerve Discharge as a Function of Sound Intensity for an Adapted Fiber (2600 cps, −110 db). A 2600 cps tone was delivered continuously to the animal while the intensity was raised in 2 db steps. The successively numbered segments of record in the figure represent the adapted response of the fiber to 2600 cps as intensity successively changes from −110 db to −80 db in 2 db steps. Points on the graph were established by counting the number of spikes appearing in 1 sec.

could be recorded.   Fig 81 is taken from their paper.   The abscissas give the relative pressure levels in the cat's ear, the zero level corresponding to a pressure level of approximately 110 db.   The ordinates are the number of spikes per second in the record of the response of a single nerve fiber.   This record is for a nerve which had a maximum response for a frequency of 2600 cps and had a threshold level at −110 db.   This level was determined as that which enabled the observer to detect an increase in response over the spontaneous or background response.

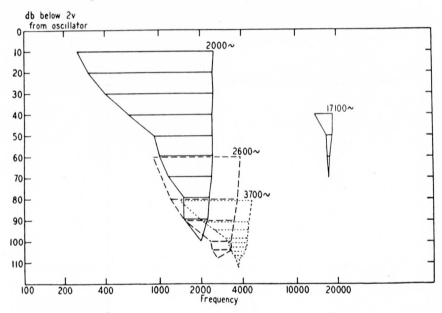

FIG. 82.—RESPONSE AREAS FOR 4 DIFFERENT FIBERS.   THE 3 AT THE LEFT OF THE FIGURE ARE THE SAME ANIMAL.

It will be noticed that as the pressure level is increased successively in 2 db steps the number of nerve discharges per second steadily increased from 24 to about 190 per second as the pressure level was raised from zero to 30 db above the threshold level.   If one counts the spikes in the first tenth second after the first discharge, then rates as high as 450 spikes per second can be obtained.

A very important discovery was made by these two observers; namely, a single fiber responded to only a limited range of stimulating frequencies. This is depicted in Fig. 82 which shows the response for four different fibers.   It is seen that at low stimulating levels the response of a single nerve fiber is limited to a very narrow range of frequencies.   As the stimulating level increases this range increases, extending principally toward the lower frequencies. As the pressure level increases above the threshold level for any frequency which will excite the nerve, then the number of discharges per second along a nerve fiber in this auditory nerve is a function of both the intensity and frequency. Fig. 83 shows this result for a 7000-cycle fiber.

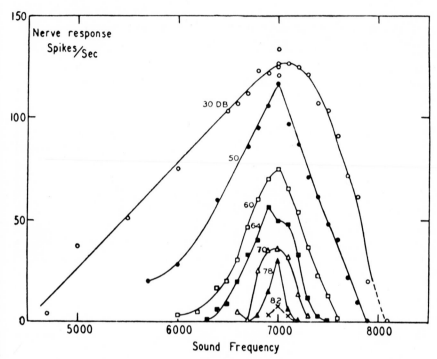

FIG. 83.—Iso-intensity Contours for a Single Fiber (7000 cps, −84 db). The way in which frequency of nerve discharge varies with sound frequency is plotted here. The number on each contour line indicates the intensity level at which the determinations were made. This figure shows that as sound intensity level increases (numbers on contour lines get smaller), (1) the fiber is excited by frequencies which lie farther away; and (2) any frequency capable of exciting the fiber elicits more discharges. Frequency of nerve response is determined by both the frequency and the intensity of the sound stimulus.

There have been many [7] theories proposed which describe the various functions performed by the different parts of the ear when sensing a sound. Most of these theories originated before there were much quantitative data concerning the facts of audition. The accumulation

[7] These are discussed in a recent book by Weaver entitled *Theory of Hearing.*

of such data during the last thirty years has produced evidence which greatly favors one of these theories which I have called the "Space-Time Pattern Theory of Hearing." [8]   It is an extension of the Helmholtz resonant theory.   Before discussing this theory it will be advantageous to consider further the important auditory information which is now available.

[8] This theory was first presented in a paper before the Acoustical Society of America, December, 1929.

CHAPTER 8

HEARING ACUITY

The hearing acuity is measured as the smallest "amount" of sound that can be perceived by the ear. To be expressed in definite physical terms, a precise definition of "amount" and of the type of sound must be made. The "amount" is expressed as pressure level (db above 0.0002 dyne/cm²).

Also, the place where the sound pressure is measured must be specified. There are two different places which have generally been used. The first place is just in front of the eardrum. Such measurements are called minimum audible sound pressures (M.A.P.) at the eardrum. The second place is at the position in a free air space where the ear will be placed. Then the listening person puts his head in such a position that he faces the source of sound and his ear is at the position where the sound pressure was measured. Such measurements are called minimum audible field pressures (M.A.F.). The kind of sound must be specified in each case. Three kinds of sound will receive most attention in this book; viz., pure tones, speech, and noise.

The acuity for pure tones depends upon the frequency of vibration of the tone. The acuity is, therefore, expressed as a curve, the abcissas

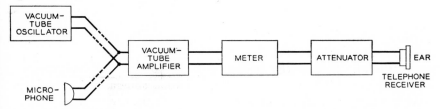

FIG. 84.—CIRCUIT ARRANGEMENT FOR TESTING THE ACUITY OF HEARING.

giving the frequency of the tone and the ordinates the pressure level in db. First, consider minimum audible pressures at the eardrum. Before the advent of the vacuum tube many ingenious methods of creating measureable amount of sound pressure near the ear were used, but they have now only historical interest. All modern methods usually use an experimental "set-up" shown in Fig. 84. If we wish to find the acuity for pure tones, the vacuum-tube oscillator is used to generate electrically the tones.   The meter reads the a.c. current I.   The attenuator box has a dial which reads decibels.   Let this reading be α db.   The dial on the oscillator reads the frequency f.   Now for a given I and f and α the sound pressure p under the receiver cup must be known.   The process of finding p for each frequency is known as calibrating the receiver.   This seems like a simple process and so it is when only approximate results are needed.   For great accuracy it becomes very difficult, and although experimenters have been working at the problem for thirty-five years since the advent of the vacuum tube, there is still no good agreement as to how it should be done.   A good discussion of the technical aspects

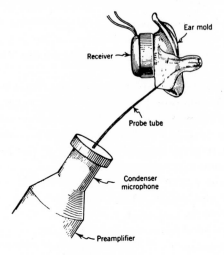

FIG. 85.—PROBE TUBE SUITABLE FOR DETERMINING THE SOUND PRESSURE PRODUCED BY A HEARING AID EARPHONE NEAR THE EARDRUM.

of this problem is given in the recent book by Beranek.[1]   In general there are two methods of making this calibration.

In the first method the receiver is held against a standard coupler (artificial ear).   The aim in constructing this standard coupler is to have the same air space and compliance as is in the ear canal and drum. The bottom of the coupler is closed by a diaphragm of a condenser microphone which measures the pressure by the voltage created at its terminals. The calibrations furnished by the Bureau of Standards are made in this way.   These are called coupler calibrations.

In the second method the receiver is held against the ear, and a small probe tube is passed through the receiver cap so that its open end is near the eardrum.   In this last method the calibration will be different for each ear because of differences in the compliances of the drum and side

[1] Beranek, *Acoustical Measurements*.

walls.   An average of a number of persons is taken as the calibration.
The experimental arrangement[2] for doing this for a receiver of a hearing
aid is shown in Fig. 85.

In the arrangement of Fig. 84 the sound pressure p is related to the
current I and attenuation setting α by the equation

$$p = KI \, 10^{\alpha/20} \tag{8-1}$$

The calibration consists in finding K at each frequency.   When this
is done the pressure level β is

$$\beta = 20 \log (p/0.0002) = \alpha + 20 \log (KI/0.0002). \tag{8-2}$$

Thus the pressure level can be determined from reading α of the attenuator
and current I in the meter.   Usually the current I is held constant by
means of the potentiometer in the amplifier so that the acuity is equal
to α plus a constant.

The arrangment in Fig. 84 when housed in a convenient form constitutes a tone range audiometer.   Such an audiometer usually has two
dials, one for showing the frequency and one for showing the attenuation.
The calibration is such that when the attenuator reads zero the sound
coming out of the receiver into the ear will be at the threshold of hearing
for an average unpracticed listener.   The number of db that the pressure
level, measuring the acuity of any listener, is above that for an average
listener is called the *hearing loss*.   An audiometer is calibrated and
arranged so that the setting of the dial when the tone is just perceived
measures directly the hearing loss.

The first commercial tone range audiometer is known as the Western
Electric 2A, shown in Fig. 86.   In this instrument eight frequencies
were obtained by throwing one of the four two-way keys shown on top
of the instrument.   These frequencies were 64, 128, 256, 512, 1024, 4096,
and 8192 cps.   Most of the audiograms taken by otologists for the first
twenty years of audiometry were referred to this instrument.   Originally
the zero marking on the dial for each frequency was determined by taking
the average of the threshold settings for one hundred ears which showed
no pathology.   More recently, however, Munson[3] has measured the pressure at the entrance of the ear canal by a search tube method while the
receiver of this audiometer is held to the ear and the attenuator set at
zero.   The results are given in Table 17.

These values give the pressure levels at about one-half inch from
the drum of the ear.   However, since the wave-length of a 4000-cycle
tone is one and one-third inches, it is safe to assume that these represent
pressures in front of the eardrum except for the 8192 cycletone.

[2] *Acoustical Measurements*, p. 732.
[3] Munson, Journal Acoustical Society America, Figure 9, p. 276, 1940.

Since 1939 the Bureau of Standards has been furnishing calibrations based on the results of a comprehensive survey by the U. S. Public Health Service of the hearing acuity in the U. S. population. In this survey it was found that the average acuity at each frequency corresponded

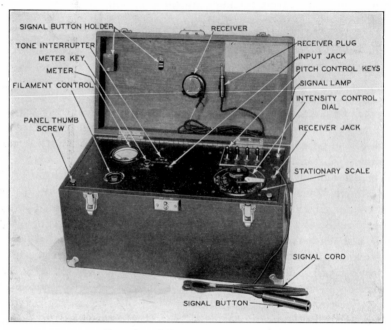

FIG. 86.—2A AUDIOMETER PHOTOGRAPH.

TABLE 17

PRESSURE LEVELS FOR ZERO ATTENUATOR SETTING ON 2A AUDIOMETER

Frequency	= 64	128	256	512	1024	2048	4096	8192
Pressure level =		47.6	39.3	39.0	22.6	23.6	20.7	259

to the following voltages (Table 18) across a typical 2A audiometer receiver. Three such Western Electric No. 552 receivers are kept as standards. The average of these three is considered typical.

These values have been adopted as a "Proposed Standard Calibration" by the Council of Physical Medicine of the American Medical Association, but the American Standard Association has not (1952) yet adopted any standard for "Normal Ear Threshold" for audiometers. It has adopted

TABLE 18

Frequency of tone	128	256	512	1024	2048	4096	8192
Voltage in 10^{-6} volt (microwatt)	224	39.8	77.94	3.55	2.82	4.47	178

what is called a zero loudness contour which will be discussed later, but this is based on minimum audible field pressures for very acute ears and is not an average threshold.

If the voltages in Table 18 are compared to those across the No. 558 receiver when the 2A audiometer's attenuator dial is set at zero db, the comparative results in Table 19 are obtained.   Then to get the acuity

TABLE 19

WHEN THE "PROPOSED STANDARD AUDIOMETER" READS ZERO

At frequency (cps)	64	128	256	512	1024	2048	4096	8192
2A audiometer reads (db)		1.5	6.0	5.0	−0.5	−1.8	3.7	3.1

as a pressure level from results of audiometers so calibrated, the values in Table 19 must be added to those in Table 17 to obtain the pressure level for the zero setting for the "Proposed Standard Audiometer."

The Bureau of Standards has determined pressure levels for the zero setting for the "Proposed Standard" given above from measurements obtained by placing the receiver on a standard coupler.   The differences between these values and those obtained by Munson by the ear-probe method are greater than one would expect, being as much as 10 db at some frequencies.   Recently (1951) the Bureau of Standards has made ear probe calibrations which give better agreement with their coupler calibrations.   Due to the great variability of ears it is difficult to reduce the differences much below 5 db.

Some of the most accurate sets of acuity measurements were reported by Sivian and White[4] in 1922.   They made extensive measurements of both M.A.P. and M.A.F. and discussed all the data taken by other observers.   First consider their minimum audible field data.   The following is their description of this work.

"The data were obtained in the field established at one meter in front of a loud speaking receiver[5] in a highly absorbing acoustic structure (referred to later as the "sound stage").   This structure is of the type developed by Wente and Bedell.[6]   It consists of 12 layers of flannel and muslin, separated by air layers, making a total thickness of 12 inches. The receiver radiates from an area of 3.8 cm diameter, in the center of a cylindrical case 16 cm in diameter.   The sound stage, the sound source and an observer are shown in Fig. 87.   This arrangement establishes in a limited volume a field approximately like that of a progressive spherical wave.   If this zone, especially its horizontal dimensions at the level

[4] Sivian and White, Journal Acoustical Society America, April, 1933.

[5] A. H. Inglis, C. H. G. Gray and R. T. Jenkins, *A Voice and Ear for Telephone Measuremenst*, Bell System Technical Journal, April, 1932.

[6] E. H. Bedell, U. S. Patent No. 1,907,712.

of the observer's ears, is several times larger than the observer's head, the effect on the latter will be nearly the same as that due to a progressive spherical wave.

"The center of the observer's ear-line (i.e., of a straight line about 18 cm long joining the two ears) is at one meter from the source, on the

FIG. 87.—THE SOUND STAGE AND SOUND SOURCE, WITH AN OBSERVER IN POSITION.

receiver axis. The ear-line nowhere departs from a circular arc by more than 0.5 cm, which is small relative to all but the shortest wave-lengths used. The difference between the diffraction effects of a plane wave and of a spherical wave of one meter radius, is quite small for our purposes. This can further be inferred from the theory of diffraction at a rigid sphere,[7] caused by plane and spherical waves, respectively. Thus Fig. 88

[7] H. T. O'Neil, Unpublished, Bell Telephone Laboratories, 1932.

shows the diffraction produced at a 20 cm diameter sphere by two 5500 cycle waves: one plane ($kR = \infty$, $k = 2\pi/\lambda$), the other spherical of 1 m radius ($kR = 100$, $k = 2\pi/\lambda$). The two are seen to be quite similar; the maximum difference of 2.5 db may in part be due to the limits of accuracy with which the zonal harmonics were evaluated. In what follows, no distinction will be made between a plane wave and a spherical wave of 1 m radius, as far as threshold of hearing is concerned.

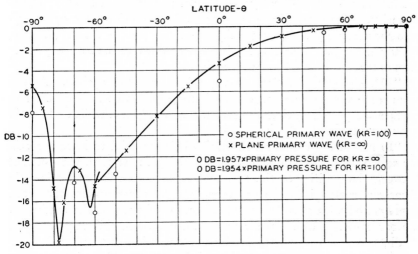

Fig. 88.—Diffraction at a Rigid Sphere.

"The sound field was measured by means of a condenser transmitter, whose 'field' calibration [8] was obtained with a Rayleigh disk. The sound stage was placed in a corner of a large, carefully sound-proofed room. At no time during the threshold measurements, was either the observer or the operator conscious of sufficient noise to affect the threshold.

The Threshold Measurement Procedure

"The observer was provided with a push button which lighted a small lamp before the operator and which was held down whenever and as long as the tone was audible. The operator allowed the observer to listen to the tone at a level well above threshold, say 30 or 40 db, for a few seconds, and then gradually reduced the intensity by turning up the receiver current attenuator until the observer signalled that he could no longer hear the tone. This level served as a convenient one at which to start interrupting the tone as usually the observer could hear an intermittent tone 10 to 20 db lower.

[8] L. J. Sivian, *Absolute Calibration of Condenser Transmitters*, Bell System Technical Journal, January, 1931.

"From this level on down, the operator reduced the sound in steps until threshold was determined, interrupting the tone several times at each attenuator setting. The tone was left on for approximately two seconds, then cut off for about the same length of time, then the tone again, etc. The transition from tone to silence and vice versa was made with no audible clicks whatever, by a gradual change in the amplifier filament current. The operator judged from the ability of the observer to follow the interruptions with his key whether or not he heard the tone at each intensity. The sizes of the steps were determined by the operator to give most rapidly an accurate figure for the threshold level and were usually about 5 db at first, becoming smaller down to the 1 db steps of the attenuator as threshold was approached.

"The element of fatigue was carefully guarded against. As soon as an observer became conscious of any appreciable fatigue, or if the operator suspected it, that observer was relieved for a while and another observer used.

"In measuring monaural threshold, it is essential to have the other ear sealed off. The seal should be definitely better than the difference between the acuities of the two ears. This was effected by inserting absorbent cotton into the ear canal; the first layer plain, the second impregnated with petrolatum which completely sealed the entrance to the ear canal. The usual attenuation obtained in this way was 30 to 34 db, and at no frequency in our range was it less than 20 db. The adequacy of the seal was proved by making threshold settings with and without seal, and comparing the difference with the acuity difference as measured on an audiometer.

"The tones used were 100, 200, 300, 400, 560, 800, 1100, 1600, 2240, 2700, 3200, 3700, 4200, 5000, 6400, 7600, 9000, 10,000, 12,000, 12,800, and 15,000 cps. The electrical circuit and the sound source were so designed and operated that the tone reaching the observer's ear at levels near threshold was completely free from extraneous frequencies. The first six tones were pure sinusoidal waves. The others were 'warble' tones centering about the nominal frequencies given. The 'warble' range progressively increased from ± 50 cycles at 1100 cps to ± 146 cycles at 15,000 cps. For all frequencies the warble was at the rate of 10 times per second. The advantage of using the warble is psychological, in that it reduces fatigue and uncertainty on the part of the observer; and physical, because of smoothing out of the residual standing wave patterns produced by reflections. A few check measurements made by the same individual with and without the warble indicated no other systematic differences between the threshold values in the two cases.

"Data were obtained on 14 ears: 10 men's, left and right of 5 observers; 4 women's, right of 4 observers. The men's ages ranged from 18 to 26, except one of 40; the women's from 20 to 23; the average age, about 23. All observers had good hearing: 'normal' or above normal, throughout the greater part of the frequency range,[9] as judged by their audiometer audiograms.   This group will hereafter be referred to as group A.

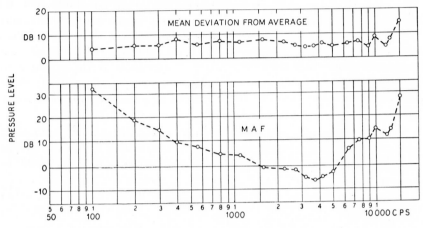

FIG. 89.—NONAURAL M.A.F., GROUP A.

The Observed M.A.F. Values

"Fig. 89 gives the M.A.F. values found, logarithmically averaged for the 14 ears in group A.   At each frequency the mean deviation from the average is indicated in the figure.

"It should be borne in mind that this M.A.F. curve is for a group of young people with generally excellent hearing, favored by freedom from fatigue and noise and by the contrast of the intermittent test tone.

Binaural M.A.F.

"The binaural M.A.F. data are based on two groups of observers. Group B consisted of the five men included in the above group A.   Group C consisted of eight men and two women, average age about 24.   The two women and three of the men were included in group A above."

The threshold measurements for group C were made under the direction of Mr. W. A. Munson.

"For group B all measurement conditions were identical with those described in the section on threshold measurement procedure.   For two members of the group data were available binaurally, as well as on each ear separately.   These data showed no significant difference between the

[9] The one exception is at 15,000 cps where one observer's left ear showed abnormally low acuity; at all other frequencies that ear was easily as good as the average of the group.

binaural M.A.F. and the best ear M.A.F. Accordingly for the three others in the group, the best ear M.A.F. was taken to be the binaural M.A.F.

"For group C at all frequencies above 240 cps the measurement conditions were the same as in the section on threshold measurement procedure, except that single frequency tones rather than 'warble' tones were employed throughout. At 60, 120, and 240 cps the sound source arrangement was somewhat different. The source was a moving coil loudspeaker, radiating from an 18-inch diaphragm. At these low frequencies the angle of incidence of the sound wave is unimportant, and it was only necessary to insure by direct measurement that the observer's head was placed in a region of substantially uniform pressure.

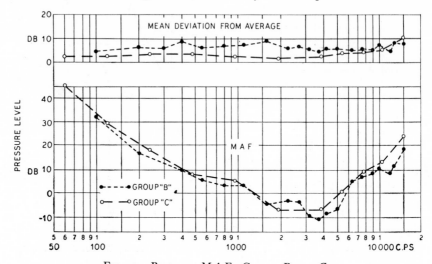

FIG. 90.—BINAURAL M.A.F., GROUPS B AND C.

"The results are shown in Fig. 90, for the two groups separately. The mean deviations from the average M.A.F. at each frequency are also shown in this figure."

The remark at the end of the section on the observed M.A.F. values, concerning the observers and the test conditions applies to groups B and C as well.

M.A.F. vs. Azimuth

"So far we have been concerned with the M.A.F. values for a progressive wave whose vertical wave front is parallel to the listener's ear-line (0° incidence). They will be different for other angles of incidence; the more so, in general, the higher the frequency. The M.A.F. values for any angle of incidence other than those corresponding to vertical wave fronts are experimentally difficult to obtain. The variation of the monaural M.A.F. with azimuth of a vertical wave are the M.A.F.—azimuth curves given in Fig. 91. The notation used is: 0° observer facing sound source; + 90°—open ear toward source. The ordinate

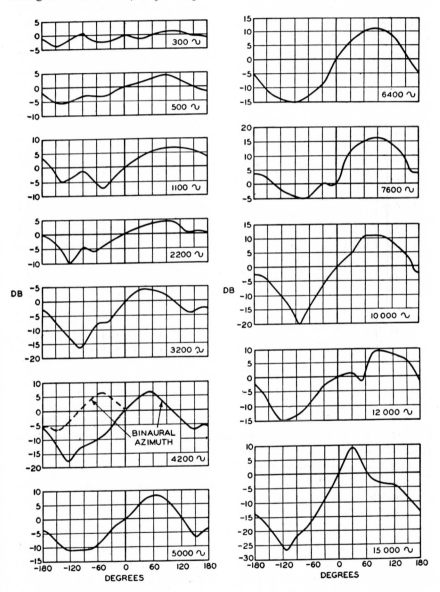

FIG. 91.—DIRECTIVITY OF MONAURAL HEARING. 0°—OBSERVER FACING SOURCE; + 90°—OPEN EAR TOWARD SOURCE.

F_θ at any angle θ gives the ratio (in db) of the M.A.F. for 0° incidence to that for θ°.

"The data were obtained in the sound field shown in Fig. 87 with the exception of the 300 cps and 500 cps values which had been obtained earlier in another connection. At the other frequencies shown, three observers were employed, two men and one woman. Readings were taken every thirty degrees, as well as at the postions of maxima and minima located by each observer in a preliminary exploration of the field. The curves shown were obtained not by averaging the three individuals' values for each angle, but by estimating a single curve to present the characteristic features of the individual curves.

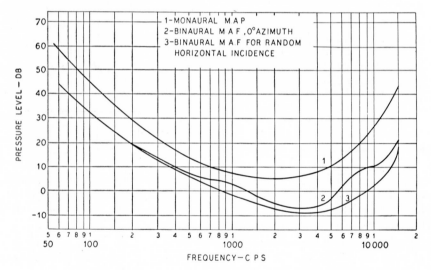

FIG. 92.—HEARING ACUITY FOR TYPICAL YOUNG OBSERVERS.

"The azimuth data, particularly those at high frequencies, indicate shadows so deep that one cannot be certain of their accuracy because of residual reflections modifying the sound field used. However, at a few frequencies similar data were available, which had been obtained outdoors in the field of a nearly perfectly progressive wave. They are so similar to the indoor data that the latter are inferred to present a fairly correct picture."

In Fig. 92 the two bottom curves give the average of the results for M.A.F. for typical young observers such as were used in those tests.

Two sets of data were taken by the search tube method, one by Sivian and White and one by Munson using the technique described above. In the first group eight ears were used and in the second, twenty-two ears were used. The upper curve in Fig. 92 gives the final results given by Sivian and White for the M.A.P. acuity of young adult observers. It must be remembered that the results in this figure are for young adults who are expertly trained in making threshold level determinations by the technique outlined above. These authors concluded that within the observational error the curve for monaural and binaural listening were the same. Since the two ears seldom have exactly the same acuity, the binaural threshold is usually determined by the level in the better ear. Munson made a study of eighty audiograms of persons having normal hearing and found the average for the better ear exceeded the average for all ears by the amounts shown in Fig. 93.

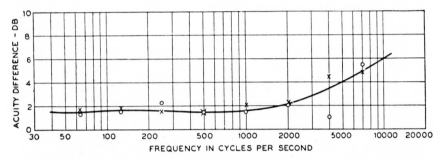

FIG. 93.—DIFFERENCE IN ACUITY BETWEEN THE BEST EAR AND THE AVERAGE OF BOTH EARS.

This is considered to be statistically the difference between monaural and binaural listening. The least difference on a single individual should be obtained when both ears are alike and is between 2 and 3 db. The larger difference shown in Fig. 93 for frequencies above 3000 cps is due to the wide spread in the acuity of the two ears. To illustrate, let the acuity at 8000 cps of the right ear be 14 db pressure level, and for the left ear be 30 db. The average is 22 db. The best ear is 8 db above the average of the two ears. But if a test were made with a person having such ears, he would obtain 14 db both binaurally and monaurally. However, if one treats the data statistically, since the curve 1 in Fig. 92 is average for both ears, the curve obtained for binaural listening is obtained by subtracting the values of Fig. 93 from the ordinates of curve 1 of Fig. 92. Similarly, for monaural listening the M.A.F. curves can be obtained from curves 2 and 3 of Fig. 92 by adding the values of Fig. 93 to the ordinates of these curves.

We are now in a position to compare the Sivian and White values for average acuity with those determined as average by 2A audiometer tests. In Fig. 94 the crosses represent the values of pressure level for the zero setting of the 2A audiometer and are the values shown in Table 17. The lower curve in this figure is the No. 1 curve from Fig. 92. This curve below 100 cps is adjusted downward to run parallel to the top

curve since no data was available in this region for the lower curve.
It is seen that these points are considerably above the M.A.P. curve
determined by Sivian and White.

A curve through these points joins a curve determined by Bekesy
for very low frequencies as shown in this figure. It will now be shown that
the difference between the two curves is due to a difference in technique
of testing and difference in experience in observing threshold levels.

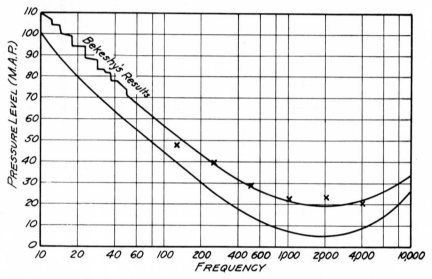

FIG. 94.—COMPARISON OF SIVIAN AND WHITE DATA ON ACUITY OF HEARING
WITH 2A AUDIOMETER ZERO.

The tabulation in Table 20 will assist in understanding this difference.
In the second line of the table the values of pressure levels are given which
are produced in an average ear by the receiver of the 2A audiometer
when the dial is set for zero hearing loss. In line 3 the values are given
of the hearing loss measured with the 2A audiometer when the listeners
used in determining the Sivian and White threshold curve were inexperienced in listening. Routine audiometric tests of all observers used
in the work in hearing studies were made, and the values given are an
average of all the audiograms available for the listeners. This did not
include all but a majority of those used in making threshold measurements
both by Munson and by Sivian.

In line 4 is given the sum of the values in lines 2 and 3, which should
give the acuity (pressure level at threshold) for these listeners. In line
5 are given values of acuity determined directly by Sivian and White
(Fig. 92) after listeners were experienced in such tests and with a more
refined technique. As indicated above, this technique consisted of lower-

ing the level in 1 db steps until the listener signaled that he could not hear the tone.   Then the level was increased until the observer signaled that he could again hear the tone.   Several reversible levels were obtained in this way, and the average was taken as the threshold level.

In line 6 the difference in the calculated and observed values of acuity is given.   It was considered that 2.5 db should be substracted from these differences because of the differences in technique explained above.

TABLE 20

THRESHOLD LEVELS

(1) Frequency	128	256	512	1024	2048	4096	8192
(2) Pressure level for 2A audiometer zero	47.5	39.3	29	22.6	23.6	20.7	25.9
(3) Hearing loss of inexperienced listeners	−3.4	−1.0	−0.9	−5.0	−4.0	−0.7	0.0
(4) Cal. acuity of listeners	44.1	38.3	28.1	17.6	19.6	20.0	25.9
(5) Obs. acuity (Sivian & White)	40	25.5	14	7	5	8.5	20
(6) Difference (line 4 − line 5)	4.2	12.8	14.1	10.6	14.5	11.5	5.9
(7) Correction for difference in techniques	2.5	2.5	2.5	2.5	2.5	2.5	2.5
(8) Difference (probably due to practice)	1.7	10.3	11.6	8.1	12.1	9.0	2.4

This leaves the differences shown in line 8 unaccounted for.   It was concluded that this difference was about what one would expect between expertly practiced observers and unpracticed ones.   The average difference is seen to be 8 db.   Any difference from this value must be ascribed to observational error.   One concludes from this that an improvement of about 8 db can be obtained over that obtained in the usual audiometer technique if a more refined technique is used, and the listeners have considerable practice in making such tests.   This is based on Munson's probe tube data.   If the new (1951) Bureau of Standards data is excepted this practice effect is reduced almost to zero.

In order to establish a zero loudness reference curve, threshold level measurements were made.[10]   These data were reported in the Sivian and White paper discussed above.   However, the zero loudness contour was finally adopted to be consistent with eleven of the other loudness contours, and is slightly different from curve 2 shown in Fig. 92.   Since both of these curves are still in considerable use, they are given together in Fig. 95.

The top curve in this figure gives the level where the ear feels a tickling sensation.   Levels above this start to give pain.   Measurements

[10] Fletcher and Munson, Journal Acoustical Society America, October, 1933.

made by Davis during the war indicated that the human ear can tolerate for short periods of time levels 10 or 15 db above this level without permanent damage, although temporary deafness may be caused. Ears receiving these high levels recovered their acuity, some in a few minutes, others taking a few months. The top curve therefore serves as a practical limit for the high levels. The zero loudness contour and the feeling level curve, joined by the dotted lines at the extreme frequencies, confine what is called the auditory area. All tones represented in this area can be sensed as sound. The data for the dotted lines are very uncertain

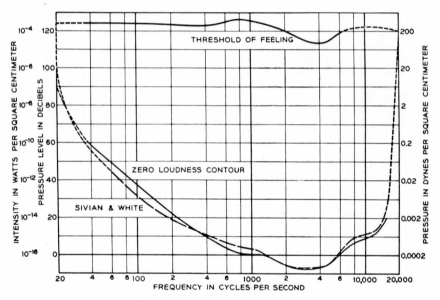

FIG. 95.—AUDITORY AREA BETWEEN THRESHOLD OF FEELING AND THE
THRESHOLD OF HEARING.

and vary greatly with various individuals. The vibrations can be felt for vibration rates down to zero. In the area below 20 cps it is difficult to distinguish between hearing and feeling. Similarly, at the high frequencies it is difficult to distinguish the hearing sensation from pain.

It will be seen that the intensities of sound in the auditory area have a range of 1000 billion to 1 and that pressures have a range of the square root of this or a million to one. It is for this reason that the decibel is so much more practical to use in acoustical work. For a 60-cycle tone at the feeling intensity the amplitude of the air particles are about 1/4 mm.

To fill a hemisphere whose center is 15 meters from a loudspeaker with the maximum tolerable sound intensity by the ear requires a sound power of about 1½ kilowatts. Of course, the electrical power necessary to drive the loudspeaker may be three or four times this value, depending on the efficiency of the loudspeaker. So it is apparent that, although powers involved in sounds are ordinarily very small, still it is necessary to have a good-sized power plant to produce in a large room the loudest sound that the ear can tolerate.

As stated before, this curve is for an individual having very acute hearing. About one in one hundred persons will have as acute hearing as that shown. The U. S. Public Health Service made a general survey of the hearing acuity of a typical American group. The results of this sur-

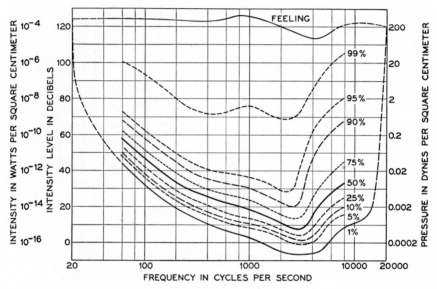

FIG. 96.—AUDITORY AREAS WHEN HEARING IS IMPAIRED. THE CURVES ARE INDICATED BY THE PERCENT OF A TYPICAL AMERICAN GROUP WHO CAN HEAR SOUNDS BELOW THE GIVEN LEVEL.

vey were given in terms of 2A audiometer readings. By using the pressure levels for zero reading given in Table 20 these results can be reduced to pressure levels. From these results the chart in Fig. 96 was constructed. Hearing tests made at the World's Fairs in San Francisco, and New York by the Bell Telephone Laboratories confirm this general picture, except for the higher frequencies the contours are lower. In a general audience if there were no noise present, one percent of the listeners could hear sounds as soft as indicated by the first curve; the next contour line is for 5 percent, and so on, for the other curves as indicated. The important curve is the 50 percent curve, which is shown by the heavy line. This means that half the people can hear tones at a level as low as indicated by this curve, but the other half must have higher intensities.

However, in an average room there is always some background noise. By using the measurements of average room noise described in Chapter 6, it is possible to calculate (method to be discussed later) the masking effect of the noise, which is shown by the darkened areas on the chart of Fig. 97. It will be seen that for at least 50 percent of the observers the threshold of audibility in an average room is determined by the noise present.

In clinical practice the acuity of hearing is usually expressed as an audiogram which is a curve that shows the hearing loss versus frequency, the zero being that given on the audiometer.

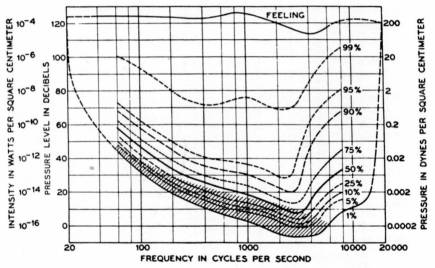

Fig. 97.—Auditory Areas with Average Room Noise Present.

If β is the acuity (pressure level at threshold) for a person at any frequency and β_A is the average acuity for a typical group of listeners without apparent impairment, then the

$$\text{hearing loss} = \beta - \beta_A = 20 \log \frac{p}{p_A} \qquad (8\text{--}3)$$

where p and p_A are the corresponding acoustic pressures near the eardrum. The values of β_A are:

$f =$	128	256	512	1024	2048	4096	8192
$\beta_A =$	47.5	39.5	29	22.6	23.6	20.7	25.9 (2A audiometer)
$\beta_A =$	46	33.3	24	23	25.4	17.0	22.8 (Bureau of Standards)

Even if the audiometer zero agrees with the manufacturing specification it has been seen above that the audiometers may differ from -1.8 at 2000 cps to 6.0 at 256 cps (see Table 19). For diagnostic purposes, however, these differences are unimportant.

In Fig. 98 are shown two typical audiograms, one for an ear that was diagnosed as having nerve deafness (shown by the solid line), and one that was diagnosed as having conductive deafness (shown by the dotted curve). The ordinates of the hearing loss curve are usually plotted downward rather than upward to indicate losses. Values above zero indicate acuities better than average.

In clinical practice the usual procedure for taking the audiogram is as follows: The levels are reduced in 5 db steps. At levels near the threshold the tone is interrupted intermittently, and the patient is asked to push a button when he hears the tone and release it when he does not.

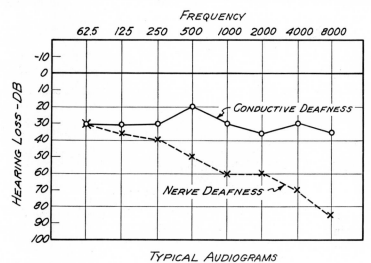

FIG. 98.—TWO TYPICAL AUDIOGRAMS, ONE FOR NERVE DEAFNESS AND ONE FOR CONDUCTIVE DEAFNESS.

The reading on the audiometer where the patient just hears the tone is taken as the hearing loss. If the steps were 1 db instead of 5, then statistically the value for hearing loss, taken this way, would average 2.5 db more hearing loss.

It is well known that the acuity of hearing decreases as one grows older particularly for the high frequencies. The loss below 1000 cycles is usually less than 10 db. At 8000 cps, however, the losses due to age run from 10 db at forty years to 40 db at sixty years.

The hearing loss in db can be obtained by using a set of calibrated tuning forks. In making such tests the fork is given a standard blow of some sort to set it into vibration. It is then held close to the ear, preferably with the flat part of the prong directly facing the opening in the ear. The time, t_0 in seconds, after striking the fork until the patient

signals that he no longer hears the tone is taken with a stopwatch. A
similar time, t_A, is taken with an ear known to have average normal hearing and with the same tuning fork in a similar position with respect to
the ear.

It is well known that the sound radiated by the tuning fork decays
with time according to the following equation:

$$p = p_0 \; 10^{-(\Delta t/20)} \tag{8-4}$$

where p is the sound pressure at any time t and p_0 is the initial sound
pressure created at the same position at the time zero, that is, when the
stopwatch is started, and Δ is the damping constant in db per second.
But the hearing loss is defined

$$\text{hearing loss} = 20 \log \frac{p}{p_A} = 20 \log \frac{p}{p_A} - \Delta \cdot t \tag{8-5}$$

where p_A is the acoustic pressure for an average ear.   If one always uses
the standard blow technique, then p and p_A are always the same.   Therefore, if t_A is the time for an average normal ear,

$$0 = 20 \log \frac{p}{p_A} - \Delta \cdot t_A.$$

Putting this value of t_A in the above equation,

$$\text{hearing loss} = \Delta \, (t_A - t).$$

Thus, the hearing loss in db is determined directly from the damping
constant in db per second of the fork, and the differences in the time for an
average normal ear and of the patient's ear.   The calibration of the fork

TABLE 21

TYPICAL VALUES FOR A SET OF TUNING FORKS

Frequency (cps)	24	48	64	100	200	400	500	800	1000	1200	1800	2000
Dampening constant Δ (db/sec.)	.3	1.9	1.6	1.75	.9	.46	.59	.87	1.19	1.14	2.29	2.41
t_A (sec.)	75	51	41	30	110	140	135	112	71	69	44	45

consists in having values of Δ and t_A and a technique for giving a standard
blow to the fork.   A tester does not need to use the standard blow if his
hearing loss is known at each frequency.   It is evident from these equations that

$$\text{hearing loss for patient} - \text{hearing loss for tester} = \Delta(t_t - t_p) \tag{8-7}$$

where t_p is the time in seconds before the patient loses the sound and t_t
the time before the tester loses it.

In Table 21 are given typical values for a set of tuning forks at the Bell Telephone Laboratories when the forks were given what was considered to be a standard blow. These are for air conduction. Hearing loss by bone conduction can be obtained in a similar way, but a new t_A must be obtained or values of t_t for tester must be taken each time.

The usual technique used is to hold the base of the fork directly against the mastoid. In this way tuning fork results can be reduced to decibel hearing loss and compared directly with those made on an audiometer.

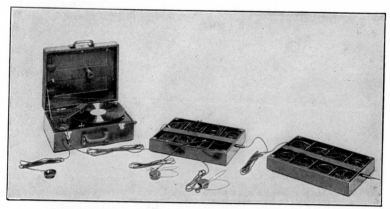

FIG. 99.—PHOTOGRAPH OF 4A AUDIOMETER.

One of the most important aspects of a person's hearing is the acuity for speech. It has been seen that speech is very variable. Nevertheless, great efforts have been made to devise a test which will give a single figure for acuity, that is, for the hearing loss for speech. When using meaningless syllables of the CVC type as the speech material, it was found that an ear which had a zero hearing loss at frequencies between 250 and 4000 cps could just detect the presence of speech when its average pressure level at the ear was 12 db. This is also approximately the average pressure level when spoken numbers, spondee words,[11] and PB words [11] are used for the speech sounds.

Phonograph audiometers have been developed for making hearing loss tests for speech. One of the first of these is known as the Western Electric No. 4A and is shown in Fig. 99. It consists of a phonograph to which is attached several telephone receivers which are distributed to the groups being tested as depicted in Fig. 100. On the disc record numbers have been recorded in such a way that each successive one is at a 5 db lower level than the preceding one. So when these numbers are repro-

[11] Hudgins, Hawkins, Karlin, Stevens, *Laryngoscope*, Vol. LVII, pp. 57–89.

duced in the ear of the listener, each number corresponds to a definite
pressure level. The persons being tested are asked to write the numbers
which they hear. The numbers become fainter and fainter until the
listener fails to write the numbers correctly. The pressure level corresponding to this number is taken as the hearing acuity. The hearing
loss for speech is the difference between the average acuity for a large
group having normal hearing and that of the individual being tested.

FIG. 100.—PHOTOGRAPH OF 4A IN USE IN A SCHOOL ROOM.

When using the spondee or P.M. lists (samples are shown in Table 22)
the level on an attenuator where 50 percent of the words are interpreted
correctly is determined. The difference between this and the average
level for a large group is the hearing loss for speech.

TABLE 22

TWO SPONDEE AND ONE SAMPLE P.B. LIST

Spondee	Spondee	P.B.—50 list 13
airplane	although	bat
armchair	beehive	been
backbone	blackout	change
bagpipe	cargo	climb
baseball	cookbook	corn
birthday	daybreak	curb
blackboard	doormat	deaf
bloodhound	duckpond	dog

TABLE 22—*Continued*

Spondee	Spondee	P.B.—50 list 13
bobwhite	eardrum	elk
bonbon	farewell	elm
buckwheat	footstool	few
coughdrop	grandson	fell
cowboy	greyhound	fold
cupcake	horseshoe	for
doorstep	hotdog	gem
dovetail	housework	grape
drawbridge	iceberg	grave
earthquake	jacknife	hack
eggplant	lifeboat	hate
eyebrow	midway	hook
firefly	mishap	jig
hardware	mushroom	made
headlight	nutmeg	mode
hedgehog	outside	mop
hothouse	padlock	moth
inkwell	pancake	muff
mousetrap	pinball	mush
northwest	platform	my
oatmeal	playmate	nag
outlaw	scarecrow	name
playground	schoolboy	nice
railroad	soybean	ought
shipwreck	starlight	owe
shotgun	sundown	patch
sidewalk	therefore	pelt
stairway	toothbrush	plead
sunset	vampire	price
watchword	washboard	pug
whitewash	whizzbang	scuff
wigwam	woodchuck	side
wildcat	workshop	sled
woodwork	yardstick	smash
		smooth
		soap
		stead
		taint
		tap
		thin
		tip
		wean

The experimental errors in making such tests are necessarily large, between 5 and 10 db. Within this range the three types of lists; namely, numbers, spondee, and P.B. lists, give the same values for hearing loss for speech. From considerations to be discussed later in connection with methods of making articulation tests, the use of the P.B. lists would be expected to give a somewhat higher hearing loss for speech than by using either of the other two lists, the amount depending upon the type of hearing loss.

Sometimes the minimum level for detecting the presence of the speech sound is used instead of the 50 percent interpretation level. Such tests also give results for the hearing loss which differ by no more than the observational error.

Fairly accurate values for the hearing loss for speech can be obtained from an audiogram. It has been seen that the important range of frequencies for determining pressure levels in speech are from 500 to 2000. Indeed, the average of the hearing loss for pure tones for the frequencies of 500, 1000, and 2000 give a fairly reliable value. It has been found recently [12] that a better rule for determining hearing loss for speech from an audiogram is the following one:

Examine the hearing losses at the frequencies of 500, 1000, and 2000 cps. Select the two that have the smallest loss. Then the average of these two losses gives the hearing loss for speech. This rule was tried out on the data available on about 200 ears, and it gave results well within the experimental error.

A test for hearing loss for speech is sometimes made by varying the distance that the speaker is from the listener. As stated above, the acuity (pressure level) for speech for a normal average ear is 12 db. If one speaks with an average talking level of 66, such a normal listener will have, at one meter distance, a sensation level of $66 - 12 = 54$ db. At 10 meters this level will drop to 34 db. This is about as far as one can go in a room and is usually about the level of noise. Therefore, even rough measurements cannot be made for people having hearing losses less than 34 db.

On the assumption that the walls are totally absorbing, Table 23 gives the hearing loss for persons who can just detect that speech is present at the distance shown in the table when the speaker trains himself to use average speech $\beta_t = 66$ db or a loud whisper $\beta_t = 46$ db at one meter distance.

The values marked (?) in the last column would be valid only if no noise were present, a condition that does not exist except in experimental rooms treated to make them noise free. If instead of the detectable threshold one uses the distance when 50% of numbers or spondee words are interpreted correctly, then 10 db must be subtracted from these hearing losses to obtain the correct hearing loss. For example, if a person obtains correctly 50% of numbers spoken in a loud whisper at a distance of 60 cm from the ear of the patient, then the hearing loss for speech is

---

[12] Fletcher, Journal Acoustical Society America, January, 1950.

approximately 48 db.   It is interesting to note that a person with average hearing in a quiet place can just hear the average voice at a distance of about 2 kilometers.   He can interpret numbers at about 700 meters. The maximum tolerable average level for speech for a normal ear is about 118 db, so the level audible range is about 106 db.   At maximum tolerable level for speech, during 10 percent of the time of talking the peak levels are above 132 db and the R.M.S. levels in 1/8 second intervals are above 123 db.

TABLE 23

Distance	Hearing Loss for Speech	
	average voice $\beta_t = 66$	loud whisper $\beta_t = 46$
10 meters	34.0 db	14 db
8	36.0	16 ?
6	38.4	18.4 ?
4	42	22 ?
2	48	28 ?
1	54	34 ?
80 cm	56	36
60	58.4	38.4
40	62	42
20	68	48
10	74	54

A watch tick, although unreliable, is sometimes used for determining acuity.   A test showed that when such watches are held to the ear the sensation level of the sound produced in a normal ear is from 40 to 70 db.   For an average grade of watch a value of about 45 db may be taken. If a person cannot hear such a watch tick when held close against the ear, his hearing loss is greater than 45 db for a watch tick.   This is essentially a test at about 2000 cps.   From contact to six inches away the level drops about 30 db.

A method of calculating the percent hearing loss for compensation cases due to varying amounts of hearing loss in both ears is given in the last chapter.

CHAPTER 9

MINIMUM PERCEPTIBLE CHANGES IN FREQUENCY AND SOUND PRESSURE LEVEL

Let the position representing a pure tone on the plot in Fig. 95 be f cps and β db. Then how far can it move from this position before the ear detects that there has been some change? If the changes are vertical, they are called minimum perceptible changes in pressure level or fractional changes in intensity. If in the horizontal direction, they are called fractional changes in frequency.

A schematic of the circuit arrangement for making tests on differential sensitivity is shown in Fig. 101. For determining differential sensitivity to frequency changes, one of the oscillators is provided with an arrangement for changing the capacity in the oscillating circuit usually by means of a variable air condenser such as is used in radio circuits. The dial on such a variable condenser can be calibrated so that it reads frequency changes in cps.

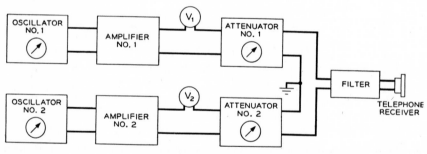

FIG. 101.—ARRANGEMENT FOR DETERMINING DIFFERENTIAL SENSITIVITY OF THE EAR.

For determining differential sensitivity to pressure level changes, the two oscillators are used and the frequencies brought close together so as to cause beats, which is a fluctuating intensity. From the readings on the two attenuator dials one can calculate the magnitude of the pressure level change in db.

A number of observers have made such measurements, but the most comprehensive set of data on differential intensity sensitivity was made by Riesz [1] of the Bell Telephone Laboratories, using the method of beats.

[1] Physical Review, May, 1928.

144

The two dials were set so that for the listener both tones were at the threshold of hearing or zero sensation level.   The db above this setting gives directly the sensation level for each tone separately.

Let the oscillator dials be set so that beats are heard, and the attenuation dials so that α_1 and α_2 are the respective sensation levels for the tones.   When the sound vibration from the two tones are in phase, the combined sound pressure is $p_1 + p_2$ where p_1 and p_2 are amplitudes of the sound pressure.   Similarly, when the tones have opposite phase, the combined pressure is $p_1 - p_2$.   Therefore, the pressure level change $\Delta\alpha$ is given by

$$\Delta\alpha = 20 \log \frac{p_1 + p_2}{p_1 - p_2} = 20 \log \frac{1 + 10^{-\frac{\alpha_1-\alpha_2}{10}}}{1 - 10^{-\frac{\alpha_1-\alpha_2}{10}}}. \qquad (9\text{--}1)$$

Riesz first determined the minimum perceptible differences in $\Delta\alpha$ for the 1000-cycle tone when the beat frequency was changed from 0.2 to 34 times per second and for two different sensation levels α_1; namely, 25 db and

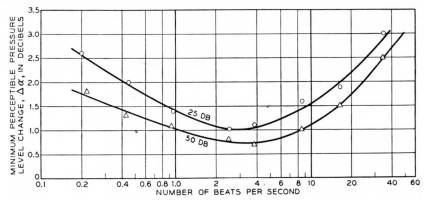

FIG. 102.—Minimum Perceptible Pressure Level Change $\Delta\alpha$ DB.

50 db.   The results of these tests are shown in Fig. 102.   It is seen that there is a broad minimum rate near three times per second.   The values of $\Delta\alpha$ at other frequencies were obtained by using this rate. Measurements were made with twelve male observers.   The values are tabulated in Table 24.

It is seen that for sensation levels near zero it requires about 3 db to notice a change when the frequency is in the speech range.   For sensation levels above 40 it requires changes less than 1 db to be noticeable, and as low as 0.3 db for the speech frequencies having sensation levels above 60 db.

Several investigators have measured the minimum perceptible frequency change, but probably the most extensive set of data were taken

TABLE 24

MINIMUM DETECTABLE CHANGES IN PRESSURE LEVEL

Sensation level=	5	10	20	30	40	50	60	70	80	90	100	110
Frequency												
35	9.3	7.8	4.3	1.8	1.8							
70	5.7	4.2	2.4	1.5	1.0	.75	.61	.57				
200	4.7	3.4	1.2	1.2	.86	.68	.53	.45	.41	.41		
1000	3.0	2.3	1.5	1.0	.72	.53	.41	.33	.29	.29	.25	.25
4000	2.5	1.7	0.97	0.68	.49	.41	.29	.25	.25	.21	.21	
8000	4.0	2.8	1.5	.9	.68	.61	.53	.49	.45	.41		
10000	4.7	3.3	1.7	1.1	.86	.75	.68	.61	.57			

by Shower and Biddulph [2] of the Bell Telephone Laboratories. To reduce transients, due to making the frequency change, to a minimum, the frequency was changed by a rotary air condenser, as shown in Fig. 103.

FIG. 103.—ROTARY AIR CONDENSER.

This condenser is so shaped that when introduced into the oscillating circuit the frequency of oscillation varies in the manner shown in Fig. 104. The dashed curve gives an ideal sinusoidal variation; the points were observed values. This rotary air condenser is connected in parallel with a fixed condenser. The setting of this fixed condenser controlled the base frequency about which the frequency fluctuated. The amount of this fluctuation is controlled by the amount that the two plates are separated by the mechanism shown. The small stationary plate may be completely separated from the rotary one. The general circuit arrangement is the same as in Fig. 101.

[2] Journal Acoustical Society America, October, 1931.

In making the measurements the attenuator dial was set so that the tone was at a known sensation level. Then from the setting of the sliding head at which the listener can just detect a change one obtains the value of Δf, the minimum perceptible change at a sensation level of

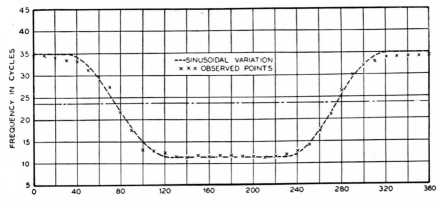

Fig. 104.—Frequency Change Produced by Rotary Condenser.

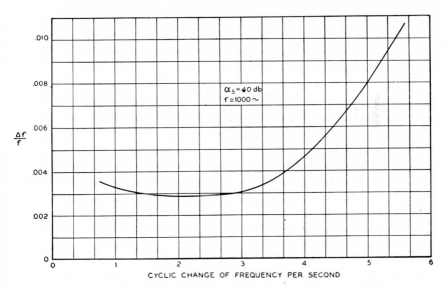

Fig. 105.—Variations of $\Delta f/f$ as a Function of the Rate of Change of Δf.

40 db. Observations were made at various speeds of the rotary condenser. The results are shown in Fig. 105 for the values of $\Delta f/f$ vs. rotation rate, where Δf is the difference between the maximum and the minimum ordinate in Fig. 104, and f is the base frequency.   It is seen that there is a broad minimum at rates corresponding to 2 or 3 rotations per second.

By using an air conduction telephone receiver held tightly to one ear, the results shown in Table 25 were obtained. These are average values obtained on ten ears of men between twenty and thirty years of age. The relation between the number of semitones change and $\Delta f/f$ is given by

$$\text{no. of semitones} = 12 \log_2 \frac{\Delta f + f}{f} \doteq 17.3 \frac{\Delta f}{f} \qquad (9\text{--}2)$$

when $\Delta f/f$ is small compared to 1. The values of Δf and minimum perceptible changes expressed in semitones are given in Fig. 106.

TABLE 25

Values of $\Delta f/f$.

Sensation level=	5	10	15	20	30	40	50	60	70	80	90
Frequency (cps)											
31	.1290	.0873	.0702	.0563	.0438	.0406					
62	.0975	.0678	.0546	.0491	.0461	.0426	.0351	.0346			
125	.0608	.0421	.0331	.0300	.0266	.0247	.0276	.0269			
250	.0355	.0212	.0158	.0130	.0109	.0103	.0099	.098	.0100	.0107	
500	.0163	.0110	.0081	.0067	.0055	.0052	.0042	.0035	.0042		
1000	.0094	.0061	.0044	.0039	.0036	.0036	.0036	.0034	.0031	.0030	.0026
2000	.0079	.0036	.0029	.0021	.0019	.0019	.0019	.0018	.0017	.0018	
4000	.0060	.0044	.0038	.0031	.0027	.0023	.0023	.0020			
8000	.0063	.0051	.0045	.0038	.0036	.0029	.0025				
11700	.0069	.0058	.0042	.0038	.0036	.0035	.0030				

It is seen that the number of cycles change Δf is between 2 and 4 cycles for the greater part of the frequency range and only exceeds the latter values for frequencies above 2200 cps. From 2200 to 8000 the ratio $\Delta f/f$ is approximately constant so that Δf doubles for each octave shift in the base frequency f.

Fig. 106 also shows that the change, in fractions of a semitone that are perceptible, varies from one-half semitone for the first octave on the piano to about one-tenth of this, or 0.05 semitones for the last two octaves. The apparent anomaly at the low frequency end of the curve was tested with frequencies between those shown in Table 26, and the bend downward at 45 cycles was found to be real.

The value of $\Delta f/f$ depends upon the method of changing Δf as is evident from comparing the three sets of measurements shown in Fig. 107. The set shown on curve A was taken with sinusoidal variations as described above. The next set B was taken by switching in and out of the circuit a fixed capacity. This method produces much greater transients than in method A and so curve B is considerably lower than curve A, especially at the low frequencies. The curve C represents results taken by Knudsen[3] by a method similar to B. All three curves were taken at a sensation level of 40 db.

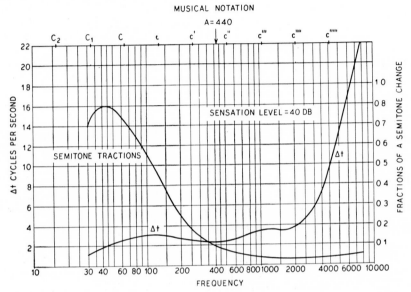

FIG. 106.—Minimum Perceptible Differences Expressed in Semitones and Cycles.

By using the rotary air condenser, results were obtained for binaural listening and also by bone conduction listening. These results are shown in Fig. 108 for only two of the ten ears. The bone conduction curve follows closely the binaural air conduction curve as one would expect since a bone conduction receiver stimulates both ears. The stimulation of the ear opposite the receiver is reduced by only a small amount from that in the ear near the bone conduction receiver.

It is interesting to calculate the number of distinguishable tones from 31 cycles to 11,700 cycles. If one keeps the tone at 40 db above threshold, then this number N_{40} is given by

$$N_{40} = \int_{31}^{11,700} \frac{df}{\Delta f} = 1400$$

where Δf are values on the curve in Fig. 106. By using these values of Δf the integrated value of N_{40} was 1400. At the higher sensation levels this number will be somewhat larger and at lower sensation levels somewhat smaller.

[3] Physical Review, January, 1923.

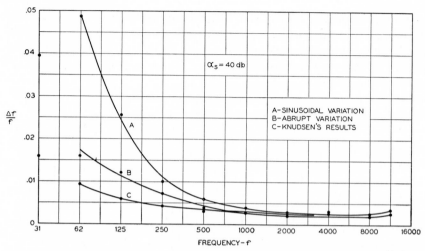

FIG. 107.—VARIATION OF $\Delta f/f$ FOR VARIOUS METHODS OF CHANGING THE FREQUENCY.

Similarly, the number of distinguishable tones N_{1000} at 1000 cps due to changes in the sensation level from 0 to 120 db is given by

$$N_{1000} = \int_0^{120} \frac{d\alpha}{\Delta\alpha} = 280$$

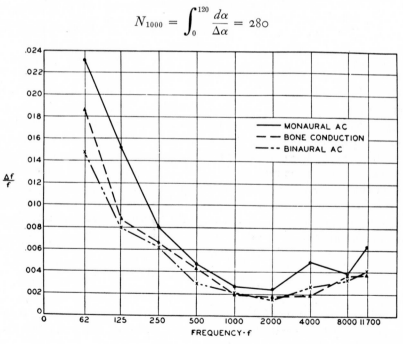

FIG. 108.—VARIATION OF $\Delta f/f$ WITH f FOR MONAURAL, BINAURAL AND BONE CONDUCTION STIMULATION.

where the values of $\Delta\alpha$ at each sensation level are given opposite 1000 in Table 26. The integrated result was found to be 280. For the 200-cycle tone this number is 190 and for the 8000-cycle tone it is 220. Therefore, the total number of tones that may be distinguished by changing either the frequency or the intensity a perceptible step is between 300,000 and 400,000 in the audible range below 120 db sensation level. The number of complex tones exceeds this number many times, but it is difficult to make even a very rough estimate of it. This is enough to show what a wealth of tone colors a musician has at his disposal if he uses all the possibilities furnished by the mechanism of hearing.

TABLE 26

POSITION COORDINATE x VERSUS FREQUENCY

Sensation level =	20	30	40	50	Average
Frequency					
100	0	0	0	0	0
250	3	4	3	3	3
500	9	9	10	10	10.5
1000	20	20	21	22	21
2000	42	40	39	39	40
4000	65	65	64	62	64
8000	83	83	83	82	83
10000	91	92	92	92	92
15000	94	94	94	94	94
25000	100	100	100	100	100

The data in Table 24 also enable one to calculate the positions along the basilar membrane where the maximum stimulation occurs for tones of different frequencies. For example, it was shown that there are 1400 perceptible steps in a frequency change from 31 to 11,700. Now let us assume that each step passes over the same number ΔN of nerve endings on the basilar membrane. Then the number of nerve terminals passed over in going from the position of maximum stimulation for the 100-cycle tone to that for the 25,000-cycle tone position is just the number of steps times ΔN or

$$\Delta N \int_{100}^{25,000} \frac{df}{\Delta f}.$$

The number of nerve terminals passed over in going from 100 cycles to f cycles is

$$\Delta N \int_{100}^{f} \frac{df}{\Delta f}.$$

If x is percent of nerve terminals passed over by the maximum stimulation when a tone is changed from 100 cps to f cps, then

$$x = 100 \frac{\int_{100}^{f} \frac{df}{\Delta f}}{\int_{100}^{25,000} \frac{df}{\Delta f}}.$$ (9-3)

The reason 100 cycles is chosen for the lower limit is because data to be discussed later indicate that frequencies below this have no definite maximum, or rather all these low tones have a maximum stimulation near the helicotrema.

The values obtained by using the data in Table 25 for sensation levels of 20, 40, 50, and 60 db are shown in Table 26. It is seen that the values of x obtained by using either of these sensation levels are the same within the observational error. This fraction x would correspond to fractional lengths on the basilar membrane if the nerve terminals were uniformly distributed along it. Anatomists have shown that this is only approximately true. Later these fractions x will be converted to lengths by using data on nerve ending distributions found by anatomists. Before doing this another method of determining x will be considered.

CHAPTER 10

MASKING EFFECTS

It is a common experience that when any sound is impressed upon the ear it reduces the ability of the ear to sense other sounds. If while a sound A is being impressed upon the ear, another sound B is gradually increased in intensity until the sound A can no longer be heard, the sound A is said to be masked by the sound B. The sound A will be called the "maskee" tone and the tone B the "masker" tone. When the ear is stimulated by a sound, particular nerve fibers terminating in the basilar membrane are caused to discharge their unit loads. Such nerve fibers then can no longer be used to carry any other message to the brain by being stimulated by another source of sound. Masking experiments appropriately chosen, then, should enable us to determine what portions of the membrane are stimulated by an external sound.

A. A. Mayer[1] was one of the first to point out the experimental fact that low-pitched sounds had a masking effect different from that of high-pitched sounds. He stated that a tone of low pitch will completely mask one of higher pitch but that a tone of high pitch will not mask a tone of lower pitch. The apparatus which he used, however, made it very difficult to control the intensity or the purity of the tones used. On account of its importance, the problem of masking was studied rather extensively at Bell Telephone Laboratories.

Masking of Pure Tones by Pure Tones

The masking effect of one pure tone by another was determined by means of apparatus which was similar to that used in the determination of the acuity of hearing described in Chapter 8. A damped telephone receiver was used for generating the pure tones. Connected to this receiver were two vacuum tube oscillators equipped with filters for eliminating any harmonics and with attenuators for controlling the magnitude of current. The attenuators were arranged so that by turning a dial the intensity level of the tone could be reduced very quickly from the maximum value to a value below the threshold. The intensity level for the threshold was determined both for the masked and the masker tones. The *masker tone was then kept at a constant sensation level while the maskee*

[1] Mayer, A. A., Philosophy Magazine, 11, 500, 1876.

tones of other pitch were gradually increased in intensity until they were just perceptible in the presence of the masker tone.   The level, expressed in decibels, that the maskee tone was raised above its threshold level in the quiet is called the threshold shift in db or the masking in db.

The results of these measurements are shown in the curves of Fig. 109. The frequency of vibration of the masker tone is given by the number at the top of each chart and its sensation level by the number on each curve. The frequency of vibration of the maskee tone is given by the abscissa and the threshold shift of the maskee tone by the ordinate.

For example, in the fourth chart the masker tone has a frequency of 1200 cycles, and curves are shown for the sensation levels of 20, 40, 60, 80, and 100 db.   It is seen that the greatest masking effect is near 1200 cycles, which is the frequency of the masker tone.   A tone of 1250 cycles must be raised to 46 db above the threshold to be perceived in the presence of a 1200-cycle tone which is 60 db above its threshold, or it must be raised to within 14 db of the masker tone before it is perceived.   This corresponds to an intensity ratio between the tones of only 25.   A tone of 3000 cycles, however, can be perceived in the presence of a 1200-cycle tone having a sensation level of 60 db when it is only 8 db above its threshold or at a sensation level of 8 db.

However, as the intensity of the masker tone is increased, all of the high tones must be increased to fairly large values before they can be heard.   For example, the high frequencies must be raised to sensation levels above 75 db to be heard in the presence of a 1200-cycle tone having a sensation level of 100 db.   But even for such high intensities for the masker tone, those frequencies below 300 are perceived by raising their loudness only slightly above the threshold value.   It should be noticed that maskee tones having frequencies near that of the masker tone have large threshold shifts.

It is thus seen that Mayer's conclusion that a low-pitched sound completely obliterates higher pitched tones of considerable intensity, and that higher pitched frequencies will never obliterate lower pitched tones is true only under certain circumstances.   A low tone will not obliterate to any degree a high tone far removed in frequency, except when the former is raised to very high intensities.   Also a tone of higher frequency can easily obliterate a tone of lower frequency if the frequencies of the two tones are near together.   When the two tones are very close together in pitch, the presence of the maskee tone is perceived by the beats it produces.   This accounts for the sharp drop in the curves at these frequencies.   A similar thing happens for those frequency regions corresponding to harmonics of the masker tone.   In the charts for the 200- and 400-cycle masker tones these drops are not shown, inasmuch as they were small, but in an accurate picture they should be shown.

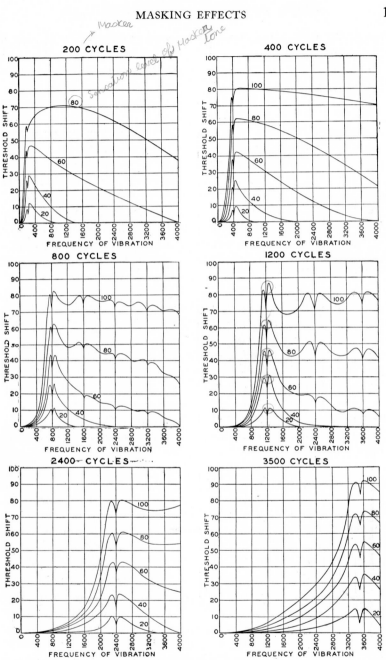

FIG. 109.—MASKING DATA FOR 200, 400, 800, 1200, 2400, AND 3500 CPS.

These results are plotted in a different way in Fig. 110. The abscissas represent the sensation level of the masker tones, the frequency of which is indicated near the top of each of the charts. The amounts that the threshold of the maskee tone is shifted are plotted as ordinates as in the previous figure.

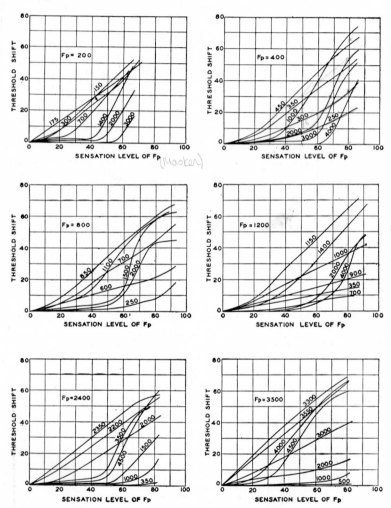

FIG. 110.—MONAURAL MASKING OF PURE TONES.

For example, in the first chart the results are shown for a masker tone of 200 cycles. The curve marked 3000 indicates the masking effect of a 200-cycle masker tone upon a 3000-cycle maskee tone. It is seen that the sensation level of the low-pitched tone can be raised to 55 db before it has any interfering effect upon the high-pitched tone.   For higher levels than this it has a very marked effect.

It will be noticed that in nearly all of the charts the curves for different frequencies intersect,   This leads to some rather interesting conclusions regarding the perception of a complex tone./ If, for example, a complex tone had three frequencies of 400, 300, and 2000 cycles with levels of 50, 10, and 10, respectively, the ear would hear only the 400- and 2000-cycle tone as is evident from the masking curves for 400 cycles./ It would be necessary to raise the 300-cycle tone an additional 6 db for it to be heard in the presence of 400 cycles at a sensation level of 50, However, if the complete sound were magnified 30 db without distortion so that the three tones had levels of 80, 40, and 40, respectively, then the 400- and 300-cycle tones only would be heard.   Under such conditions, the 300-cycle tone could be attenuated approximately 8 db before it would disappear./ These conclusions will be somewhat modified when all of the tones are sounding simultaneously, as the data were taken for two tones only, but the general picture given above will still be true./ It follows that the sensation produced by a complex sound is different in character as well as in intensity when the sound is increased or decreased in intensity without distortion/ In general, as the tone becomes more intense, the low tones will become more prominent because the high tones are masked./ Because of the nonlinearity of the ear transmitting mechanism, the low-pitched tones produce more subjective harmonics, harmonics in the sensed sound but not in the original pressure variations, and for that reason increases in loudness faster than the high-pitched tones/ It is a common experience of one working with complex sounds to have the low frequencies always gain in prominence as the sound is amplified.   This phase of the subject will be discussed again in a later section.

The question arises: "Does the same interfering effect exist when the two tones are introduced into opposite ears instead of both being introduced into the same ear?"   The answer is "No."   Curves showing the results of such tests are shown in Fig. 111.

For comparison the results for the case when the tones are both in the same ear are given by the light lines.   Take the case of 1200 and 1300 cycles.   It is rather remarkable that a tone in one ear can be raised to 60 db, that is, increased in intensity one million times, before the threshold value for the tone in the other ear is noticeably affected.   If the 1300-cycle tone were introduced into the same ear as the 1200-cycle tone, its sensation level would need to be shifted 40 db, corresponding to a 10,000-fold magnification in intensity above its threshold intensity in the free ear before it could be heard.   It is seen that if one set of curves is shifted about 50 db it will coincide with the second set.   This strongly suggests that the interference in this case is due to the loud tone being transmitted

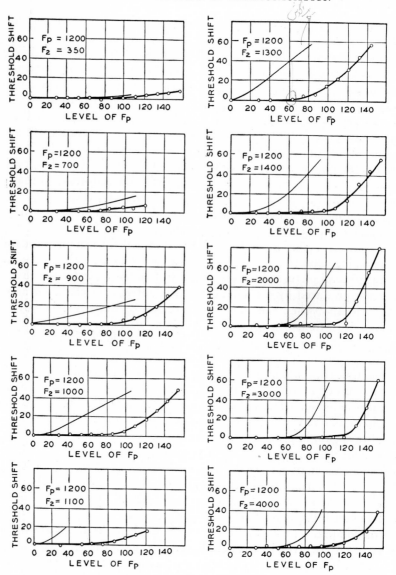

FIG. 111.—BINAURAL MASKING.

by bone conduction through the head with sufficient energy to cause masking.

That this is the case is substantiated by experiments on persons having unilateral deafness. If the telephone receiver is held to the deaf ear of such a person and the intensity of the tone gradually increased, the threshold value will be reached when it has a sensation level of approxi-

mately 50 db.   That the sound has been transmitted to the good ear
by bone conduction is shown by the fact that under such circumstances
the tone is greatly enhanced by placing the finger in the good ear.   Another fact which is discussed in more detail later is that binaural beats
are most pronounced when the intensity of the tones in the two ears has
a sensation level difference of approximately 50 db.

These experiments indicate that when a receiver of the type used in
these experiments is placed on the ear it communicates a certain amount of
its vibration to the bones of the head.   This vibration then is transmitted
through the head to both ears, the intensity of the stimulation being
approximately at a level of 50 db below that produced by the diaphragm
of the receiver acting upon the air in the ear canal.   It is claimed by some
otologists that the vibration communicated to the cap of the telephone
receiver used in practice is a great aid for a person having a certain type
of deafness in transferring the speech vibrations to the end organ of hearing by means of bone conduction.   It is seen from these experiments that
in order for this to be true, the acuity of hearing by the air path must be
at least reduced 50 db without in any way interfering with the acuity
of hearing by the bone path.   The value 50 db is dependent upon the
type of telephone receivers used.   This value may be decreased or
increased, depending upon the type of apparatus used in communicating
the tones to the ear.

This suggests that interference of room noise to telephone conversation
is not principally due to that which goes to the free ear, but to that which
gets into the same ear to which the telephone receiver is being held,
mainly due to leaks under the receiver cap.   Even when the receiver is
held very tightly to the ear, enough noise is conducted through the hard
shell of the receiver and then to the air in the auditory canal to produce
greater interference than that caused by noise coming into the free ear.
This conclusion has been confirmed by direct experiments with telephone
users.

Subjective Tones

The sharp dips in the curves of Fig. 109 at frequencies corresponding
to multiples of the masking frequency require explanation.   These dips
suggest that they may be produced by harmonics of the masker tone.
For example, the curves for the masker tone having a frequency of 1200
cycles and sensation levels of either 100, 80, or 60 db look like those which
would be produced if the masking were caused by three tones having
frequencies of 1200, 2400, 3600.   A careful analysis of the tone by means
of the harmonic analyzer showed no harmonics.   At the frequency corresponding to the dips, beats were plainly audible.   This indicates that
the masker tone creates harmonic frequencies in the ear.

As stated in Chapter 7, these harmonic frequencies are due to the nonlinear response of the hearing mechanism. The tones introduced by this nonlinearity are called subjective tones. The magnitude and the frequency of such tones may be determined by using the principle of beats mentioned above. If while the master tone is present, an exploring tone is changed in frequency and intensity until the beats are most prominent, then the intensity and frequency of such an exploring tone can be taken as the intensity and frequency of the subjective tone. It was found that there are three classes of subjective tones which are called harmonics, summation tones, and difference tones, respectively. When a single tone stimulates the ear, tones of the first class are produced. The frequencies of such tones are exact multiples of the frequencies of the stimulating tone. When two tones stimulate the ear, a series of subjective harmonics for each tone and also a series of difference and summation tones are produced. The subjective difference tones have frequencies which are equal to the differences obtained by subtracting the frequency of one tone from that of the other and also by subtracting the frequency of any harmonic from that of any other harmonic. Similarly, the summation subjective tones have frequencies which are obtained by taking sums instead of differences. When more than two tones stimulate the ear these three classes of tones are produced, but the situation then becomes very complex. It was found that the sensation levels of the first two subjective harmonic tones produced by a 1200-cycle tone having a level of 80, were 60 and 50 db, respectively. For a level of 60, the subjective harmonics were 20 and 15 db, respectively. For levels below 40, the subjective tones were undetectable.

The results of some experiments reported by Wegel and Lane[2] are given in the chart of Fig. 112. One tone, called the primary tone, was held at a constant level while a second tone, called the secondary tone, was varied both in frequency and intensity. The resulting sensations are represented on the chart. For levels below the masking curves only the 1200-cycle tone can be perceived. / For levels just above the masker curve and in the frequency range between 1200 and 2400 cycles, only the primary and the difference tones can be perceived. In other words, in this region, the presence of the secondary tone is detected by hearing the subjective difference tone between the primary and the secondary tones. For higher levels, the primary, the secondary, and the difference tones can be perceived. For example, if the secondary tone is held at a frequency of 1600 and at a level of 60 db, the ear will perceive three tones, namely, the 1200-, the 1600-, and the 400-cycle tones. For still higher levels for the secondary, very complicated mixtures of tones are perceived.

[2] Physical Review, Feb., 1924.

A careful analysis was made of the mixture of tones present in the ear when a primary tone of 1200 cycles at a sensation level of 80 db was present along with a secondary tone of frequency 700, and at the same level. The component frequencies were determined by introducing an exploring tone and determining the frequencies at which beats occur. If f_1 represents the primary, and f_2 the secondary, the frequencies found in the mixture were f_1, 1200 cycles; f_2, 700; $f_1 + f_2$, 1900; $f_1 - f_2$, 500; $2f_1$, 2400; $2f_2$, 1400; $3f_1$, 3600; $3f_2$, 2100; $2f_1 + f_2$, 3100; $2f_1 - f_2$, 1700; $2f_2 - f_1$, 2600; $2f_2 - f_1$, 200 (?); $4f_2$, 2800; $2f_1 + 2f_2$, 3800; $2f_1 - 2f_2$, 1000; $3f_1 + f_2$, 4300; $3f_1 - f_2$, 2900; $3f_2 + f_1$, 3300; $3f_2 - f_1$, 900. No attempt was made to determine their magnitudes, although approximate values

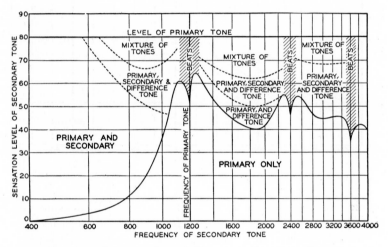

FIG. 112.—SENSATION LEVELS CAUSED BY TWO PURE TONES.

can be obtained by measuring the intensity of the exploring tone at which the beats at each frequency are most prominent. Such measurements are rather difficult when so many tones are present. Except for the absence of frequency $4f_1$, this series is all that would be expected if the response of the ear were nonlinear and represented by the equation,

$$x = a_0 - a_1p - a_2p^2 - a_3p^3 - a_4p^4. \qquad (10\text{--}1)$$

In this equation x is the response of the mechanism of the middle ear; a_0, a_1, a_2, etc., are constants, and p is the pressure in the ear canal. While frequencies introduced by higher powers of the pressure were probably present, they were very faint and no careful search was made for them.

A study of the levels of a primary tone which is necessary to produce detectable subjective harmonics reveals some interesting and important data. To do this, the pure tone was held at a convenient level while the presence of the harmonic was determined by the beating effect produced by an exploring tone as described above. In this way the sensation level for tones of various frequencies at which the second, the third, the fourth, and the fifth harmonic first appeared was determined. These data are shown in the curves of Fig. 113. For tones above 1000 cps no subjective harmonics appear until the sensation level is 50 db, where the second

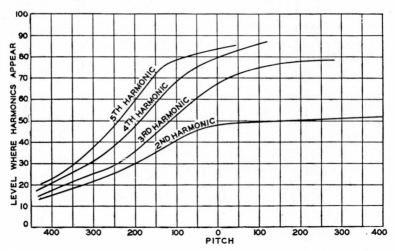

Fig. 113.—Level Where Subjective Harmonics Become Audible.

harmonic just becomes detectable. In the low-pitched range the harmonics appear when the tone is very faint. For example, for a tone of frequency 62 cps, the fifth harmonic appears before a sensation level of 25 db is reached.

TABLE 27

	Harmonic Number								
	I	2	3	4	5	6	7	8	9
Pressure level =	120	109	99	90	83	75	68	60	53 db
Threshold level β_0 =	59	45	36	31	26	22	20	18	16 db
Sensation level =	61	65	63	59	57	53	48	42	37 db

From these data and additional data taken by Graham, the chart in Fig. 114 was calculated. The ordinate gives the pressure levels of the harmonics indicated by the abscissas. The pressure level for harmonic 1 is the level of the fundamental frequency. The levels corresponding to the harmonics for any fundamental is on the same curve. For example, a tone at a pressure level of 120 db has harmonic tones at levels 109, 99, 90, 83, 75, 68, 60, and 53 db. If the frequency of the tone is 50 db, then the threshold level β_0 for a young adult ear with training is from Fig. 94 (lower curve) about 59 db. For the other harmonics β_0 is given in Table 27.

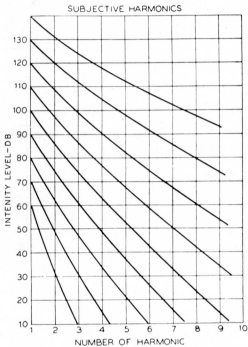

SUBJECTIVE HARMONICS

INTENITY LEVEL–DB

NUMBER OF HARMONIC

Fig. 114.—Pressure Levels of Subjective Harmonics.

It is seen that the second and third harmonics are at greater sensation levels than the fundamental. In Fig. 115 are some data for 50 cps which confirm this general picture. The sensation level of the subjective harmonic was determined by finding the level of the test tone that gave best beats.

TABLE 28

$f_0 = 1000$ cps	Harmonic Number								
	1	2	3	4	5	6	7	8	9
Pressure level =	120	109	99	90	83	75	68	60	53 db
Threshold level β_0 =	8	4	6	9	11	14	17	20	23 db
Sensation level =	112	105	93	81	72	61	51	40	30 db

If the fundamental frequency is 1000 cps, then for these same high levels the sensation level of the harmonics are those shown in Table 28.

Masking Effects of Complex Sounds

The masking effects of complex sounds are what one would expect after considering the data on pure tones. When the masking sound is composed of two components, the masking is a combination of the masking produced by each component plus the effects due to the summation and

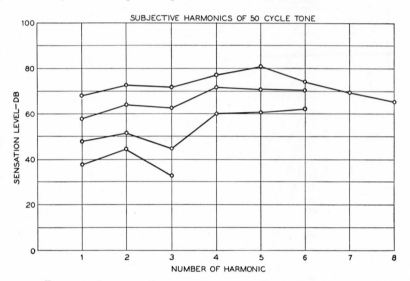

FIG. 115.—SENSATION LEVEL OF SUBJECTIVE HARMONICS OF 50 CPS.

difference subjective tones. In the previous section such curves were described for a complex tone with components having frequencies of 1000, 1500, and 2000 cycles and having the common sensation level of 80 db.

Masking curves for a musical hum having components 60 cycles apart are shown in Figs. 116, 117, 118, and 119. The pressure exerted on the eardrum by each component is given by the lower curve on each chart. Fig. 116 shows the effect when the components of appreciable size are above 3000 cycles; Fig. 117 when they are above 1500 cycles; Fig. 118 when they are below 1500 cycles; and Fig. 119 when they are below 500 cycles. No attempt was made to explore the detail of the curve near each component.

Such masking curves are known as noise audiograms and they show the loss in hearing as truly as though it were a deafness audiogram with no noise present.

Special interest attaches to masking by white noise since from such data the relation between the frequency *f* and the position coordinate

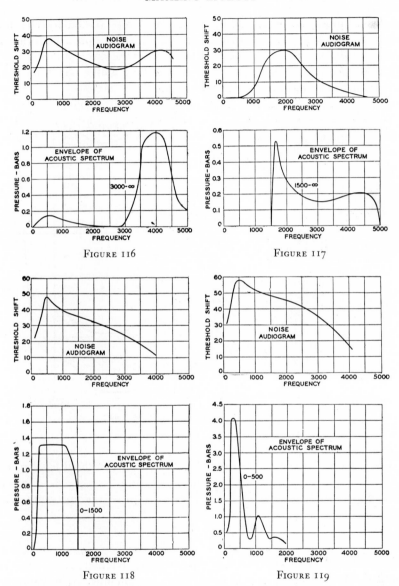

FIGURE 116

FIGURE 117

FIGURE 118

FIGURE 119

FIGS. 116, 117, 118, AND 119.—MASKING CURVES PRODUCED BY A 50-CYCLE HUM WITH VARIOUS MAGNITUDES OF THE HARMONICS.

x along the basilar membrane can be obtained. In Fig. 120 is show the spectrum level for a particular kind of noise defined by the upper curve bounding the cross-hatched area. The lower curve is the M.A.P. curve for young acute ears used in this investigation. The level of the maskee tone when it is just perceived in this noise is represented by the dots above the hatched area. It will be noticed that they are 50 db above this lower curve at all frequencies. The shape of the spectrum level curve was chosen so this would be true. The masking audiogram for such a noise is then a straight horizontal line at 50 db.

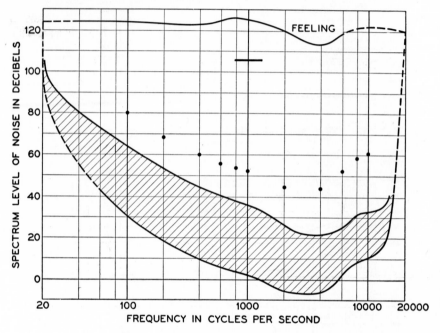

FIG. 120.—MASKING EFFECT OF A NOISE.

Let the level of the maskee tone be β_m and its threshold level in the absence of noise be β_0; then the threshold shift is $\beta_m - \beta_0$. It was found experimentally that if B_N is the ordinate to the spectrum level curve for the noise, then at any frequency f

$$B_N + \kappa = \beta_m \qquad (10\text{-}2)$$

This means that if the curve in Fig. 120 is moved up and down on the level scale the dots will move up and down the same amount. The value κ is the number of db above the spectrum level curve to reach the dots. These values have already been given in Chapter 6, Table 16, in connection with defining a rational signal to noise ratio. With the value of κ known, then the masking level curve is obtained directly from the spectrum level curve by adding values of κ.

A sample set of data showing this linear relation between B_N and β_m is given in Fig. 121 for two frequency regions $f = 9500$ and $f = 480$

cps.   The indicated values of κ in Fig. 121 were calculated from this set of data.   The values given in Chapter 6 are values obtained from considering all available data.

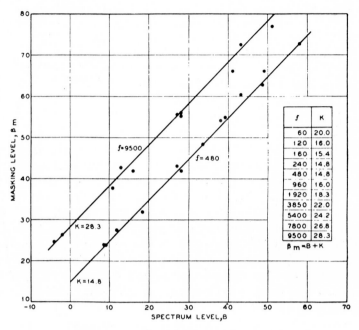

f	κ
60	20.0
120	16.0
160	15.4
240	14.8
480	14.8
960	16.0
1920	18.3
3850	22.0
5400	24.2
7800	26.8
9500	28.3

$\beta_m = B + \kappa$

FIG. 121.—RELATIONS BETWEEN SPECTRUM LEVEL OF NOISE AND THE RESULTING MASKING LEVEL OF A PURE TONE.

Equation (2) cannot hold when β_m is near the threshold because $\beta_m - \beta_0$ cannot be less than zero.   It has been found that a more general formula holds, namely

$$10^{\frac{\beta_m}{10}} = 10^{\frac{B_N + \kappa}{10}} + 10^{\frac{\beta_0}{10}}. \qquad (10\text{--}3)$$

The last term has the effect of adding a fictitious noise whose masking level is β_0, the threshold pressure level in the absence of noise.   This equation gives a good fit for the entire range of values of β_m and B_N and throughout the range of frequencies.   Since the threshold shift is $\beta_m - \beta_0$, this equation then enables one to calculate this shift or masking from the spectrum level curve of the noise.   Or if this shift is measured one can calculate the spectrum level curve.   It is convenient to define a quantity Z by

$$Z = B_N + \kappa - \beta_0 \qquad (10\text{--}4)$$

and let

$$\beta_m - \beta_0 = M,$$

the threshold shift or masking M db. Then (3) becomes

$$10^{\frac{M}{10}} = 10^{\frac{Z}{10}} + 1. \qquad (10\text{--}5)$$

Equation (10–5) has two restrictions on its validity: (1) The slope of the curve Z vs. f must not exceed certain critical slopes; and (2) the peaks must not be too sharply resonant. The empirical equation which gives approximately the critical slope in db per octave is

$$\sigma = 75 - \frac{Z}{2} \qquad (10\text{--}6)$$

for negative slopes, and $\sigma = 80$ db per octave for positive slopes. Equation (10–6) holds only very approximately but still is useful.

In Figs. 139 and 140 of Chapter 11 are shown the results of experiments on the masking of pure tones by bands of white noise. For all of these tests at the edges of the filter the critical slope is exceeded so that the slope of the masking curves gives this critical slope. The value of Z is equal to the masking at the top of the curves. It is seen that Equation (10–6) is only a very rough approximation to the experimental facts. The value of M at the peaks of the Z vs. f curve is approximately equal to the ordinate in a band-pass filter having a flat top and a band width equal to a critical band at the frequency of the peak. This hypothetical band-pass filter has the same noise power in it as in the actual peak. This is an estimated value without much experimental confirmation.

However, equation (10–5) applies for most noises because they do not have sharp peaks or high slopes for the Z curve unless they are produced in the laboratory by use of electrical networks. The relation between the acoustic pattern and the corresponding stimulation pattern on the nerves is illustrated in Fig. 122. A 500-cycle band of noise between 500 and 1000 is spread into a wide stimulation pattern of 16 percent of the nerve endings, while this same band width between 7500 and 8000 of the same acoustic intensity acts upon only one percent of the nerve endings at position 88 as indicated. Consequently, one must raise the level of a pure tone in this high frequency region to a higher value to be perceived than the level needed in the low frequency region where the stimulation per nerve is not nearly so great. Conversely, if the masking level, compared to the spectrum level, is higher for the high frequency region than for the low frequency region, it shows that the frequencies are less spread out in the high and more spread out in the low frequency regions. For example, in the case illustrated the intensity of the masker tone would be sixteen times greater for one than for the other.

Let us consider this relation in a quantitative way. The power $I_f \cdot \Delta f$ in the thermal noise band between f and $f + \Delta f$ goes mostly to stimulate those nerve endings between x and $x + \Delta x$, where x corresponds to the position of maximum stimulation for a pure tone having a frequency f, and $x + \Delta x$ to the position of maximum stimulation for a pure tone having a frequency of $f + \Delta f$. In other words, the band Δf located at the frequency position f will be chosen so that the power in this particular noise band is spread over the particular patch of nerves Δx located at the position x. As illustrated in Fig. 122 the patches adjacent to Δx will also be stimulated if a single band Δf is impressed upon the ear. However, for any type of noise whose spectrum is not changing rapidly with

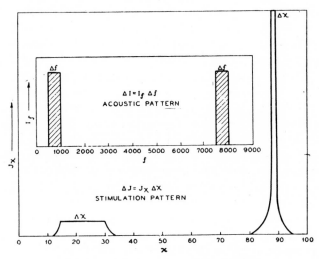

FIG. 122.—RELATION BETWEEN ACOUSTIC PATTERNS AND
CORRESPONDING STIMULATION PATTERN.

frequency these adjacent patches will already be stimulated by the adjacent bands. For this type of noise it is fairly accurate to assume that all the intensity in the band Δf goes to stimulate patch Δx. Then let the stimulation due to this noise power $I_f \Delta f$ be $J_x \Delta x$, and let the stimulation due to the sound power I_m of the maskee tone be J_m. Since the noise band and the maskee tone are in the same frequency region, they will experience the same frequency discrimination by the electrical circuits generating the sounds and by the transmission mechanism of the ear. Therefore,

$$\frac{I_f \Delta f}{I_m} = \frac{J_x \Delta x}{J_m} \qquad (10\text{--}7)$$

or, integrating,

$$x = \int_0^f \frac{J_m}{J_x} \frac{I_f}{I_m}\, df. \qquad (10\text{--}8)$$

The quantity J_m/J_x is the ratio of the two kinds of stimulation when the pure tone is just masked. It would be expected to be a constant c independent of frequency and it will be so assumed.

$$x = c \int_0^f \frac{I_m}{I_f}\, df = c \int_0^f 10^{\frac{B_N - \beta_m}{10}}\, df = c \int_0^f 10^{\frac{-\kappa}{10}}\, df. \qquad (10\text{--}9)$$

By using the same limits for f as before; namely, 100 cps to 25,000 cps, the constant c is determined by the condition $x = 100$ when $f = 25,000$ cps. Therefore,

$$x = 100\, \frac{\displaystyle\int_{100}^f 10^{\frac{-\kappa}{10}}\, df}{\displaystyle\int_{100}^{25,000} 10^{\frac{-\kappa}{10}}\, df}. \qquad (10\text{--}10)$$

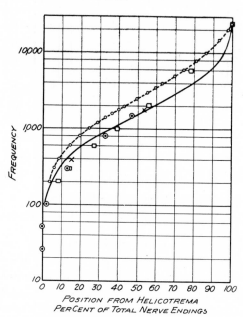

Fig. 123.—The Position Coordinate x versus Frequency as Obtained by Several Methods.

Using the values of κ given in Table 16 of Chapter 6, the values of x vs. f were calculated to be those given in Fig. 123 top curve.

If equation (10–10) is compared to equation (9–3), Chapter 9, it will be seen that the minimum difference in frequency Δf which is perceptible is proportional to

$$10^{\frac{\kappa}{10}}.$$

It is found experimentally that the constant of proportionality is 0.05.   So

$$\Delta f = 0.05 \quad 10^{\frac{\kappa}{10}}. \qquad (10\text{--}11)$$

This analysis relates two very different sets of experimental values; namely, the minimum perceptible change in frequency to values of κ obtained from masking by noise.   It will be remembered that κ is the db above the spectrum level B of the noise that the level of a pure tone may be raised before it is masked by the noise.   The question now arises how values of κ vary as the width of the frequency band Δf of noise containing the frequency of the maskee tone is changed from a wide band to a very narrow one.   It is obvious that when Δf becomes very small the value of κ will become large; that is, the maskee tone can be

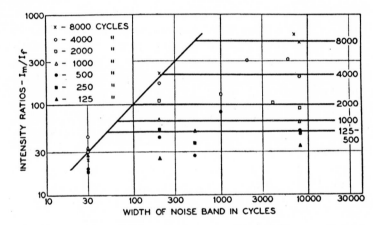

FIG. 124.—EXPERIMENTAL DETERMINATION OF THE CRITICAL BONDS OF FREQUENCY.

raised to much higher levels.   But there must be a critical band width above which the value of κ will become constant and equal to $\beta_m - B$ as indicated above for a wide band.   Experiments were made to determine these critical bands and to confirm the above expectations.   The noise was passed through an electrical filter of variable width Δf.   Let f be the frequency of the maskee tone.   Then this band was placed so that the edges were $f - (\Delta f / 2)$ and $f + (\Delta f / 2)$.   The results are shown in Fig. 123.

For reasons which will become obvious the values

$$10^{\frac{\kappa}{10}} = \frac{I_f}{I_m} \qquad (10\text{--}12)$$

are plotted as ordinates and the band width Δf as abscissas.   The variable parameter which identifies the different curves is the frequency of the maskee tone, which is also the frequency region of the band of noise. It is evident from the results for the 30-cycle band of noise that this ratio is the same for all frequencies and is approximately equal to 30. This result makes the relations very simple. For these smaller bands and for this type of statistical noise, the intensity of the masked tone must be adjusted to be equal to the average intensity of the noise in the band in order for it to be perceived. It will be seen that as the band widths increase this ratio I_m/I_f also increases until the critical band widths are reached, which are indicated by the intersection of the horizontal lines with the 45-degree line.

For example, consider the case for the 2000-cycle tone being masked by variously sized bands of noise indicated by the squares in Fig. 123. The ratio of I_m/I_f increased until the band width Δf reached 100 cps; then it remained constant for larger band widths. The value 100 is the critical band width for this frequency. The horizontal part of the curves as drawn was determined from measurements with wide bands. Their intersection with the 45° line drawn through the point (30,30) determines the critical band widths. The experimental points, although having a large observational error, are consistent with this point of view. Then, if $(\Delta f)_c$ be designated the critical band width

$$(\Delta f)_c = \frac{I_m}{I_f} = 10^{\frac{\kappa}{10}}. \qquad (10\text{--}13)$$

It is because of this relation that κ is called the critical band width expressed in db. Comparing (10–13) to (10–4) it is seen that

$$\Delta f \text{ (perceptible frequency change)} = 0.05 \ (\Delta f)_c. \qquad (10\text{--}14)$$

This means that a frequency change which is just 1/20 of a critical band width can be perceived.

Since it was shown in Chapter 9 that there are about 1500 perceptible steps of Δf then each corresponding Δx is 0.07% of the total and each critical band width is 1.5% of the total. If the nerve endings are scattered uniformly over about 35 mm length of basilar membrane, then each critical band would occupy 1/2 mm and for each perceptible change in frequency the maximum stimulation position would shift 0.025 mm.

However, it will appear in Chapter 14 that values calculated by equation (10–10) disagree with values observed by Bekesy and also those calculated from fundamental dynamical equations. Instead of assuming that the critical shift corresponds to a constant $(\Delta x)_c$, that is, a constant number of nerve endings and independent of position, if one assumes the critical shift in cm is equal to the width of the basilar membrane, then a relation is obtained which does give calculated results which gives a better agreement with the observed ones.

Let the position coordinate be changed from x to z where z is the distance in centimeters from the stapes to the position on the basilar membrane. Then if b is the width of the basilar membrane at the position z and l its length, then this assumption leads to the following relations:

$$(\Delta x)_c = b \text{ and } (\Delta f)_c = 10^{\frac{\kappa}{10}},$$

$$\frac{dz}{df} = \frac{(\Delta z)_c}{(\Delta f)_c} = b \times 10^{-\frac{\kappa}{10}},$$

so that

$$z = l \frac{\displaystyle\int_f^{2\,5000} b \, 10^{-\frac{\kappa}{10}} \, df}{\displaystyle\int_{50}^{2\,5000} b \, 10^{-\frac{\kappa}{10}} \, df}. \tag{10-15}$$

Before values from this equation can be compared to those obtained from (10-10) a relation between z and x must be established.

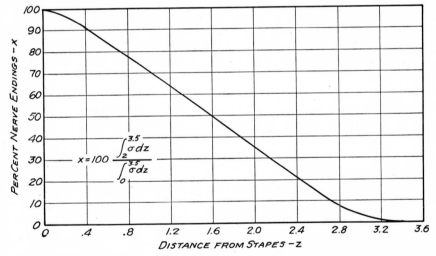

Fig. 125.—The Relation Between the Percent x of Nerve Endings and the Distance z Passed Over in Going from the Stapes to the Helicotrema End of the Basilar Membrane.

If σ is the number of nerve terminals per mm, then by definition of x

$$1 - \frac{x}{100} = \frac{\displaystyle\int_0^z \sigma \, dz}{\displaystyle\int_0^1 \sigma \, dz}. \tag{10-16}$$

SPEECH AND HEARING IN COMMUNICATION

TABLE 29

z =	0	.1	.2	.3	.4	.5	.7	.9	1.1	1.3	1.5
σ =	0	300	800	1000	1050	1050	1000	1060	1150	1200	1200
z =	2.0	2.5	2.7	2.9	3.0	3.1	3.2	3.3	3.4	3.5	
σ =	1200	1150	1000	600	500	400	300	200	100	0	

The average values of σ obtained from 23 specimens of the human ear by Guild at Johns Hopkins University are given in Table 29. As reported these were given in terms of the various lengths of the basilar membrane. They were reduced to the common length 3.5 cm by multiplying by the proper ratios of lengths.

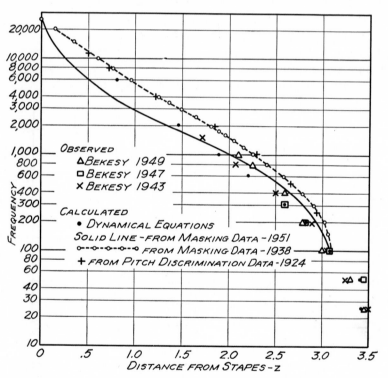

FIG. 126.—THE RELATION BETWEEN THE RESONANT FREQUENCY f_0 AND THE DISTANCE FROM THE STAPES OBTAINED BY VARIOUS METHODS.

Using these values in equations (10–16) the relation between x and z was calculated to be that given by the curve in Fig. 125. The shape of this curve near the helicotrema end shows why there has been so much uncertainty in experimental values of masking for frequencies below 100 cps.

By using this relation the relation between f_0 and x can be converted to one between f_0 and z. The top curve in Fig. 123 obtained from masking data was so converted and shown by the circles in Fig. 126. The values of z and f obtained by using data in Table 26 are shown by the plus signs. There is good agreement between the data obtained from masking and from pitch discrimination under the assumptions made. However, if equations (10–15) are used with the masking data then the solid line shown in Fig. 126 is obtained. The distances where the displacement of the basilar membrane becomes a maximum as observed by Bekesy are shown by the points $\triangle$, $\square$. The solid points are calculated ones obtained from hydrodynamical equations as outlined in Chapter 14. These same data are shown in Fig. 123 with x as the abscissa.

It is seen that the assumptions underlying equations (10–15) give results which agree better with observed data than the assumptions used earlier. It may be that a combination of these assumptions may best correspond to the observed data.

CHAPTER 11

LOUDNESS

Loudness is a psychological term used to describe the magnitude of an auditory sensation. Although we use the terms "very loud," "loud," "moderately loud," "soft" and "very soft," corresponding to the musical notations ff, f, mf, p, and pp, to define the magnitude, it is evident that these terms are not at all precise and depend upon the experience, the auditory acuity, and the customs of the persons using them. If loudness depended only upon the intensity of the sound wave producing the loudness, then measurements of the physical intensity would definitely determine the loudness as sensed by a typical individual and therefore could be used as a precise means of defining it. However, no such simple relation exists.

The magnitude of an auditory sensation, that is, the loudness of the sound, is probably dependent upon the total number of nerve impulses that reach the brain per second along the auditory tract. It is evident that these auditory phenomena are dependent not alone upon the intensity of the sound but also upon their physical composition. For example, if a person listened to a flute and then to a bass drum placed at such distances that the sounds coming from the two instruments are judged to be equally loud, then the intensity of the sound at the ear produced by the bass drum would be many times that produced by the flute.

If the composition of the sound, that is, its wave form, is held constant, but its intensity at the ear of the listener varied, then the loudness produced will be the same for the same intensity only if the same or an equivalent ear is receiving the sound and also only if the listener is in the same psychological and physiological condition, with reference to fatigue, attention, alertness, etc. Therefore, in order to determine the loudness produced, it is necessary to define the intensity of the sound, its physical composition, the kind of ear receiving it, and the physiological and psychological condition of the listener. In most engineering problems we are interested mainly in the effect upon a typical observer who is in a typical condition for listening.

In Chapter 4 it was shown how to specify a pure tone by giving its frequency in cycles per second and its pressure level (same as intensity level except for a small correction as described in Chapter 4). A complex tone is similarly defined by giving the pressure levels and frequencies of each component. The loudness of pure and complex tones will be considered first. Then such sounds as white noise, room and street noise, and speech will be considered.

Definitions

In making loudness measurements, use is made of a *reference tone*. This reference tone has been adopted by the American and European Standards Associations as a 1000-cycle tone produced by a source at a distance greater than a meter from the ear of the listener. It is then essentially a plane wave when it passes the head. The room in which such a source is used must be such that the reflected waves are small compared to the original wave.

The *loudness level* of any sound is the intensity level of the equally loud reference tone at the position where the listener's head is to be placed. The unit of loudness level is the phon.

Manner of Listening to the Sound

In observing the loudness of the reference sound, the observer faces the source, which should be small, and listens with both ears at a position so that the distance from the source to a line joining the two ears is greater than one meter.

The value of the intensity level of the equally loud reference sound depends upon the manner of listening to the unknown sound and also to the standard of reference. The manner of listening to the unknown sound may be considered as part of the characteristics of that sound. The manner of listening to the reference sound is as specified above.

Loudness has been briefly defined as the magnitude of an auditory sensation, and more will be said about this later, but it will be seen from the above definitions that the *loudness level* of any sound is obtained by adjusting the intensity level of the reference tone until it sounds equally loud as judged by a typical listener. The only way of determining a typical listener is to use a number of observers who have normal hearing to make the judgment tests. The typical listener, as used in this sense, would then give the same results as the average obtained by a large number of such observers.

A pure tone having a frequency of 1000 cycles per second was chosen for the reference tone for the following reasons: (1) it is simple to define, (2) it is sometimes used as a standard of reference for pitch, (3) its use makes the mathematical formulae more simple, (4) its range of auditory intensities (from the threshold of hearing to the threshold of feeling) is as large and usually larger than for any other type of sound, and (5) its frequency is in the mid-range of audible frequencies.

It is frequently more convenient to use two matched head receivers for introducing the reference tone into the two ears. This can be done provided they are calibrated against the condition described above. This consists in finding by a series of listening tests by a number of observers the electrical power W_1 in the receivers which produces the same loudness as a level β_1 of the reference tone. The intensity level β_r of an open air reference tone equivalent to that produced in the receiver for any other power W_r in the receivers is then given by

$$\beta_r = \beta_1 + \text{10} \log (W_r/W_1). \tag{11-1}$$

Or, since the intensity level β_r of the reference tone is its loudness level L phons,

$$L = \text{10} \log W_r + C_r \tag{11-2}$$

where C_r is a constant of the receivers which is independent of W_r but varies with frequency.

A steady sound can be represented by a finite number of pure tones called components. Since changes in phase produce only second order effects upon the loudness level it is necessary to specify only the magnitude and frequency of the components. The magnitudes of the components at the listening position where the loudness level is desired are given by the intensity levels β_1, β_2, . . . β_k . . . β_n of each component at that position. In case the sound is conducted to the ears by telephone receivers or tubes, then a value W_k for each component must be known such that if this component were acting separately it would produce the same loudness for typical observers as a tone of the same pitch coming from a source at one meter's distance and producing an intentisy level of β_k.

In addition to the frequency and magnitude of the components of a sound it is necessary to know the position and orientation of the head with respect to the source, and also whether one or two ears are used in listening. The monaural type of listening is important in telephone use and binaural type when listening directly to a sound source in air. Unless otherwise stated, the discussion and data which follow apply to the condition where the listener faces the source and uses both ears, or uses head telephone receivers which produce an equivalent result.

Method for Calculating the Loudness Level of a Steady Complex Tone

It is well known that the intensity of a complex tone is the sum of the intensities of the individual components. Similarly, in finding a method of calculating the loudness level of a complex tone one would naturally try to find numbers which could be related to each component in such a way that the sum of such numbers will be related in the same way to the equally loud reference tone. Such efforts have failed because the amount contributed by any component toward the total loudness sensation depends not only upon the properties of this component but also upon the properties of the other components in the combination. The answer to the problem of finding a method of calculating the loudness level lies in determining the nature of the ear and brain as measuring instruments in evaluating the magnitude of an auditory sensation.

One can readily estimate roughly the magnitude of an auditory sensation; for example, one can tell whether the sound is soft or loud. There have been many theories to account for this change in loudness. One that seems very reasonable is that the loudness experienced is dependent upon the total number of nerve impulses per second going to the brain along all the fibers that are excited. Although such an assumption is not necessary for deriving the formula for calculating loudness it aids in making the meaning of the quantities involved more definite.

Let us consider, then, a complex tone having n components each of which is specified by a value of intensity level β_k and of frequency f_k. Let N be a number which measures the magnitude of the auditory sensation produced when a typical individual listens to a pure tone. *Since by definition the magnitude of an auditory sensation is the loudness, then N is the loudness of this simple tone.* The unit of loudness is the sone. Loudness as used here must not be confused with loudness level. If we accept the assumption mentioned above, N is proportional to the number of nerve impulses per second reaching the brain along all the excited nerve fibers when the typical observer listens to a simple tone.

Let the dependency of the loudness N upon the frequency f and the intensity β for a simple tone be represented by

$$N = G\,(f, \beta) \tag{11-3}$$

where G is a function which is determined by any pair of values of f and β. For the reference tone, f is 1000 and β is equal to the loudness level L, so a determination of the relation expressed in equation (11-3) for the reference tone gives the desired relation between loudness and loudness level.

If now a simple tone is put into combination with other simple tones to form a complex tone, its loudness contribution, that is, its contribution toward the total sensation, will in general be somewhat less becasue of the interference of the other components. For example, if the other components are much louder and in the same frequency region, the loudness of the simple tone in such a combination will be zero. Let $1 - b$ be the fractional reduction in loudness because of its being in such a combination. Then bN is the contribution of this component toward the loudness of the complex tone. It will be seen that b by definition always remains between zero and unity. It depends not only upon the frequency and intensity of the simple tone under discussion but also upon the frequencies and intensities of the other components. It will be shown later that this dependence can be determined from experimental measurements.

The subscript k will be used when f and β correspond to the frequency and intensity level of the kth component of the complex tone, and the subscript r used for reference tone when f is 1000 cycles per second. The "loudness level," L by definition, is the intensity level of the reference tone when it is adjusted so it and the complex tone sound equally loud. Then

$$N_r = G\,(100,L) = \sum_{k=1}^{k=n} b_k N_k = \sum_{k=1}^{k=n} b_k G(f_k, \beta_k). \qquad (11-4)$$

Now let the reference tone be adjusted so that it sounds equally loud successively to simple tones corresponding in frequency and intensity to each component of the complex tone.

Designate the experimental values of loudness level thus determined as $L_1, L_2, L_3, \ldots L_k, \ldots L_n$. Then from the definition of these values

$$N_k = G\,(1000, L_k) = G(f_k, \beta_k), \qquad (11-5)$$

since for a single tone b_k is unity. On substituting the values from (11-5) into (11-4) there results the fundamental equation for calculating the loudness N of a complex tone

$$N = \sum_{k=1}^{k=n} b_k N_k = G(L), \qquad (11-6)$$

since the loudness N_r is judged to be equal to the loudness N of the combination. Since the frequency is always 1000 for the reference tone this function is dependent only upon the single variable, the loudness level L.

This formula has no practical value unless we can determine b_k and G in terms of quantities which can be obtained by physical measurements. The methods and results for these determinations are described below, but values of the loudness levels L_k for pure tones will first be discussed.

Loudness Level of Pure Tones

To determine these values of L_k, the loudness level of a pure tone of frequency f_k when its intensity level is β_k, the following experimental procedure was used. This consists of listening alternately to the tone and the 1000-cycle reference tone and adjusting the level of the latter until the two are judged to be equally loud. If the intensity level of the reference tone is L decibels when this condition is reached, the sound is said to have a loudness level of L decibels. When the character of the sound being measured differs only slightly from that of the reference tone, the comparison is easily and quickly made, but for other sounds the numerous

factors which enter into a judgment of equality of loudness become important, and an experimental method should be used which will yield results
typical of the average normal ear and normal physiological and psychological conditions.

A variety of methods have been proposed to accomplish this, differing
not only in general classification, that is, the method of average error,
constant stimuli, etc., but also in important experimental details such as
the control of noise conditions and fatigue effects.   In some instances
unique devices have been used to facilitate a ready comparison of sounds.
one of these, the alternation phonometer,[1] introduces into the comparison
important factors such as the duration time of the sounds and the effect
of transient conditions.   The merits of a particular method will depend
upon the circumstances under which it is to be used.   The one to be
described here was developed for an extensive series of laboratory tests.

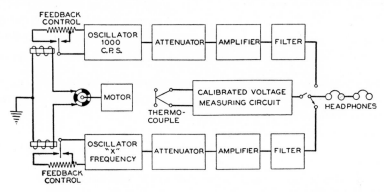

Fig. 127.—System Schematic for Making Loudness Tests.

To determine when two sounds are equally loud it is necessary to
rely upon the judgment of an observer, and this involves, of course, not
only the ear mechanism, but also associated mental processes, and
effectively imbeds the problem in a variety of psychological factors.
These difficulties are enhanced by the large variations found in the judgments of different observers, necessitating an investigation conducted
on a statistical basis.   The method of constant stimuli, wherein the observer listens to fixed levels of the two sounds and estimates which sound
is the louder, seemed best adapted to control the many factors involved,
when using several observers simultaneously.   By means of this method
an observer's part in the test can be readily limited to an indication of his
loudness judgment.   This is essential as it was found that manipulation
of apparatus controls, even though they were not calibrated, or participa-

[1] D. Mackenzie, *Relative Sensitivity of the Ear at Different Levels of Loudness*, Physical
Review, 20, 331, 1922.

tion in any way other than as a judge of loudness values, introduced undesirable factors which were aggravated by continued use of the same observers over a long period of time. Control of fatigue, memory effects, and the association of an observer's judgments with the results of the tests or with the judgments of other observers could be rigidly maintained with this method, as will be seen from the detailed explanation of the experimental procedure.

TABLE 30

LOUDNESS BALANCE DATA SHEET

125 cps Pure Tone Test No. 4 Crew No. 1.   1000 cps Voltage Level (db)

Obs.		6	2	−2	−6	−10	−14	−18	−22	−26
125 cps	CK	+	+	+	+	+	o	o	o	o
Volt. level =	AS	+	+	+	+	o	o	o	o	o
+9.8 db	DH	+	+	o	o	o	o	o	o	o
	CK	+	+	+	+	+	o	o	o	o
	AS	+	+	+	+	o	o	o	o	o
	DH	+	+	o	o	+	o	o	o	o
	CK	+	+	+	+	o	o	o	o	o
	AS	+	+	+	o	o	o	o	o	o
	DH	+	+	o	o	o	o	o	o	o
		o	−4	−8	−12	−16	−20	−24	−29	−32
125 cps	CK	+	+	+	+	o	+	+	o	o
Volt. level =	AS	+	+	+	+	+	o	o	o	o
−3.2 db	DH	+	+	+	+	o	o	o	o	o
	CK	+	+	+	+	+	+	+	o	o
	AS	+	+	+	+	+	+	o	o	o
	DH	+	+	+	o	+	o	+	o	o
	CK	+	+	+	+	+	+	o	o	o
	AS	+	+	+	+	+	o	o	o	o
	DH	+	+	+	o	+	o	o	o	o
		−15	−19	−23	−27	−31	−35	−39	−43	−47
125 cps	CK	+	+	+	+	+	o	o	o	o
Volt. level =	AS	+	+	+	+	o	o	o	o	o
−14.2 db	DH	+	+	o	+	o	+	o	o	o
	CK	o	+	+	+	+	+	o	o	o
	AS	+	+	+	+	o	+	o	o	o
	DH	+	+	o	+	o	o	+	o	o
	CK	+	+	o	+	+	+	o	o	o
	AS	+	+	o	o	+	+	o	o	o
	DH	+	+	o	o	o	o	+	o	o

The circuit shown in Fig. 127 was employed to generate and control the reference tone and the sounds to be measured. Vacuum-tube oscillators were used to generate pure tones, and for complex tones and other sounds, suitable sources were substituted. By means of the voltage measuring circuit and the attenuator, the voltage level (voltage level = 20 log V) impressed upon the terminals of the receivers could be determined. For example, the attenuator, which was calibrated in decibels, was set so that the voltage measuring set indicated 1 volt was being impressed upon the receiver. Then the difference between this setting and any other setting is the voltage level. To obtain the intensity level of the sound we must know the calibration of the receivers.

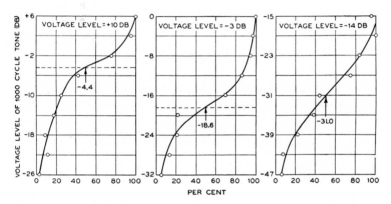

FIG. 128.—PERCENT OF OBSERVATIONS ESTIMATING 1000-CYCLE TONE TO BE LOUDER THAN 125-CYCLE TONE.

The observers were seated in a sound-proof booth and were required only to listen and then operate a simple switch. These switches were provided at each position and were arranged so that the operations of one observer could not be seen by another. This was necessary to prevent the judgments of one observer from influencing those of another observer. First they heard the sound being tested, and immediately afterwards the reference tone, each for a period of one second. After a pause of one second this sequence was repeated, and then they were required to estimate whether the reference tone was louder or softer than the other sound and indicate their opinions by operating the switches. The levels were then changed and the procedure repeated. The results of the tests were recorded outside the booth.

The typical recording chart shown in Table 32 contains the results of three observers testing a 125-cycle tone at three different levels. Two marks were used for recording the observers' judgments, a cipher indicating the 125-cycle tone to be the louder, and a plus sign denoting the

184   SPEECH AND HEARING IN COMMUNICATION

reference tone to be the louder of the two.   No equal judgments were permitted.   The figures at the head of each column give the voltage level of the reference tone impressed upon the receivers, that is, the number of decibels from 1 volt, plus if above and minus if below, and those at the side are similar values for the tone being tested.   Successive tests were chosen at random from the twenty-seven possible combinations of levels shown, thus reducing the possibility of memory effects.   The levels were, selected so the observers listened to reference tones which were louder and softer than the tone being tested, and the median of their judgments was taken as the point of equal loudness.

The data on this recording chart, combined with a similar number of observations by the rest of the crew (a total of eleven observers), are shown in graphical form in Fig. 128.   The arrow indicates the median level at which the 1000-cycle reference, in the opinion of this group of observers, sounded equally loud to the 125-cycle tone.

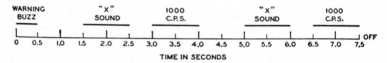

Fig. 129.—Time Sequence for Loudness Comparisons.

The testing method adopted was influenced by the efforts to minimize fatigue effects, both mental and physical.   Mental fatigue and probable changes in the attitude of an observer during the progress of a long series of tests were detected by keeping a record of the spread of each observer's results.   As long as the spread was normal it was assumed that the fatigue, if present, was small.   The tests were conducted on a time schedule which limited the observers to five minutes of continuous testing, during which time approximately fifteen observations were made. The maximum number of observations permitted in one day was 150.

To avoid fatiguing the ear, the sounds to which the observers listened were of short duration and in the sequence illustrated on Fig. 129. The duration time of each sound had to be long enough to fatigue the ear. The reference tone followed the x sound at a time interval short enough to permit a ready comparison, and yet not be subject to fatigue by prolonging the stimulation without an adequate rest period.   At high levels it was found that a tone requires nearly 0.3 second to reach full loudness and if sustained for longer periods than one second, there is danger of fatiguing the ear.[2]

To avoid the objectionable transients which occur when sounds are interrupted suddenly at high levels, the controlling circuit was designed to

[2] G. V. Bekesy, *Theory of Hearing* Physical Zeitsung, 30, 115, 1929.

start and stop the sounds gradually.   Relays, operating in the feedback
circuits of the vacuum-tube oscillators and in the grid circuits of amplifiers, performed this operation.   The period of growth and decay was
approximately 0.1 second as shown on the typical oscillogram in Fig. 130.

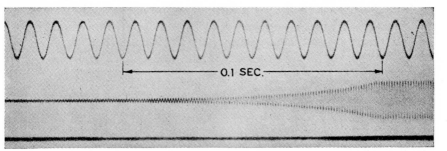

Growth

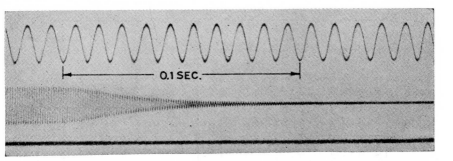

Decay

FIG. 130.—GROWTH AND DECAY OF 1000-CYCLE REFERENCE TONE.

With these devices the transient effects were reduced and yet the sounds
seemed to start and stop instantaneously unless attention was called to
the effect.   A motor-driven commutator operated the relays which started
and stopped the sounds in proper sequence, and switched the receivers
from the reference tone circuit to the sound under test.

Threshold measurements were made before and after the loudness
tests by turning off the reference tone and slowly attenuating the other
tone below threshold and then raising the level until it again became audible.   The average of these two levels was taken as the threshold.   These
are the measurements which were called Munson's data in Chapter 8
on acuity.   They served to establish what is now known as the zero
loudness contour.

The results on the loudness level of pure tones were obatined by
using receivers held to the two ears.   These receivers were of the electro-

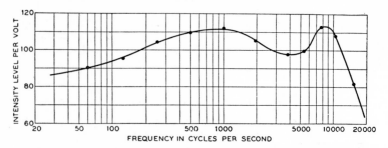

FIG. 131.—FIELD CALIBRATION OF LOUDNESS BALANCE RECEIVERS.
(CALIBRATION MADE AT $L = 60$ DB.)

dynamic type and were practically free of nonlinear distortion for the entire range of intensity levels used. The highest level of any generated harmonic was less than 20 db below the fundamental. In most cases it was 50 db down. The calibration of these receivers are shown in Fig. 131.

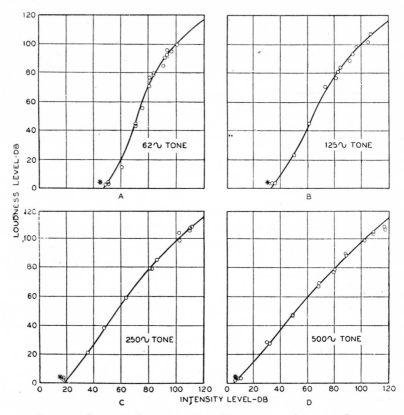

FIG. 132.—LOUDNESS LEVELS OF PURE TONES VERSUS INTENSITY LEVEL.

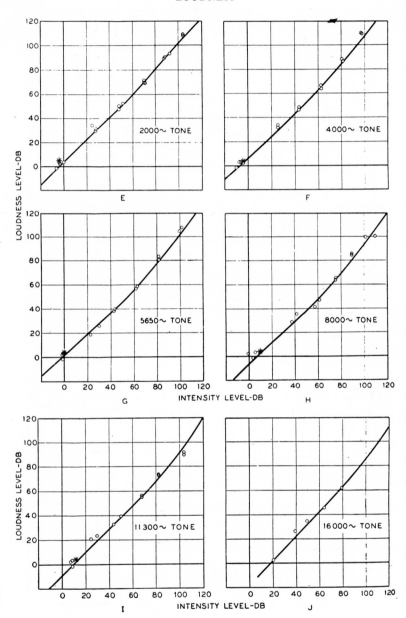

FIG. 133.—LOUDNESS LEVELS OF PURE TONES VERSUS INTENSITY LEVEL.

The values of voltage level on the receivers could then be transferred to field intensity levels. The results for the loudness level L_k of pure tones are shown in Figs. 132 and 133. This set of data enables one to plot the loudness level contours shown in Figs. 134 and 135. The peculiar shape of these contours above 1000 cycles in Fig. 135 is due to the diffraction effects of the head.   Since the curves in Figs. 134 and 135 are essentially flat for the range between 500 and 5000 cps, then for this

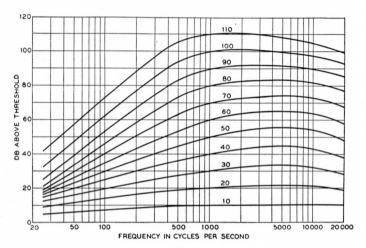

FIG. 134.—LOUDNESS LEVEL CONTOURS VERSUS SENSATION LEVEL.

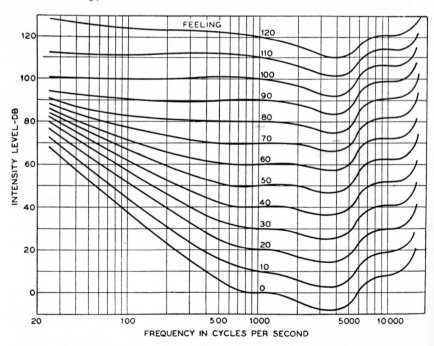

FIG. 135.—LOUDNESS LEVEL CONTOURS VERSUS INTENSITY LEVEL.

range the intensity level and loudness are equal. This is the principal range concerned with speech.

The Loudness Scale

A true loudness scale must be one such that when the number of units on this scale is doubled, the magnitude of the sensation as experienced by typical observers will be doubled, or when trebled the loudness sensation is trebled, etc. The existence of such a scale is dependent upon the supposition that consistent judgment tests of loudness can be obtained. Experimental tests indicate that such judgments are sufficiently consistent to warrant choosing such a scale. To find the relation which has been designated $G(L)$ between the loudness level L and the loudness N on the proposed new scale, various types of experiments were performed.

The general scheme of these experiments is to find experimentally pairs of values of loudness level L_1 and L_2 phons, which correspond to pairs of values of the loudness N_1 and N_2 sones. The first type of experiment is concerned with a comparison of the loudness experienced by a typical observer when listening first with one ear and then with both ears. Since we are dealing with the typical observer, the two ears will be alike in sensitivity. Consequently, if loudness is proportional to the total nerve energy sent to the brain, then it follows that the loudness experienced when using two ears will be double that when using one ear. To obtain such data the sound is first produced at any convenient intensity and listened to with only one ear, and its loudness level measured. Let us call this value L_1. Without chaniging the intensity of the sound, the observer listens with both ears, and the loudness level is measured. Let us call its value L_2. If N_1 is the number of loudness units corresponding to listening with one ear and N_2 to that corresponding to listening with both ears, then it is evident that N_2 must be just double N_1. We will again listen with one ear, but increase the intensity of the sound until a loudness level of L_2 is obtained. If now again the intensity of the sound is held constant and we listen with both ears, we will find a loudness level L_4. This must correspond to a loudness N_4 which is four times N_1. An so we might continue throughout the entire intensity range. If we now choose N_1 arbitrarily equal to some convenient number, we will have a set of corresponding values of loudness units and loudness levels from which we can draw a curve giving the relation which we are seeking.

The experiments as outlined could not be carried out because our typical observer was hypothetical. To obtain results corresponding to that which would be obtained by such a typical observer, one must deal with a large group of observers, taking the average value as that corresponding to a typical observer. For this reason, pairs of loudness levels L_1 and L_2 were obtained starting with L_1 at various values throughout the audible range. The points indicated by the open square in Fig. 136 are such observed points. A solid curve is drawn to give the best fit of

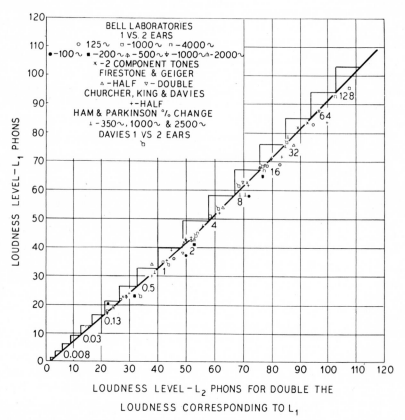

FIG. 136.—EXPERIMENTAL VALUES OF TWO LOUDNESS LEVELS L_1 AND L_2 SUCH THAT THE SOUND CORRESPONDING TO THE LATTER IS TWICE AS LOUD AS THAT CORRESPONDING TO THE FORMER.

the observed points corresponding to N_1, $2N_1$, $4N_1$, and $8N_1$. From this curve the proper values of L_1, L_2, L_4, L_8, etc., can be obtained to build the scale in the manner described above.

In the second type of experiment the following procedure is used. A 1000-cycle reference tone is balanced against a pure tone having a frequency far removed from 1000 until they are equally loud. Then the two tones are combined to form a complex tone having two components. Let L_1 be the loudness level of each component alone and L_2 the loudness level of the combination. Since the components were adjusted to produce equal loudness, it is assumed that each is producing the same nerve stimulation and that when they act together they will produce twice the loudness. This hypothesis is reasonable provided in the mechanism of hearing the two sets of nerves do not interfere with each other. It can be shown by experiments on the masking of one tone by another that such interference is negligibly small when their frequencies are widely separated. Consequently, balancing such a two-component tone against the reference tone should give pairs of values of L_1 and L_2 which can be used in the same way as indicated by the one versus two ear method described above; that is, L_2 corresponds to a loudness number which is just twice that corresponding to L_1. Such observed points are also shown in Fig. 136.

In the third type of experiment a typical observer is asked to listen to a sound, first at a loudness level L_1 and then to the same sound when its loudness level has been raised to a value L_2 such that to him the loudness seems to have doubled. The experiment is repeated, starting with another initial value of L_1, and thus a series of pairs of values of L_1 and L_2 are obtained which have the same relation to our loudness scale as those obtained by the first two methods. A much greater amount of data is required by this method because the probable error of a single judgment is very large. However, this method is related more directly to the scale we are seeking than the two preceding ones. Four different investigators [3] in different parts of this country and England have taken a very large number of observations by this method, not only on the 1000-cycle reference tone but on many types of tones. The data taken by Laird have been omitted since they were so far out of line from those obtained by the other three groups of investigators; namely, Ham and Parkinson, Firestone and Geiger, and Churcher-King-Davies. Their observations are also given in Fig. 136 by the points indicated.

It will be seen that the observed points obtained by these diverse methods fit consistently on one curve, particularly well in the range of loudness usually experienced in everyday life; namely, from $L_2 = 40$ to $L_2 = 80$ phons. It was sufficiently consistent to justify choosing the resulting loudness scale as a true loudness scale. This curve can now be used to determine the relationship between the loudness level L and the loudness N. The unit of loudness is called the sone.[4] The scale is chosen so that when $L = 40$ phons $N = 1$ sone. The first step downward from $L = 40$ to decrease the loudness to $1/2$ or $N = .5$ is seen to be 7.8.

---

[3] In these experiments the loudness level was not measured but only the number of db above the threshold. For the 1000-cycle tone this was taken as the loudness level L. For other pure tones the loudness level was computed from our data on the loudness level of pure tones.

[4] This name was suggested by S. S. Stevens.

So the loudness level $L = 32.2$ phons correspond to .5 sones. The next step is 6.6 phons so the loudness level 25.6 phons corresponds to the loudness .25 sones. The steps and corresponding values of N and L are given in Table 31.

TABLE 31

L_2	L_1	Δl	N	L_2	L_1	Δl	N
2.0	0	2.0	.001	67	58	9	4
4.0	2.0	2.0	.002	76	67	9	8
6.3	4.0	2.3	.004	85	76	9	16
8.9	6.3	2.6	.008	94	85	9	32
12.0	8.9	3.1	.016	103	94	9	64
15.8	12.0	3.8	.031	112	103	9	128
20.2	15.8	4.4	.062	121	112	9	256
25.6	20.2	5.4	.125	130	121	9	512
32.2	25.6	6.6	.25		130		1024
40.0	32.2	7.8	.50				
49.0	40.0	9.0	1				
58	49	9.0	2				

It is seen that above $L = 40$ phons the steps for doubling the loudness are all equal to 9 db. Consequently for values of L above 40 phons the value of N, is given by

$$N = 2^{\frac{L-40}{9}} = 046 \times 2^{\frac{L}{9}} \doteq 046 \times 10^{\frac{L}{30}}. \qquad (11-7)$$

A plot of the values of L and N from Table 31 is shown in Fig. 137. The resulting curve gives the desired relation between loudness and loudness level.

This same scale can be developed from data obtained by balancing a three-component tone against the reference tone or by judging when a threefold increase in loudness has been produced. Or we could use any other number besides 2 or 3 and get the same scale if it is a real loudness scale. An extreme case would be to use a ten-component tone and use judgment tests for 1/10 and ten times as loud. Tests of this kind have been made which I shall now describe.

A complex tone [5] was generated having ten harmonics of a fundamental frequency of 530 cps. The components were each adjusted so that when listened to separately they had the same loudness level L_1 phons. They were then combined into a complex tone, and it was found that the loudness level was raised to a value L_{10} phons. So in this way pairs of

[5] The description of this generator is given in the paper by Fletcher and Munson, Journal Acoustical Society America, 5, 82–108, 1933.

values of loudness levels L_1 and L_{10} were obtained starting with L_1 at different intensities of sound.   If the patches of nerve stimulation cor- responding to each component do not overlap, then the complex tone should be ten times as loud as each component.   Such pairs of intensities were obtained by using a group of observers, and are shown by the points

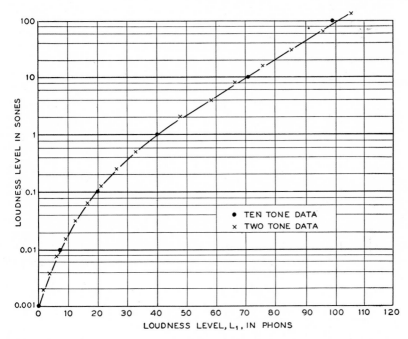

FIG. 137.—RELATION BETWEEN LOUDNESS LEVEL IN PHONS AND THE
LOUDNESS IN SONES.

in Fig. 138.   Ham and Parkinson, and Firestone and Geiger made judg- ment tests to find a pair of loudness levels L_1 and L_{10} such that the tone for L_1 was one-tenth the loudness of that for L_{10}.   Their results are shown by the points △ and ▽, respectively.   The points are somewhat scattered, but I think it is remarkable that the two sets of points determine the single curve within the observational error, for such judgment tests are extremely difficult to make.   It is surprising that the agreement is as good as indicated.   The judgment tests and the ten-tone balance tests were all made in different laboratories and before any loudness scale of the type discussed here was constructed.

Now the curve of Fig. 138 can be used to construct a loudness scale. In this case the width of the steps of the staircase corresponds to the phons increase necessary to make the sound ten times as loud.   The corresponding values of N and L can be used to determine the curve of Fig. 137. The solid curve of Fig. 138 was drawn so that points on it would yield the same loudness scale as shown in Fig. 137. It is seen that such a curve does indeed fit the observed data except for high values of L_{10}. For these high intensities, the stimulated patches of nerves in the inner ear overlap, so the observed values of L_{10} should be less than indicated by the points on the curve.

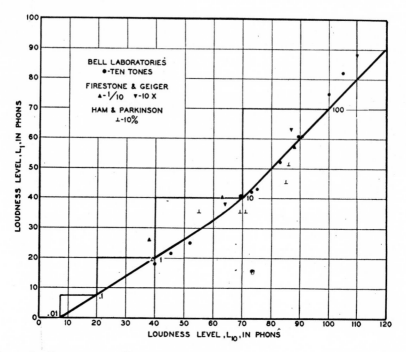

FIG. 138.—EXPERIMENTAL VALUES OF TWO LOUDNESS LEVELS L_1 AND L_{10} SUCH THAT THE SOUND CORRESPONDING TO THE LATTER IS TEN TIMES LOUDER THAN THE FORMER.

The following empirical equation was found to represent the curve of Fig. 137 and therefore represents the relation between loudness and loudness level.

$$N = \frac{10^{\frac{L-40}{30}}}{1 + 50 \times 10^{\frac{L}{10}}} = G(L). \qquad (11\text{-}8)$$

The points indicated by circles were calculated from this equation. The crosses are taken from the data in Table 31.

Method of Calculating the Loudness Level of a Complex Tone

By using the curves shown in Fig. 135 together with the relation in equation (11–8) one can determine the loudness N_k of a pure tone in terms of its intensity level and frequency.   If b_k were unity one would add the values of N_k corresponding to each component to find the loudness of the complex tone.   However in general b is not unity.

First, when the components are very close together they act on the same set of nerve endings.   Therefore, one must first add together all the intensities of the components in a critical band width and treat the combined intensity as a single component having a frequency equal to the mid-frequency of the band.

After this is done it was found by purely empirical methods that b_k could be calculated approximately by the rather complicated formula

$$b_k = [(250 + f_k - f_m)/1000]\ 10^{(L_k - L_m)/T}\ Q(\beta_k + 30 \log f_k - 95) \quad (11\text{–}9)$$

where

f_k is the frequency of the component expressed in cycles per second,
f_m is the frequency of the masking component expressed in cycles per second,
L_k is the loudness level of the kth component when souding alone,
L_m is the loudness level of the masking tone,
Q is a function depending upon the intensity level β_k and the frequency f_k of each component and is given in Table 32 as a function of

$$X = \beta_k + 30 \log f_k - 95$$

T is the masking and is given by the curve of Fig. 139.

TABLE 32

VALUES OF $Q(X)$

X	0	1	2	3	4	5	6	7	8	9
0	5.00	4.88	4.76	4.64	4.53	4.41	4.29	4.17	4.05	3.94
10	3.82	3.70	3.58	3.46	3.35	3.33	3.11	2.99	2.87	2.76
20	2.64	2.52	2.40	2.29	2.16	2.05	1.95	1.85	1.76	1.68
30	1.60	1.53	1.47	1.40	1.35	1.30	1.25	1.20	1.16	1.13
40	1.09	1.06	1.03	1.01	0.00	0.97	0.95	0.94	0.92	0.91
50	0.90	0.90	0.89	0.89	0.88	0.88	0.88	0.88	0.88	0.88
60	0.88	0.88	0.88	0.88	0.88	0.88	0.88	0.89	0.89	0.90
70	0.90	0.91	0.92	0.93	0.94	0.96	0.97	0.99	1.00	1.02
80	1.04	1.06	1.08	1.10	1.13	1.15	1.17	1.19	1.22	1.24
90	1.27	1.29	1.31	1.34	1.36	1.39	1.41	1.44	1.46	1.48
100	1.51	1.53	1.55	1.58	1.60	1.62	1.64	1.67	1.69	1.71

It is important to remember *that b_k can never be greater than unity so that all calculated values greater than this must be replaced with values equal to unity.* Also all components *within the limiting frequency bands must be grouped together as indicated above.* It is very helpful to remember that any component for which the loudness level is 12 db below the kth

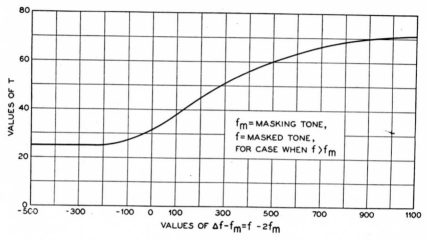

FIG. 139.—VALUES OF THE MASKING T.

component, that is, the one for which b is being calculated, need not be considered as possibly being the masking component. If all the components preceding the kth are in this class, then b_k is unity.

The masker component is usually the component preceding the kth. In general, it is the one which produces the smallest value of T.

TABLE 33

COMPUTATIONS

k	f_k	β_k	L_k	N_k	b_k	
1	60	50	0	.001	1.0	
2	180	45	25	.25	1.0	$N = 1.39$ sones
3	300	40	30	.42	1.0	
4	540	30	27	.30	1.0	$L = 42$ phons
5	1200	25	30	.42	1.0	

To illustrate the method of using the formula the loudness of two complex tones will be calculated. The first may represent the hum from a dynamo. Its components are given in Table 33.

The first step is to find the values of N_k from f_k and β_k. Since the values of N_k are low and the frequency separation fairly large, one familiar with these functions would readily see that the values of b would be unity and a computation would verify it so that the sum of the N_k values gives the total loudness of 1.4 sone.   This corresponds to a loudness level of 42 phons.

The second tone calculated is this same hum amplified 30 db.   It better illustrates the use of the formula.

TABLE 34

COMPUTATIONS

k	f_k	β_k	L_k	N_k	f_m	L_m	X	Q	b	$b_k \cdot N_k$
1	60	80	69	9.2	—	—	—	—	1.0	9.2
2	180	75	72	11.8	60	69	48	.92	.42	4.8
3	300	70	71	11.0	180	72	49	.91	.37	4.0
4	540	60	60	4.6	300	71	47	.94	.19	0.9
5	1200	55	55	3.2	300	71	52	.89	.57	1.8

$N = 21$ sones; $L = 81$ phons.

The loudness level of the combined tones is only 7 phons above the loudness level of the second component.   If only one ear is used in listening, the loudness of this complex tone is one-half, corresponding to a loudness level of 72 phons.

Comparison of Observed and Calculated Results on the Loudness Levels of Complex Tones

In order to show the agreement between observed loudness levels and levels calculated by means of the formula developed in the preceding

TABLE 35

TWO COMPONENT TONES ($\Delta L = 0$)

Frequency Range	Δf	Loudness Levels (db)				
1000–1100	100	L_k	83	63	43	23	2
		$L_{obs.}$	87	68	47	28	2
		$L_{calc.}$	87	68	47	28	4
1000–2000	1000	L_k	83	63	43	23	−1
		$L_{obs.}$	89	71	49	28	2
		$L_{calc.}$	91	74	52	28	1
125–1000	875	L_k	84				
		$L_{obs.}$	92				
		$L_{calc.}$	92				

TABLE 36
Ten Component Tones ($\Delta L = 0$)

Frequency Range	Δf		Loudness Levels (db)									
50–500	50	L_k	67	54	33	21	11	−1				
		$L_{obs.}$	83	68	47	38	20	2				
		$L_{calc.}$	81	72	53	39	24	8				
50–500	50	L_k	78	61	41	23	13	−1				
		$L_{obs.}$	92	73	53	42	25	2				
		$L_{calc.}$	91	77	60	42	27	8				
1400–1895	55	L_k	78	69	50	16	6	−1				
		$L_{obs.}$	94	82	62	32	22	2				
		$L_{calc.}$	93	83	65	31	17	0				
1400–1895	55	L_k	57	37	20	3						
		$L_{obs.}$	68	50	34	2						
		$L_{calc.}$	73	52	36	5						
100–1000	100	L_k	84	64	43	24	2	84	64	43	24	2
		$L_{obs.}$	95	83	59	41	2	94	80	63	44	2
		$L_{calc.}$	100	83	68	47	12	100	83	68	47	12
100–1000	100	L_k	81	64	43	23	13	−4				
		$L_{obs.}$	93	82	65	49	33	2				
		$L_{calc.}$	98	83	68	45	27	3				
100–1000	100	L_k	83	63	43	23	0					
		$L_{obs.}$	95	79	59	43	2					
		$L_{calc.}$	99	82	68	45	9					
3100–3900	100	L_k	83	63	43	23	78	59	48	27	−7	
		$L_{obs.}$	100	82	59	32	99	81	62	38	2	
		$L_{calc.}$	100	80	60	38	95	77	65	42	0	
1100–3170	230	L_k	79	60	41	17	7	−4				
		$L_{obs.}$	100	81	65	33	22	2				
		$L_{calc.}$	100	83	64	34	18	3				
260–2600	260	L_k	79	62	42	23	13	−2				
		$L_{obs.}$	97	82	65	44	28	2				
		$L_{calc.}$	100	85	68	45	27	5				
530–5300	530	L_k	75	53	43	25	82	61	43	17	−2	
		$L_{obs.}$	100	83	73	52	105	90	73	40	2	
		$L_{calc.}$	101	82	72	48	108	89	72	34	5	
530–5300	530	L_k	61	41	21	−3						
		$L_{obs.}$	89	69	45	2						
		$L_{calc.}$	89	70	42	4						

sections, the results of a large number of tests are given here, including those from which the formula was derived. In Tables 35-41 the first column shows the frequency range over which the components of the tones were distributed, the figures being the frequencies of the first and last component. Several tones having two components were tested, but as the tables indicate, the majority of the tones had ten components. But a number of them contained eleven components, so for purposes of identification these are placed in a separate group. In the second column of the tables, next to the frequency range of the tones, the

TABLE 37

Eleven Component Tones ($\Delta L = 0$)

Frequency Range	Δf	Loudness Levels (db)						
1000–2000	100	L_k	84	64	43	24	−1	
		$L_{obs.}$	97	83	65	43	2	
		$L_{calc.}$	103	84	64	45	7	
1000–2000	100	L_k	84	64	43	23	1	
		$L_{obs.}$	99	82	65	42	2	
		$L_{calc.}$	103	84	64	45	11	
1150–2270	112	L_k	79	60	40	20	10	−5
		$L_{obs.}$	99	78	62	41	25	2
		$L_{calc.}$	98	81	61	40	23	1
1120–4520	340	L_k	77	62	42	22	7	−7
		$L_{obs.}$	102	86	66	46	20	2
		$L_{calc.}$	101	88	69	44	19	−1

TABLE 38

Ten Component Tones ($\Delta L = 5$ db)

Frequency Range	Δf	Loudness Levels (db)						
1725–2220	55	L_k	82	62	43	27	17	−6
		$L_{obs.}$	101	73	54	38	30	2
		$L_{calc.}$	95	76	56	40	30	−1
1725–2220	55	L_k	80	62	42	22	12	−2
		$L_{obs.}$	94	66	50	33	22	2
		$L_{calc.}$	93	76	54	35	22	4

TABLE 39

ELEVEN COMPONENT TONES ($\Delta L = 5$ DB)

Frequency Range	Δf	Loudness Levels (db)					
57–626	57	L_k	79	61	41	26	16	1
		$L_{obs.}$	91	73	56	41	28	2
		$L_{calc.}$	90	76	59	43	28	8
3420–4020	60	L_k	76	61	42	25	15	−9
		$L_{obs.}$	95	77	55	33	25	2
		$L_{calc.}$	89	75	54	36	26	−4

TABLE 40

TEN COMPONENT TONES ($\Delta L = 10$ DB)

Frequency Range	Δf	Loudness Levels (db)					
1725–2220	55	L_k	79	59	40	19	9	−5
		$L_{obs.}$	95	71	54	33	22	2
		$L_{calc.}$	91	73	51	31	17	−1
1725–2220	55	L_k	79	61	41	27	17	−1
		$L_{obs.}$	89	67	48	37	27	2
		$L_{calc.}$	92	75	53	39	28	4

TABLE 41

ELEVEN COMPONENT TONES ($\Delta L = 10$ DB)

Frequency Range	Δf	Loudness Levels (db)					
57–627	57	L_k	80	62	42	27	17	2
		$L_{obs.}$	88	70	53	40	27	2
		$L_{calc.}$	90	76	59	45	30	8
3420–4020	60	L_k	81	62	42	27	17	−4
		$L_{obs.}$	100	70	50	33	26	2
		$L_{calc.}$	94	75	53	37	27	0

frequency difference Δf between adjacent components is given. The remainder of the data pertains to the loudness levels of the tones. Opposite L_k are given the common loudness levels to which all the components of the tone were adjusted for a particular test, and in the next line the results of the test, that is, the observed loudness levels $L_{obs.}$, are given. Directly beneath each observed value, the calculated loudness levels $L_{calc.}$ are shown. The three associated values of L_k, $L_{obs.}$, and $L_{calc.}$ in each column represent the data for one complete test. For example, in Table 36, the first tone is described as having ten components, and for the first test shown each component was adjusted to have a loudness level L_k of 67 db. The results of the test gave an observed loudness level $L_{obs.}$ of 83 db for the ten components acting together, and the calculated loudness level $L_{calc.}$ of this same tone was 81 db. The probable error of the observed results in the tables is approximately $\pm$ 2 db.

In the next series of data, adjacent components had a difference in loudness level of 5 db, that is, the first, third, fifth, etc., components had the loudness level given opposite L_k, and the even numbered components were 5 db lower (Tables 38 and 39).

In the sets of tests given in Tables 40 and 41 the difference in loudness level of adjacent components was 10 db.

Calculations of Loudness from Noise Audiograms

In sounds of the type where the components are closely spaced, the loudness contribution of one component depends to a large extent upon the masking effects of other components, and the situation can become exceedingly complex when the number of components is large. For this reason a computing method which deals with each component separately is always tedious and may be inadequate when applied to sounds having a large number of components. A quantitative relationship was found between loudness and masking which enables one to calculate the loudness of such a sound. Although this method seems to have a general application to all types of sounds, it is particularly well suited to the complicated types which approach a continuous spectrum where the previous loudness formula has doubtful application. The method can also be applied to single frequency tones, or sounds having only a few components, but in these cases it is more difficult to obtain the masking audiogram accurately.

As outlined in Chapter 10, the masking audiogram, sometimes called the noise audiogram, is a curve which gives the number of db at each frequency, f, that the threshold level of a pure tone is shifted when heard in the presence of the noise. Let M be the ordinate of such a curve. Then at an abscissa corresponding to f, the ordinate, M, gives the difference between the threshold of hearing in the presence of the sound and in a quiet place or the threshold shift.

When masking occurs, it is evident that the nerves along the basilar membrane are excited. The excitation is most where the masking is greatest. If we let N_x be excitation per unit of length at the position x, then it follows that the total excitation N is given by

$$N = \int N_x \, dx \qquad (\text{11-10})$$

where the integration extends over the entire length of the basilar membrane where the nerve endings are located. Now if we can identify excitation with loudness, we will have the relation desired.

The relation between x and f was established and given in Chapter 10 (Fig. 123, solid curve) so that each frequency can be identified with a particular position coordinate x which has also been related to the distance from the stapes along the basilar membrane.

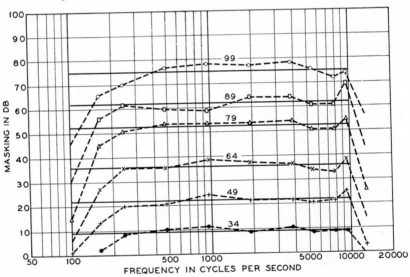

FIG. 140.—MASKING VS. FREQUENCY AND INTENSITY FOR A WIDE BAND OF THERMAL NOISE.

The N_x in equation (11-10) can be considered a function of M only, where M is the threshold shift at the frequency f. If M is constant over a portion of the membrane from x_1 to x_2, then if N is the measured loudness of the noise producing such masking,

$$N_x(M) = N/(x_1 - x_2) \qquad (\text{11-11})$$

or the loudness per one percent of the total number of nerves. For convenience this will be called a patch of nerve endings.

It will be seen from Table 29 that there are about 300 nerve endings in such a patch. The function N_x can be determined from measurements of the loudness N of the noise producing such masking. However, there is no noise that will ideally produce a sharp band of masking. One can produce such a sharp band of frequencies by electrical filters, but the corresponding masking audiogram will not have sharp sides.

However, if we take a wide band of noise which covers practically the entire length of the membrane the error introduced by not having M constant for a short distance will not be appreciable. Such a sound was obtained by amplifying thermal noise and passing it through appropriate networks so the masking was approximately constant over a wide range of frequencies.

The results of masking tests made at various intensity levels of this sound are shown in Fig. 140. The intensity levels, measured in db

TABLE 42

VALUES OF N_x

M	0	10	20	30	40	50	60	70	80	90	100
0	0	.015	.067	.176	.370	.70	1.27	2.30	3.90	6.2	9.4
1	.0003	.018	.075	.190	.39	.74	1.35	2.40	4.10	6.5	9.7
2	.0007	.021	.083	.207	.42	.79	1.43	2.55	4.30	6.8	10.0
3	.0013	.026	.091	.224	.45	.84	1.51	2.70	4.50	7.1	10.3
4	.0023	.030	.100	.243	.48	.89	1.60	2.85	4.70	7.4	10.6
5	.0036	.035	.111	.263	.51	.95	1.70	3.00	5.0	7.7	10.9
6	.0054	.040	.123	.282	.54	1.01	1.80	3.15	5.2	8.0	11.2
7	.0072	.047	.135	.304	.57	1.07	1.90	3.35	5.4	8.4	11.6
8	.0095	.053	.148	.326	.61	1.14	2.02	3.50	5.7	8.6	12.0
9	.0123	.060	.162	.348	.65	1.20	2.15	3.70	5.9	9.0	12.3

above 10^{-16} watts per square centimeter, are marked on the masking spectrums. As will be seen, the masking levels obtained are not uniform with frequency, particularly at the high intensities, but considering the experimental difficulties involved in making such measurements, the data were sufficiently accurate to determine the function N_x. The sounds for the different intensity levels were obtained by changing an attenuator in the circuit. So to each attenuator setting experimental values of M and N were obtained. Such experimental values are shown by the dots in Fig. 143. Now N_x can be determined if we can choose the correct values of x_1 and x_2 corresponding to f_1 and f_2 for the cut-off frequencies in Fig. 140. It is seen that these are approximately 200 and 10,000 cps corresponding to $x_1 = 5$ and $x_2 = 96$ as seen from Fig. 123. Values obtained in this way were used as a first trial. Slight adjustments were then made to make the calculations using them give a better fit of the observed loudness data.   The final values chosen are given in Table 42.

If we call the loudness per patch of nerves N_x, then the function $F(M)$ has been identified as equal to N_x and

$$N = \int_0^{100} N_x \, dx. \qquad (11\text{-}12)$$

For example if $M = 47$ db, then $N_x = .57$ sones.

Comparison of Observed and Computed Loudness Levels from Noise Audiograms

Loudness and masking tests have been made on a number of sounds so a comparison between calculated, and observed results are possible.   The masking tests were similar to the loudness tests in that the observers listened to the sounds with receivers on both ears, and the constant stimulus method was used.

In making a masking test on a noise at the frequency f, the observer first made a threshold test on the maskee tone of frequency f with the noise turned off.   Then the noise was turned on and the threshold repeated in the presence of the noise.   Actually the noise was not on continually during the latter test but came on at intervals five seconds apart and stayed on for two seconds each time.   The tone came on after the noise had been on for one second and was turned off shortly before the noise was stopped, so the tone was only presented in the presence of the noise. Each time the noise and tone came on the tone was at a slightly different level so that it varied above and below the observer's threshold.   The masking level was chosen as the point where the tone was audible 50 percent of the time.

Subtracting the threshold level of the tone from the masking level gives the masking of the noise at the frequency f.   After the masking tests on a large number of sounds had been completed, it was found that the threshold taken with the noise off were close to the zero loudness contour line, so for the sake of uniformity this contour was chosen as the threshold for all tests.   The masking audiograms were plotted then in terms of db above zero loudness instead of db above observed threshold.

Results will first be given for various intensity spectra of thermal noise.   In Fig. 141 the masking audiograms for narrow bands are given. The intensity level of the noise is marked on each audiogram.   In the same figure a comparison of the calculated and observed loudness levels of these bands is shown.   The agreement is good except for the high-frequency band where in the middle range of intensities the calculated results are somewhat too high.   Masking audiograms for thermal noise

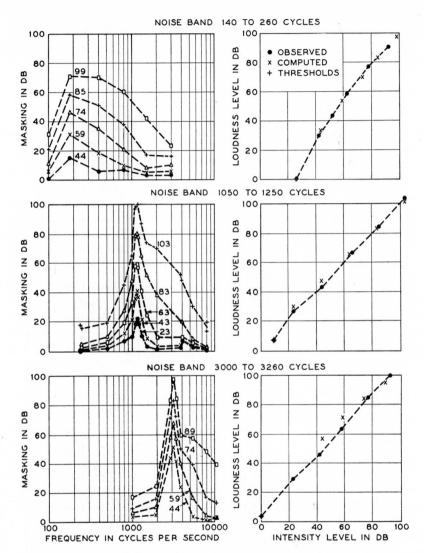

FIG. 141.—MASKING AUDIOGRAMS AND A COMPARISON OF OBSERVED AND COMPUTED LOUDNESS LEVELS FOR NARROW BANDS OF THERMAL NOISE.

bands of intermediate widths are given in Fig. 142, and curves giving a comparison of observed and calculated results are shown also. In Fig. 143 is shown a comparison of observed and computed loudness levels for the very wide band from which the function F was determined. It would be expected that this agreement would be good, as is found in this curve. It is seen that there is a fairly good agreement for thermal noise bands of almost any width and in all frequency regions. An extreme case would be the loudness of a pure tone since the noise audiogram is very different from the flat one for thermal noise.

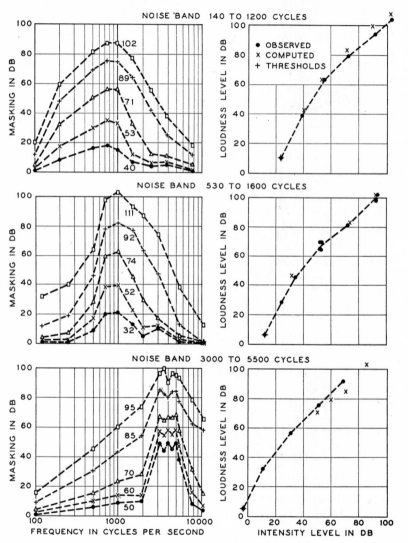

FIG. 142.—MASKING AUDIOGRAMS AND A COMPARISON OF OBSERVED AND COMPUTED LOUDNESS LEVELS FOR THERMAL NOISE BANDS OF MEDIUM WIDTH.

In Fig. 144 is shown a comparison of calculated and observed results for 200-, 1000-, and 4000-cycle tones, and the masking audiograms are shown opposite, marked with the intensity levels of the tones. The observed levels, indicated by the dotted lines, are taken from the data on loudness contours. The audiograms have recently been obtained by using a narrow band of thermal hoise as an exploring tone. The previous data which have been given for the masking of single frequencies are very uncertain in the neighborhood of the masking tone principally because of beats. When a narrow band of thermal noise is used this

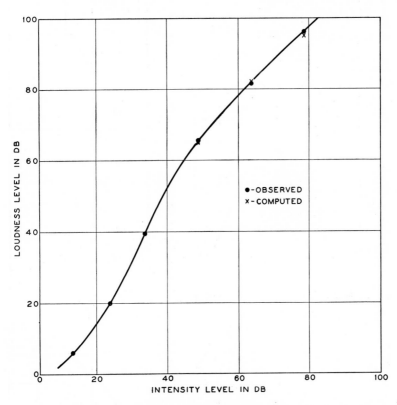

FIG. 143.—COMPARISONS OF COMPUTED AND OBSERVED LOUDNESS LEVELS FOR A WIDE BAND OF THERMAL NOISE.

uncertainty is less, but it is still difficult to determine accurately the masking in the neighborhood of the frequency of the masking tone.

It is found that a better agreement between calculated and observed results for single frequency tones is obtained if the masking at the frequency of the masking tone is taken as about 4 db below the level of the masking tone. This was done in the calculations for the three single frequency tones. The masking at other frequencies was that which was directly observed.

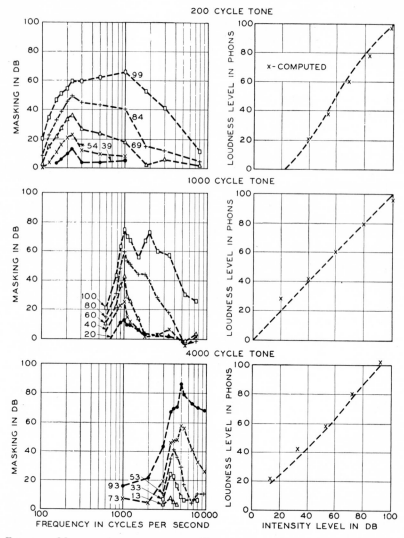

FIG. 144.—MASKING AUDIOGRAMS AND A COMPARISON OF OBSERVED AND COMPUTED
LOUDNESS LEVELS FOR SINGLE FREQUENCY TONES.

Calculation of Loudness from the Spectrum Level Curve

It was seen in Chapter 10 that the masking curve can be calculated from the spectrum level B curve if the slope of this curve does not exceed critical values.   Under this condition (see equation (10–5),

$$M = 10 \log (10^{Z/10} + 1) \qquad (11\text{–}13)$$

where $Z = B + \kappa - \beta_0$.   Therefore, for every value of Z there corresponds a definite value of M. The corresponding loudness per patch then can be found from Table 42. A set of such values of N_x and Z are given in Table 43.

TABLE 43

VALUES OF N_x (SONES) VS. Z

Z	-20	-10	0	10	20	30	40	50	60	70	80	90	100
0	0	.00002	.0007	.016	.067	.176	.37	.70	1.27	2.3	3.9	6.2	9.4
1		.00005	.001	.018	.075	.190	.39	.74	1.35	2.4	4.1	6.5	9.7
2		.0001	.002	.021	.083	.207	.42	.79	1.43	2.55	4.3	6.9	10.0
3		.0002	.003	.026	.091	.224	.45	.84	1.51	2.7	4.5	7.1	10.3
4		.0003	.004	.030	.100	.243	.48	.89	1.60	2.85	4.7	7.4	10.6
5		.0004	.006	.035	.111	.263	.51	.95	1.70	3.0	5.0	7.7	10.9
6		.0004	.007	.040	.123	.282	.54	1.01	1.80	3.15	5.2	8.0	11.2
7		.0005	.009	.047	.135	.304	.57	1.07	1.90	3.35	5.4	8.4	11.6
8		.0005	.011	.053	.148	.326	.61	1.14	2.02	3.5	5.7	8.6	12.0
9		.0006	.013	.060	.162	.348	.65	1.20	2.15	3.7	5.9	9.0	12.3

TABLE 44

f	B	κ	β_0 (Pressure level)	Z	N_x (sones)	x
100	26	19	38	7	.009	1
200	20	17	21	16	.040	4
400	14	17	10	21	.075	12
600	11	17	3	25	.111	21
800	9	18	1	28	.148	29
1000	8	18	0	26	.123	37
2000	4	20	-5	29	.162	59
4000	-2	23	-6	27	.135	79
6000	-7	26	1	18	.053	89
8000	-10	28	8	10	.016	93
10000	-15	29	9	5	.006	96

$N = 10$ sones; $L = 70$ phons.

To illustrate this method of calculation the loudness for average room noise is computed in Table 44. The frequencies are given in the first column. The values of B are taken from the curve in Fig. 70 of Chapter 6, and the values of β_0 from the zero loudness contour, Fig. 95, Chapter 8, and values of x from Fig. 123, Chapter 10. The value $\int_0^{100} N_x dx$ was found graphically to be 9.7 sones which corresponds to a loudness level of 70 phons.

It should be remembered that the method just outlined for calculating loudness gives results for the case of listening with two ears since the values of κ and $\beta_0 + N_x$ correspond to this method of listening. When listening with only one ear the loudness is only 5 sones corresponding to a loudness level of 61 phons.

CHAPTER 12

BINAURAL HEARING EFFECTS

When listening to a sound produced in the air, normally both ears are used and certain sensations are dependent upon this fact. Changing the normal condition for such listening produces certain effects known as binaural effects. Some of these effects have already been mentioned because they were directly related to the material being discussed. These and other effects are described in this chapter.

Pure binaural effects are probably produced in the brain itself and because of the difficulty of interpreting the sensations produced, there have been very large differences in results obtained by different observers. In general, it has been found that the two ears aid in locating the direction and distance of a sound source. This is particularly true of sources giving pure tones, for it has been found that persons having a total loss of hearing in one ear have great difficulty in locating the direction of such tones. Even when using both ears, however, it is very difficult to locate the source of pure tones when the pitch is high.

Binaural Effects Due to Changes in the Phase and Intensity of the Sound at the Two Ears

If a sound is conducted from a source to the two ears by different acoustic paths, some very interesting effects are produced. If the apparatus is arranged so that the phase in one of the paths can be changed, the following sensations are experienced by most persons who try the experiment. When the difference in phase between the two paths conducting the sound to the ear is zero, then the source appears to be in the median plane, that is, directly *in front* of the individual. As the difference in phase increases, the sound image travels, apparently, along a circle toward the ear which is leading in phase. When the image appears to be opposite the ear, it suddenly seems to jump through the head to the other side, finally coming back again to the median plane.

Several methods of producing the phase difference have been used by various investigators. The results obtained by G. W. Stewart and his students are typical.[1] For a source of sound he used an instrument called the "Phaser." This instrument consisted essentially of a rotating

[1] Physical Review, p. 433, May, 1920.

toothed wheel with two telephone bipolar receiver magnets placed radially close to the teeth and capable of being separated from each other by a variable known number of degrees of rotation of the wheel. The currents induced in the windings of these small magnets were conducted to two telephone receivers which were placed on the ears of the observer. It was thus possible to secure any difference in phase between the sounds at the two ears by moving the bipolar receiver magnets to different positions around the tooth wheel. By including selective networks in the circuit, tones of a fair degree of purity were obtained. The observer sat at the center of a circular scale and was asked to point in the direction from which the sound appeared to come.

A second method made use of two tuning forks placed at the end of rubber tubes, the sound being conducted to the ear by means of stethoscopes connected to these tubes. The tuning forks were slightly out of tune so that the difference in phase would change periodically. Under such circumstances, the image appeared to rotate around the head. By recording the time necessary for the image to rotate through a given angle, and comparing it with the time to produce a complete cycle, results were obtained which showed the relation between the phase shift at the ears and the angular displacement of the sound image.

In a third method the source of sound was two tuning forks which were electrically driven with the same frequency. The sound was conducted to the ear by means of stethoscope tubes as described above. Means were provided for changing the attenuation in the acoustic paths so as to keep the intensity at the ear constant while varying the phase. The phase difference was produced by choosing different lengths of the air path from the tuning forks to the ears.

In all these methods it was found that within the experimental error the angular displacement of the image was proportional to the difference in phase at the two ears, the constant of proportionality varying somewhat with frequency. The following formula represents the average results obtained by such experiments:

$$\Phi/\theta = 0.0034 f + 0.8 \text{ (approx.)}$$

where Φ is the phase difference at the two ears, θ the angular displacement of the sound image from the median plane, and f the frequency of vibration. For example, the phase difference of a pure tone having a frequency of 500 cycles is always about 2.6 times the angular displacement of the sound image. When the phase difference has reached 180°, the image has been displaced 70°. As the phase difference increases, the image jumps to −70° and then again returns to the median plane when the phase difference reaches 360°. For a pure tone of 60 cycles the phase difference is approximately equal to the angular displacement of the image.

If the phase of sound reaching the two ears is kept constant while the intensity is varied, an angular displacement in the sound image is also produced. However, the results are very much less definite and the variations from one individual to another are very great. Stewart concluded from his results that for any one individual the angular displacement of the image was proportional to the difference in intensity level at the two ears. However, his results show that for some individuals the angular displacement for a given difference in intensity level was twice as great as for another. As the frequency of the exciting tone approaches about 1000 cycles, the uncertainty of locating the image becomes greater, and for many persons there is no localization for the higher frequencies.

The phase difference produced at the two ears is undoubtedly preserved in the composite nerve current going to the brain. The discharges from any particular nerve fiber occur at intervals which are exact multiples of the period of the sound wave. As the intensity of the sound becomes greater, this interval becomes less and approaches the period of the sound wave. The effect of all of the impulses from the individual nerve fibers is to produce a stimulation pattern in the brain which has a periodicity of the sound wave. The maximum stimulation at the brain center is definitely related to the maximum pressure in the sound wave in front of the eardrum. The interval of occurrence between the two depends upon the time of transmission of the mechanical vibration from the drum of the ear through the middle ear and through the cochlea to the basilar membrane, and also the time of transmission of the nerve impulses from the nerve endings on the basilar membrane to the brain. The two maxima produced in the brain from the stimulation coming from the two ears will occur at approximately the same time if the phase of the sound vibration at the two ears is the same. However, when this phase is different, there will be a corresponding time interval between the occurrence of the two maxima produced in the brain. It is undoubtedly the recognition of this time interval that enables us to recognize phase difference.

As pointed out by Hartley and Fry,[2] when the experiments are performed as indicated above, a new experience is produced which is different from that produced by a source of sound being actually present. If a sound source is placed in the air and moved about, the change in phase and intensity produced at the two ears must take place together in a certain way so that any experiments which produce sounds which keep either the phase or intensity constant, produce an experience different from that ordinarily obtained when listening to actual sound sources. The fact that the experiments on the change in the apparent image with

[2] Physical Review, p. 431, December, 1921.

change in phase give much more definite results than those obtained when the phase is kept constant and the intensity varied, shows that the mind can more readily reconcile differences in intensity than differences in phase. Hartley and Fry give a series of calculated curves showing how the phase and intensity vary as a sound source is moved about the head. It is only when reproduced sounds have phases and intensities corresponding to points on these curves that localization as perfect as that obtained from an actual source would be expected.

Binaural Location of Complex Sounds

During the war the binaural location of complex sounds became important. Its use made it possible to locate enemy submarines and airplanes. It was found that when two microphones connected separately to two receivers were used in picking up the sound and transmitting it to the two ears, the direction of a complex source of sound could be located by the individual listening. To obtain a complete duplication of the binaural effect produced without such a transmission system, the two microphones must be mounted on something equivalent acoustically to the head and at positions corresponding to the two ears. Then if the transmission system transmits faithfully the phases and amplitudes of the component sounds to the ears, the same auditory sensation will be produced as that obtained when the head is placed in the position where the artificial head carrying the transmitters is located. Any variation from this ideal transmission system will result in producing results which are different from those ordinarily produced by direct listening.

Experiments have shown that a considerable departure from this ideal may be made and yet a fairly good sense of localization be obtained. As was the case with pure tones, so with complex tones it was found that the phase was the controlling factor. For this reason, phase compensators were introduced into such a binaural transmission system so as to bring the apparent location of the sound directly in front of the observer. The amount of compensation necessary to do this indicated the position of the complex sound. The very fact that such compensators will not produce the proper shifts for all the components, indicates that the localization of such a compensated transmission system will be somewhat indefinite. When the source of sound is a combination of a few pure tones, the compensated transmission system might very well produce a shifting of these components to different apparent positions with the result that either images in several directions are formed or confusion produced so that no localization is obtained.

The location of a complex sound under ordinary conditions is very definite and may be made even by a person who is totally deaf in one ear. It is difficult to point out definitely all the factors which contribute to this ability. Certainly the reflections in the room under ordinary circumstances give considerable aid. Our experience with such sounds has given us an education so that we unconsciously know the way these changes take place as the source is moved into different positions.

Binaural Beats

Two telephone receivers which are connected to electrical oscillators are held to the ear of a listener. The oscillators are adjusted so that the difference in frequency is 2 or 3 cycles per second. For example one tone, called the "primary," is kept at a constant sensation level of 80 db in the right ear. When the sensation level of a second tone, called the "secondary," is at about 10 db in the left ear, then faint beats are observed. As the sensation level of the secondary is increased these beats become more pronounced, reaching a maximum at a level of 30 db. For higher levels the beats again become fainter until a level of 45 db is obtained, above which they are not heard. These beats, called "*objective beats*," produce sensations which correspond in every way to those produced when the primary tone is reduced in sensation units about 50 db and introduced directly into the same ear as the secondary. These objective beats are undoubtedly due to physical interference in the left ear, the vibrations coming from the right ear by means of bone conduction. This conclusion is confirmed by the fact that the difference in intensity level for best beats increases when soft rubber pieces are placed under the receiver caps. It is important to remark here that this phenomenon is one which can easily be observed by anyone who tries it and beats are produced for all frequencies.

Keeping the primary again at a sensation level of about 80 db in the right ear, it will be found that for a sensation level of 60 db for the secondary tone in the left ear beats again appear having a maximum effect when the tones in both ears have the same sensation level. These beats, called "*subjective*" *beats*, disappear when the secondary tone is at a level of 100 db. These subjective beats are entirely different in character from those called objective beats. Some persons cannot hear them at all, and others report results which are quite discordant. It is with these subjective beats that most of the experiments on binaural beats during the past century have been concerned. For this reason it is not surprising that there was so much disagreement between results reported. In a good many of these experiments, tuning forks or other sources of sound were used which made it difficult to prevent the sound from one source going into both ears and thus directly producing beats of the ordinary kind.

The work of Stewart[3] showed that seventeen out of the twenty-three were able to hear beats sufficiently distinct to report them. The work of Lane[4] showed that eighteen out of twenty-two were able to hear the beats sufficiently well to determine their period. The kinds of sensation reported by the different observers were greatly different.

A summary of the essential facts concerning subjective beats as given by Lane is as follows:

"(a) If two tones of equal intensities and nearly the same frequencies are simultaneously presented to opposite ears, the beat frequency can be recognized by about 80 percent of the observers, provided the frequencies of the beating tones are less than 800 or 1000 cycles. For higher frequencies the beats cannot be heard.

"(b) If the beats are slow, the one outstanding phenomenon observed by all who recognized the beat is an alternate left and right localization of the sound, localization being on the side of the tone leading in phase.

"(c) Most observers who hear the slow beats experience a more or less vague notion of the localization traveling along some path through the median plane when the localization shifts from one side of the head to the other, but there is no good agreement among the observers as to the position of this path.

"(d) The passing of the localization through the median plane is generally more clearly defined during phase agreement than during phase opposition.

"(e) While all observers who heard the slow beats reported without any previous suggestions the existence of the alternate right and left localization, none reported any intensity maxima until questioned as to the existence of such maxima. However, when questioned, over 80 percent of the observers reported maxima corresponding to one or more of the following three-phase relations: (1) phase agreement, (2) 30° or 40° before opposition and (3) 30° or 40° after opposition. There was no good agreement among the observers and several during the course of the experiments shifted from one phase relation to another in their report on the time of intensity maxima.

"(f) For fast beats the chief sensation is that of an intensity fluctuation of the sound located somewhere within the head.

"(g) For intermediate beats some reported a predominating sensation of motion, others of intensity fluctuation and still others seemed to experience both sensations about equally well and could direct their attention upon either at the sacrifice of the other.

"(h) Subjective beats are heard equally well for tones introduced into

[3] Physical Review, p. 502, June, 1917.
[4] Physical Review, September, 1925.

the ears by means of telephone receivers with and without receiver cushions or presented by means of rubber tubes.

"(i) So long as the two tones are of equal intensity, the hearing of subjective beats may be heard about equally well for all intensity levels of the two tones."

It is important to note that while the objective beats are readily observed by all, the phenomenon of subjective beats is quite indefinite and differs very greatly with individuals; also, that no subjective binaural beats are obtained for frequencies higher than 700 or 800 cycles.

It seems clear that the phenomenon of subjective beats is one which is produced in the brain and is closely associated with the binaural localization described in the last section. The term "beat" is hardly descriptive of the phenomenon since the sensation obtained is that of a wandering localization. It is only occasionally that we notice the intensity maxima, and they are usually associated with positions of best localizations rather than positions of maximum loudness. Also, since the intensity and phase relations do not correspond to those ordinarily experienced in locating a source of sound, the psychological reaction of the observers must be that of experiencing a new sensation.

Other Binaural Phenomena

The following experiment suggested by Arnold showed some very interesting effects. A high quality transmission system was provided with a filter system so that all the frequency components below 1000 cycles were sent into one channel and delivered to the left ear. Those above 1000 cycles were sent into another channel and delivered to the right ear. When speech was transmitted over such a system, there was apparently no distortion produced, although if either one or the other of the two receivers were taken away the speech sound was very distorted, and it was hard to recognize what was being said. When both receivers were used, the speech seemed to be good quality, and no difficulty was experienced in following what was being said. Apparently, in this case, the brain was able to combine the sounds obtained from the two ears to complete the proper picture. However, when music was transmitted, a different situation resulted. This was particularly true when listening to music from the piano. In this case the tones appear first in one ear and then in the other ear depending upon the pitch. This causes confusion and gives a very wierd sort of sensation. When listening to sounds which have frequencies fairly well scattered in both the ranges below and above 1000 cycles, the sensation produced was about the same as that obtained by combining the frequencies into the same ear. When the sounds were predominating in either one or the other ear, localizations were produced first at one ear and then at the other as described above.

CHAPTER 13

AUDITORY PERSPECTIVE

There are two transmission systems which preserve the auditory perspective; that is, reproduce the sounds such that the original sound sources are located in their proper relative positions. If the sound sources are moving, the reproduced sound will give the listener the impression of sound source movement.

The first system is called a binaural transmission system. It consists of two independent telephone systems. The microphones are mounted in a dummy head, shaped like an average human head. Preferably, they should be mounted at the terminals of the artificial ear canal of the dummy head. The telephone receivers are then placed on the two ears of the listener. The reproduction ratio for all audible frequencies is made unity; that is, the amplitude and phase of the pressure in the dummy's ears are reproduced in the listener's ear. This constitutes an ideal binaural system. In practice this may be approached very closely so that one cannot distinguish the reproduced sound from the real sound. When one walks around the dummy's head talking as he goes, and sometimes whispering into the dummy's ear, the listener has the compelling illusion of someone walking around him. One has to hear such perfect reproduction before one realizes how far short most reproduced sounds are from realism. For speech only the frequency range from 100 to 8000 cycles is necessary, and good results are obtained by mounting microphones six inches apart on an ordinary mounting.

The second system is called a stereophonic transmission system.

Suppose in hall T there were interposed between the orchestra and the audience a flexible curtain of such a nature that it did not interfere with a free passage of the sound, and which at the same time had scattered uniformly over it microphones which would pick up the sound waves and produce a faithful electrical copy of them. Assume each microphone to be connected with a perfect transmission line which terminates in a projector occupying a corresponding position on a similar curtain in hall R. By a perfect transmission line is meant one that delivers to the projector electrical energy equal both in form and magnitude to that which it receives from the microphone. If these sound projectors faithfully transform the electrical vibrations into sound vibrations, the

217

audience in hall R should obtain the same effect as those listening to the original music in hall T.

Theoretically, there should be an infinite number of such ideal sets of microphones and sound projectors, and each one should be infinitesimally small. Practically, however, when the audience is at a considerable distance from the orchestra, as usually is the case, only a few of these sets are needed to give good auditory perspective; that is, to give depth and a sense of extensiveness to the source of the music. The arrangement of some of these simple systems, together with their effect upon listeners in various parts of the hall, is described in the paper by Steinberg and Snow.[1]

Localization Afforded by Multichannel Systems

In Fig. 145 is shown a diagram of the experimental set-up that was used. The microphones, designated as LM (left), CM (center), and RM (right), were set on a "pick-up" stage that was marked out on the floor of an acoustically treated room. The loudspeakers, designated as IS, CS, and RS, were placed in the front end of the auditorium at the Bell Telephone Laboratories and were concealed from view by a curtain of theatrical gauze. The average position of a group of twelve observers is indicated by the cross in the rear center part of the auditorium.

The object of the test was to determine how a caller's position on the pick-up stage compared with his apparent position as judged by the group of observers in the auditorium listening to the reproduced speech. Words were uttered from some fifteen positions on the pick-up state in random order. The nine positions shown in Fig. 145 were always included in the fifteen, the remaining positions being introduced to minimize memory effects. The reproducing system was switched off while the caller moved from one position to the other.

In the first series of tests, the majority of the observers had no previous experience with the set-up. They simply were given a sheet of co-ordinate paper with a single line ruled on it to indicate the line of the gauze curtain and asked to locate the apparent position of the caller with respect to this line. Following these tests, the observers were permitted to listen to speech from various announced positions on the pick-up stage. This gave them some notion of the approximate outline of what might be called the "virtual" stage. These tests then were repeated. As there was no significant difference in results, the data from both tests have been averaged and are shown in Fig. 145.

The small diagram at the top of Fig. 145 shows the caller's positions with respect to the microphone positions on the pick-up stage. The

[1] Bell Technical Journal, April, 1934.

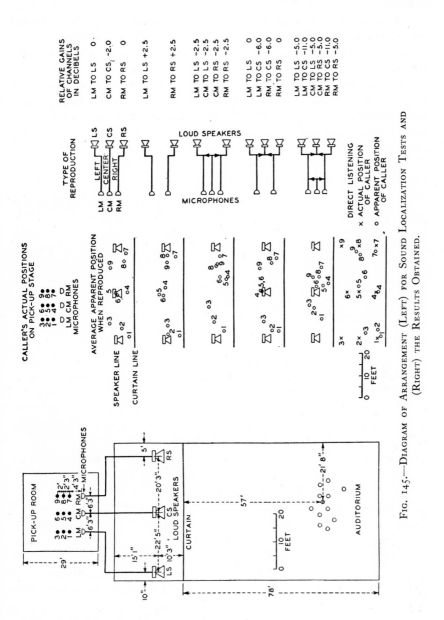

FIG. 145.—DIAGRAM OF ARRANGEMENT (LEFT) FOR SOUND LOCALIZATION TESTS AND (RIGHT) THE RESULTS OBTAINED.

corresponding average apparent positions when reproduced are shown with respect to the curtain line and the loudspeaker positions. The type of reproduction is indicated symbolically to the right of the apparent position diagrams.

With 3-channel reproduction there is reasonably good correspondence between the caller's actual position on the pick-up stage and his apparent position on the virtual stage. Apparent positions to the right or left correspond with actual positions to the right or left, and apparent front and rear positions correspond with actual front and rear positions. Thus the system afforded lateral or "angular" localization as well as fore and aft or "depth" localization. For comparison, there is shown in the last diagram the localization afforded by direct listening. The crosses indicate a caller's position in back of the gauze curtain and the circles indicate his apparent position as judged by the observers listening to his speech directly. In both cases, as the caller moved back in a straight line on the left or right side of the stage, he appeared to follow a curved path pulling in toward the rear center; e.g., compare the caller positions 1, 2, 3, with the apparent positions 1, 2, 3. This distortion was somewhat greater for 3-channel reproduction than for direct listening.

The results obtained with the 2-channel system show two marked differences from those obtained with 3-channel reproduction. Positions on the center line of the pick-up stage (i.e., 4, 5, 6) all appear in the rear center of the virtual stage, and the virtual stage depth for all positions is reduced. The virtual stage width, however, is somewhat greater than that obtained with a 3-channel reproduction.

Bridging a third microphone across the 2-channel system has the effect of pulling the center line positions 4, 5, 6, forward, but the virtual stage depth remained substantially that afforded by 2-channel reproduction, while the virtual stage width was decreased somewhat. In this and the other bridged arrangements, the bridging circuits employed amplifiers, as represented by the arrows in Fig. 145, in such a way that there was a path for speech current only in the indicated direction.

Bridging a third loudspeaker across the 2-channel system had the effect of increasing the virtual stage depth and decreasing the virtual stage width, but positions on the center line of the pick-up stage appeared in the rear center of the virtual stage as in 2-channel reproduction.

Bridging both a third microphone and a third loudspeaker across the 2-channel system had the effect of reducing greatly the virtual stage width. The width could be restored by reducing the bridging gains, but fading the bridged microphone out caused the front line of the virtual stage to recede at the center, whereas fading the bridged loudspeaker out reduced the virtual stage depth. No fixed set of bridging gains was found that would enable the arrangement to create the virtual stage created by three independent channels.   The gains used in obtaining the data shown in Fig. 145 are indicated at the right of the symbolic circuit diagrams.

Factors Affecting Depth Localization

Before attempting to explain the results that have been given in the foregoing, it may be of interest to consider certain additional observations that bear more specifically upon the factors that enter into the "depth" and "angular" localization of sounds.   The microphones on the pick-up stage receive both direct and reverberant sound, the latter being sound waves that have been reflected about the room in which the pick-up stage is located.   Similarly, the observer receives the reproduced sounds directly and also as reverberant sound caused by reflections about the room in which he listens.   To determine the effects of these factors, the following three tests were made:

1. Caller remained stationary on the pick-up stage and close to microphone, but the loudness of the sound received by the observer was reduced by gain control.   This was loudness change without a change in ratio of direct to reverberant sound intensity.

2. Caller moved back from microphone, but gain was increased to keep constant the loudness of the sound received by the observer.   This was a change in the ratio of direct to reverberant sound intensity without a loudness change.

3. Caller moved back from microphone, but no changes were made in the gain of the reproducing system.   This changed both the ratio and the loudness.

All of the observers agreed that the caller appeared definitely to recede in all three cases.   That is, either a reduction in loudness or a decrease in ratio of direct to reverberant sound intensity, or both, caused the sound to appear to move away from the observer.   Position tests using variable reverberation with a given pick-up stage outline showed that increasing the reverberation moved the front line of the virtual stage toward the rear, but had slight effect upon the rear line.   When the microphones were placed outdoors to eliminate reverberation, reducing the loudness either by changing circuit gains or by increasing the distance between caller and microphone moved the whole virtual stage farther away.   It is because of these effects that all center line positions on the pick-up stage appeared at the rear of the virtual stage for 2-channel reproduction.

It has not been found possible to put these relationships on a quantitative basis.   Probably a given loudness change, or a given change in ratio of direct to reverberant sound intensity, causes different sensations of depth depending upon the character of the reproduced sound and upon the observer's familiarity with the acoustic conditions surrounding the reproduction. Since the depth localization is inaccurate even when listening directly, it is difficult to obtain sufficiently accurate data to be of much use in a quantitative way. Because of this inaccuracy, good auditory perspective may be obtained with reproduced sounds even though the properties controlling depth localization depart materially from those of the original sound.

Angular Localization

Fortunately, the properties entering into lateral or angular localization permit more quantitative treatment. In dealing with angular localization, it has been found convenient to neglect entirely the effects of reverberant sound and to deal only with the properties of the sound waves reaching the observer's ears without reflections. The reflected waves or reverberant sounds do appear to have a small effect on angular localization, but it has not been found possible to deal with such sound in a quantitative way. One of the difficulties is that, because of differences in the build-up times of the direct and reflected sound waves, the amount or direct sound relative to reverberant sound reaching the observer's ears for impulsive sounds such as speech and music is much greater than would be expected from steady state methods of dealing with reverberant sound.

For the case of a plane progressive wave from a single sound source, and where the observer's head is held in a fixed position, there are apparently only three factors that can assist in angular localization; namely, phase difference, loudness difference, and quality difference between the sounds received by the two ears.

In applying these factors to the localization of sounds from more than one source, as in the present case, the effects of phase differences have been neglected. It is difficult to see how phase differences in this case can assist in localization in the ordinary way. The two remaining factors, loudness and quality differences, both arise from the directivity of hearing. This directivity probably is due in part to the shadow and diffraction effects of the head and to the differences in the angle subtended by the ear openings. Measurements of the directivity with a source of pure tone located in various positions around the head in a horizontal plane by Sivian and White.[2] From these measurements, the loudness level differences between near and far ears have been determined for various frequencies. These differences are shown in Fig. 146 from which, using the pure tone data given, similar loudness level differences for

[2] Fig. 88, Chapter 8.

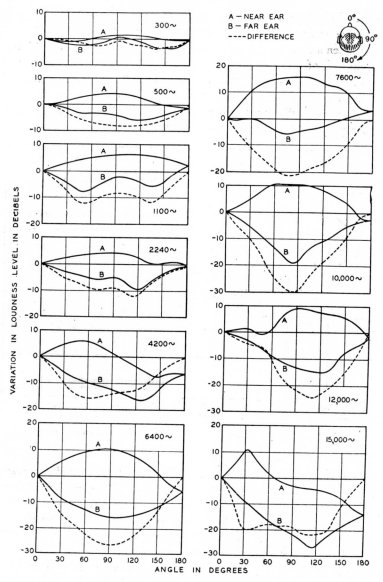

FIG. 146.—VARIATION IN LOUDNESS LEVEL AS A SOUND SOURCE IS ROTATED IN A
HORIZONTAL PLANE AROUND THE HEAD.

complex tones may be calculated. Such differences for complex tones
may be calculated. Such calculated differences for speech are shown in
Fig. 147.

As may be inferred from the varying shapes of the curves of Fig. 144, the directive effects of hearing introduce a frequency distortion at the right ear when a source of sound is moved from a position on the right to one on the left of an observer. It is a graph of the "difference" values of Fig. 146 for an angle of 90 degrees. Frequencies above 4000 cycles per second are reduced by as much as 15 to 30 decibels. This amount of distortion is sufficient to affect materially the quality of speech, particularly as regards the loudness of the sibilant sounds.

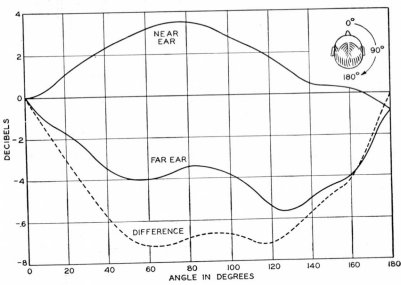

FIG. 147.—VARIATION IN LOUDNESS AS A SPEECH SOURCE IS ROTATED IN A HORIZONTAL PLANE AROUND THE HEAD.

Reference to the difference curve of Fig. 147 shows that if, for example, a source of speech is 20 degrees to the right of the median plane the speech heard by the right ear is 3 db louder than that heard by the left ear. A similar difference exists when the angle is 167 degrees. Presumably, when the right ear hears speech 3 db louder than the left, the observer localizes the sound as coming from a position 20 degrees or 167 degrees to the right, depending upon the quality of the speech. If this be assumed to be true, even though the difference is caused by the combination of sounds of similar quality from several sources, it should be possible to calculate the apparent angle.

Loudness Theory of Localization

Upon this assumption the apparent angle of the source as a function of the difference in decibels between the speech levels emitted by the loudspeakers of the 2- and 3-channel systems has been calculated. Each loudspeaker contributes an amount of direct sound loudness to each ear, depending upon its distance from and its angular position with respect to the observer. These contributions were combined on a power basis

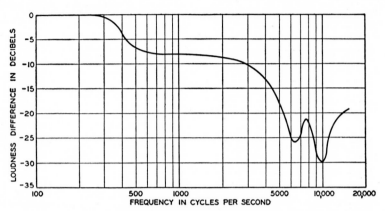

FIG. 148.—LOUDNESS DIFFERENCE PRODUCED IN THE RIGHT EAR WHEN A SOURCE OF PURE TONE IS MOVED FROM THE RIGHT TO THE LEFT OF AN OBSERVER.

to give a resultant loudness of direct sound at each ear, from which the difference in loudness between the two ears was determined. The calculated results for the 2- and 3-channel systems are shown by the solid lines in Fig. 149. The y axis shows the apparent angle, positive angle being measured in a clockwise direction. The x axis shows the difference in decibels between the speech levels from the right and left loudspeakers. The points are observed values taken from Fig. 145. The speech levels from each of the loudspeakers were calculated for each position on the pick-up stage. This was done by assuming that the waves arriving at the microphone had relative levels inversely proportional to the squares of the distances traversed. By correcting for the angle of incidence and for the known relative gains of the systems, the speech levels from the loudspeakers were obtained.

A comparison of the observed and calculated results seems to indicate that the loudness difference at the two ears accounts for the greater part of the apparent angle of the reproduced sounds. If this is true, the angular location of each position on the virtual stage results from a particular loudness difference at the two ears produced by the speech coming from the loudspeakers. When three channels are used, a definite set of loudspeaker speech levels exist for each position on the pick-up stage. To create these same sets of loudspeaker speech levels with the 3-microphone 3-loudspeaker bridging arrangement already discussed, it would be necessary to change the bridging gains for each position on the pick-up stage.   Hence it could not be expected that the arrangment as used (i.e., with fixed gains) would create a virtual stage identical with that created by 3-channel reproduction.   However, with proper technique, bridging arrangements on a given number of channels can be made to give better reproduction than would be obtained with the two channels alone.

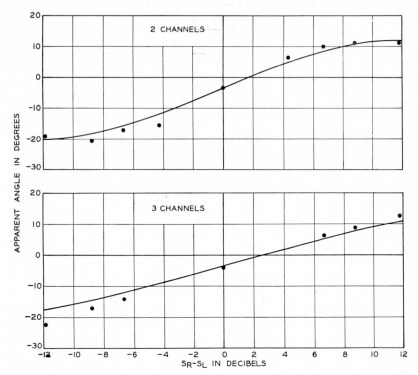

Fig. 149.—Calculated and Observed Apparent Angles for 2- and 3-Channel Reproduction.

Experimental Verification of Theory

Considerations of loudness difference indicate that all caller positions on the pick-up stage giving the same relative loudspeaker outputs should be localized at the same virtual angle.   The solid lines of Fig. 150 show a stage layout used to test this hypothesis with the 2-channel system. All points on each line have a constant ratio of distances to the microphones.   The resulting direct sound differences in pressure expressed in decibels, and the corresponding calculated apparent angles are indicated beside the curves.   The apparent angles were calculated for an observing position on a line midway between the two loudspeakers but at a distance from them equal to the separation between them. The microphones were turned face up at the height of the talker's lips to eliminate quality changes caused by changing incidence angle. It was found that a caller walking along one of these lines maintained a fairly constant virtual angle. For caller positions far from the microphones, the observed angles were somewhat greater than those computed. For highly reverberant conditions, the tendency was toward greater calculated than observed angles. Reverberation also decreased the accuracy of localization.

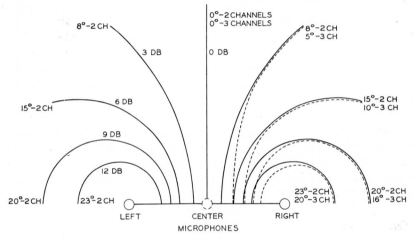

FIG. 150.—PICK-UP STAGE CONTOUR LINES OF CONSTANT APPARENT ANGLE.

A change of relative channel gain caused a change in virtual angle as would be expected from loudness difference considerations. For instance, if the caller actually walked the left 3-db line, he seemed to be on the 6-db line when the left channel gain was raised 3 db. Many of the effects of moving about the pick-up stage could be duplicated by volume control manipulation as the caller walked forward and backward on the center path. With a bridged center microphone substituted for the two side microphones, similar effects were possible and, in addition, the caller by speaking close to the microphone could be brought to the front of the virtual stage.

For the observing positions near the center of the auditorium, the observed angles agreed reasonably well with the calculations based only upon loudness differences. As the observer moved to one side, however, the virtual source shifted more rapidly toward the nearer loudspeaker than was predicted by the computations. This was true of reproduction in the auditorium, both empty and with damping simulating an audience, and outdoors on the roof. Computations and experiment also show a change in apparent angle as the observer moves from front to rear, but its magnitude is smaller than the error of an individual localization observation. Consequently, observers in different parts of the auditorium localize given points on the pick-up stage at different virtual angles.

Because the levels at the three microphones are not independent, and because the desired contours depend upon the effects at the ears, a 3-channel stage is not as simple to lay out as a 2-channel stage. For a given observing position, however, a set of contour lines can be calculated. The dashed lines at the right of Fig. 150 show four contours thus calculated for the circuit condition of Fig. 145 and the observing position previously mentioned. The addition of the center channel reduces the virtual angle for any given position on the pick-up stage by reducing the resultant loudness difference at the ears. Although the 3-channel contours approach the 2-channel contours in shape at the back of the stage, a given contour results in a greater virtual angle for 2- than for 3-channel reproduction.

Similar effects were obtained experimentally. As in 2-channel reproduction, movements of the caller could be simulated by manipulation of the channel gains. From an observing standpoint the 3-channel system was found to have an important advantage over the 2-channel system in that the shift of the virtual position for side observing positions was smaller.

Effects of Quality

If the quality from the various loudspeakers differs, the quality of sound is important to localization. When the 2-channel microphones were so arranged that one picked up direct sound and reverberation while the other picked up mostly reverberation, the virtual source was localized exactly in the "direct" loudspeaker until the power from the "reverberant" loudspeaker was from 8 to 10 db greater. In general, localization tends toward the channel giving most natural or "close-up" reproduction, and this effect can be used to aid the loudness differences in producing angular localization.

Principal Conclusions

The principal conclusions that have been drawn from these investigations may be summarized as follows:

1. Of the factors influencing angular localization, loudness difference of direct sound seems to play the most important part; for certain observing positions the effects can be predicted reasonably well from computations. When large quality differences exist between the loudspeaker outputs, the localization tends toward the more natural source. Reverberation appears to be of minor importance unless excessive.

2. Depth localization was found to vary with changes in loudness, the ratio of direct to reverberant sound, or both, and in a manner not found subject to computational treatment. The actual ratio of direct to reverberant sound, and the change in the ratio, both appeared to play a part in an observer's judgment of stage depth.

3. Observers in various part of the auditorium localize a given source at different virtual positions, as is predicted by loudness computations. The virtual source shifts to the side of the stage as the observer moves toward the side of the auditorium. Although quantitative data have not been obtained, qualitative data on these effects indicate that the observed shift is considerably greater than that computed. Moving backward and forward in the auditorium appears to have only a small effect on the virtual position.

4. Because of these physical factors controlling auditory perspective, point-for-point correlation between pick-up stage and virtual stage positions is not obtained for 2- and 3-channel systems. However, with stage shapes based upon the ideas of Fig. 145, and with suitable use of quality and reverberation, good auditory perspective can be produced. Manipulation of circuit conditions probably can be used advantageously to heighten the illusions or to produce novel effects.

5. The 3-channel system proved definitely superior to the 2-channel by eliminating the recession of the center-stage positions and in reducing the differences in localization for various observing positions. For musical reproduction, the center channel can be used for independent control of soloist renditions. Although the bridged systems did not duplicate the performance of the physical third channel, it is believed that with suitably developed technique their use will improve 2-channel reproduction in many cases.

6. The application of acoustic perspective to orchestral reproduction in large auditoriums gives more satisfactory performance than probably would be suggested by the foregoing discussions. The instruments near the front are localized by every one near their correct positions. In the ordinary orchestral arrangement, the rear instruments will be displaced in the reproduction depending upon the listener's position, but the important aspect is that every auditor hears differing sounds from differing places on the stage and is not particularly critical of the exact apparent positions of the sounds so long as he receives a spatial impression. Consequently, 2-channel reproduction of orchestral music gives good satisfaction, and the difference between it and 3-channel reproduction for music probably is less than for speech reproduction or the reproduction of sounds from moving sources.

CHAPTER 14

SPACE-TIME PATTERN THEORY OF HEARING

In 1930 I published a paper entitled *Space-Time Pattern Theory of Hearing*. The experimental data that have accumulated since then indicate that the main parts of this theory are correct. Principally because of the work of Békésy there are now good data on the mechanical constants of the cochlea with which to test such a theory. In fact, his observations leave no doubt as to the general mechanical behavior of the cochlea.

Any theory must be consistent with these data of Békésy, the data of Davis and Galambos on auditory nerve transmission and other physiological data, as well as the psycho-acoustic observations previously discussed; such as (1) the limits of the pitch and the intensity that the hearing mechanism is capable of handling, (2) the minimum changes in pitch and intensity that are perceptible, (3) subjective tones, (4) the masking effects of one sound upon another, (5) the relation of loudness to sensation level, and (6) binaural effects. Besides these effects there are other auditory phenomena which cannot be expressed in as quantitative a manner, but they are just as important. The principal ones are (1) the ability of the ear to analyze a complex tone into its component tones, (2) the effect upon the pitch, the loudness, and the quality of a musical tone when certain groups of its components are eliminated, (3) the relation of brightness and volume (as used by psychologists) to frequency and intensity of the stimulating tone, and (4) the effect of shifting the phases of the components of a musical tone.

Two general types of hearing theories have been put forth from time to time to explain these effects. One might be called a space pattern theory and the other a time pattern theory. In the first theory it is assumed that the time pattern of the wave motion in the air is transferred into a space pattern in the inner ear so that the nerve impulses reaching the brain give us information concerning the time pattern of the wave motion by means of the location of the nerves which are stimulated. In the second theory it is assumed that the time sequences are transmitted directly to the brain. It is now generally recognized that both of these effects are operating in aiding one to interpret the sounds which one hears. The term *A Space-Time Pattern Theory of Hearing* therefore best expresses this conception.

When a sound wave is created in the air, the air particles oscillate back and forth and cause small pressure changes which occur in a certain time sequence depending upon the kind of sound created.

If a small [1] pressure gauge, which follows instantly the pressure variations of the air, were placed at a certain point in the path of the wave, its fluctuations for the three classes of sound indicated in Fig. 151 would be

TIME PATTERNS

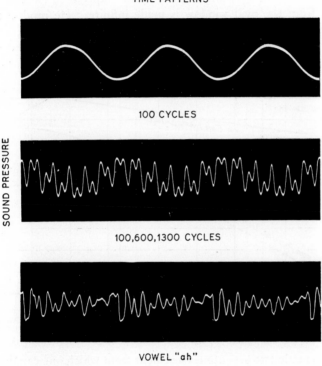

100 CYCLES

100,600,1300 CYCLES

VOWEL "ah"

TIME

Fig. 151.—Time Pattern of (a) 100 chs Tone; (b) Complex Tone
100 chs + 600 chs + 1300 chs; (c) Vowel a.

as shown. Each curve is a pressure-time pattern of the sound its represents. This pattern is transmitted through the air and communicated to the drum of the ear. It is then transferred through the ossicles of the middle ear to the liquid of the cochlea.

[1] This size must not be too small or the Brownian Movements would be superimposed upon the wave motion.

Dynamics of the Middle Ear

In the process of transmission of sound through the middle ear sound pressure is amplified for some frequencies and attenuated for others. The lever arm ratio of the ossicles is about 1.3. The ratio of the area of the ear drum to the area of the oval window ranges from 15 to 20. Thus one would expect sound pressures under the oval window which are 20 to 30 times those in front of the ear drum. Indeed, Békésy has measured values of this amount when the impedance looking into the inner ear from the oval window is made infinite. He produced known values of the pressure back of the oval window which were equal and opposite to those produced by the ear drum so that the stapes remained stationary. These values are shown by the top curve in Fig. 152.

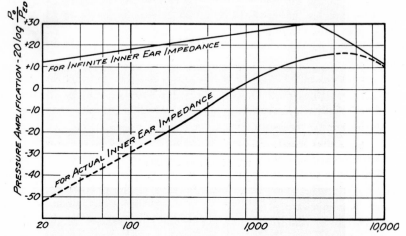

Fig. 152.—Amplification versus Frequency for the Mechanical Transformer of the Middle Ear.

He also made two sets of measurement from which one can deduce the amplification of the middle ear transformer for an ear in operating condition.

In the May 1949 issue of the Journal of the Acoustical Society, Békésy gave two experimental curves pertaining to the dynamics of the middle ear which will be seen to have an important bearing on the acuity of hearing at various frequencies. The first one (Fig. 5 of his paper) gives the amount ΔV of fluid displaced by the round window during each cycle when tones of various frequencies throughout the audible range were impressed upon the external eardrum (membrani tympani) having an acoustical pressure P_{ED}. In the curve, the values of $\Delta V/P_{ED}$ are given as ordinates and the frequency as abscissas. Similarly, in the second curve (Fig. 6 of his paper), he gives values $\Delta V/P_0$ where ΔV is again the volume of fluid displaced by the round window, and P_0 is the difference in pressure between that in fluid just back of the oval window and that just back of the round window. In order to make these measurements it was necessary to remove both the round window and the oval window. However, whether they are in place or whether they are removed and some artificial means is used to create the pressure difference P_0 at the two ends of the liquid column in the cochlea, the motion of the various parts of the cochlea will be the same. For a given P_0 in dynes, the velocity and displacement of the basilar membrane at every postion along its length will be determined. This value of P_0 must be very nearly equal to that for the pressure across the basilar membrane at the basal end, and in this analysis it will be considered equal to this pressure difference. If the acoustical pressure is impressed directly on the stapes after the ossicles have been removed, then Békésy's measurements showed pressures ranging from 10 P_0 at 200 cycles per second to 1.5P_0 at 1000 cycles per second are required to produce a pressure P_0 across the basilar membrane at the basal end.

If the values of $\Delta V / P_{ED}$ from Békésy's data are divided by those of $\Delta V / P_0$, then values P_0 / P_{ED} are obtained. Values obtained in this way were used to give the lower curve of Fig. 152. The ordinates are expressed as db difference in pressure level or 20 log P_0 / P_{ED}.

It is seen that when one dyne per square centimeter pressure exists in front of the eardrum that, at 650 cycles per second driving frequency, one dyne per square centimeter is created across the basilar membrane at the basal end. There is no amplification of the pressure as it passes through the mechanical transformer of the middle ear. For driving frequencies lower than 650 cycles per second the value of P_0 is lower than P_{ED}, so the mechanical transformer attentuates the pressure, and for frequencies higher than this value, P_0 is higher than P_{ED}, so there is amplification. Fortunately, the amplification is in the range of speech frequencies. Also this transformer action discriminates against most noises which have large acoustical pressures in the low frequency region.

It is rather surprising that for frequencies below 100 cycles per second the attenuations are greater than 30 db. This is due to the low mechanical impedance across the basilar membrane for these low frequencies.

If the intensity of the sound is increased without otherwise changing the pattern in the air, there is a change in the pattern transmitted to the cochlea not only in magnitude but also in form. For high sound intensities the elastic members in the middle ear will exceed the amplitude limits within which the strain is proportional to the stress. Also, the limit for extension is different from that for compression. Under such circumstances it is well known that frequencies other than those in the original pattern are introduced. For example, for such high intensities a pure tone of frequency f will be transmitted to the cochlea as a tone having components of frequency f, $2f$, $3f$, $4f$, etc. These components, which are added to the original tone in the process of transmission, account for the subjective tones.

Let the pressure variation of the air in front of the drum of the ear be designated by p. Since the pressure of the air in the middle ear balances the undisturbed outside air pressure, this change in pressure multiplied by the effective area of the eardrum is the only effective force that produces displacements. Let the displacement of the fluid of the cochlea near the oval window be designated by X. If Hooke's law held for all the elastic members taking part in the transmission of sound to the inner ear, then

$$X = ap \tag{14-1}$$

where a is a constant.

It would be expected from the anatomy of the ear that Hooke's law would start to break down even for small displacements. So, in general, the relation between the pressure p and the displacement X can be represented by

$$X = f(p) = a_0 + a_1 p + a_2(p)^2 + a_3(p)^3 + \cdots \tag{14-2}$$

where the coefficients a_0, a_1, $a_2 \cdots$ belong to the expansion of the function into a power series. Now if p is a sinusoidal variation, then

$$p = p_0 \cos \omega t \tag{14-3}$$

where $\omega/2\pi$ is the frequency of vibration. Substituting this value in equation (14-2), terms containing the cosine raised to integral powers are obtained. These can be expanded into multiple angle functions. For example, for the first four powers

$$\cos^2 \omega t = \tfrac{1}{2} \cos 2 \omega t + \tfrac{1}{2}, \tag{14-4}$$

$$\cos^3 \omega t = \tfrac{1}{4} \cos 3 \omega t + \tfrac{3}{4} \cos \omega t, \tag{14-5}$$

$$\cos^4 \omega t = \tfrac{1}{8} \cos 4 \omega t + \tfrac{1}{2} \cos 2 \omega t + \tfrac{3}{8}. \tag{14-6}$$

It is evident then that the displacement X will be represented by a formula

$$X = b_0 + b_1 \cos \omega t + b_2 \cos 2 \omega t + b_3 \cos 3 \omega t + \cdots. \tag{14-7}$$

In other words, when a periodic force of only one frequency is impressed upon the eardrum, this same frequency and in addition all its harmonic frequencies are impressed upon the fluid of the inner ear.

If two pure tones are impressed upon the ear, then p is given by

$$p = p_1 \cos \omega_1 t + p_2 \cos \omega_2 t. \tag{14-8}$$

If this value is substituted in equation (14–2), terms of the form $\cos^n \omega_1 t$ and $\cos^m \omega_2 t$ and $\cos^n \omega_1 t \cos^m \omega_2 t$ are obtained. The first two forms give rise to all the harmonics and the third form gives rise to the summation and difference tones. For example, the first four terms are:

$$a_0 = a_0.$$

$$a_1 p = a_1(p_1 \cos \omega_1 t + p_2 \cos \omega_2 t).$$

$$a_2(p)^2 = a_2\left[\tfrac{1}{2}p_1^2 \cos 2 \omega_1 t + \tfrac{1}{2} p_2^2 \cos 2 \omega_2 t \right.$$
$$\left. + p_1 p_2 (\cos (\omega_1 - \omega_2)t - \cos (\omega_1 - \omega_2)t) + \tfrac{1}{2}(p_1^2 + p_2^2)\right].$$

$$a_3(p)^3 = a_3(\tfrac{3}{4}p_1^3 + \tfrac{3}{2}p_1 p_2^2) \cos \omega_1 t + \tfrac{1}{4}p_1^3 \cos 3 \omega_1 t$$
$$+ (\tfrac{3}{4}p_2^3 + \tfrac{3}{2}p_1^2 p_2) \cos \omega_2 t + \tfrac{1}{4}p_2^3 \cos 3 \omega_2 t$$
$$+ \tfrac{3}{4}p_1^2 p_2 \cos (\omega_2 t + 2 \omega_1 t) + \tfrac{3}{4}p_1^2 p_2 \cos (\omega_2 t - 2 \omega_1 t)$$
$$+ \tfrac{3}{4}p_1 p_2^2 \cos (\omega_1 t + 2 \omega_2 t) + \tfrac{3}{4}p_1 p_2^2 \cos (\omega_1 t - 2 \omega_2 t). \quad (14\text{–}9)$$

Therefore, unless there is a linear relation between a force acting on the eardrum and the displacement at the oval window, that is, unless all the coefficients in equation (14–2) are zero except a_1, the harmonics and the summation and difference tones will be impressed upon the fluid in the cochlea of the inner ear.

This nonlinearity accounts for the subjective harmonics and difference tones described in Chapter 10. Since we do not have any experimental data on the values of a_1, a_2, a_3, etc., this theory accounts for the subjective harmonics only in a qualitative way.

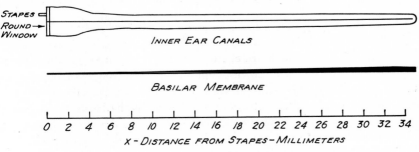

STAPES
ROUND →
WINDOW

INNER EAR CANALS

BASILAR MEMBRANE

0 2 4 6 8 10 12 14 16 18 20 22 24 26 28 30 32 34
X – DISTANCE FROM STAPES – MILLIMETERS

FIG. 153.—BASILAR MEMBRANE AND INNER EAR CANALS DRAWN TO SCALE.

The Dynamics of the Cochlea

The basilar membrane is very long compared to its width, as illustrated by the drawing in Fig. 153. It is with this long ribbon-like membrane that we are principally concerned when dealing with the dynamics of the cochlea, for the nerve endings of hearing are stimulated as it vibrates.

In the upper portion of Fig. 153 the two inner ear canals (scala tympani and scala vestibuli) are also drawn to scale. Now if one turns the diagram of the basilar membrane through 90° and slips it between the two canals along the line dividing them, one obtains the dynamical system to be investigated.

The dimensions of the canals and the basilar membrane are given by the solid curves in Fig. 154. The meaning of the dotted line will be discussed later.

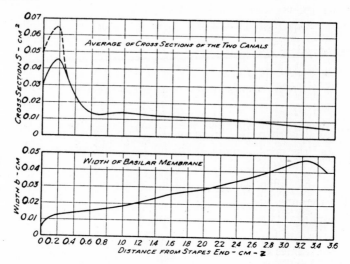

FIG. 154.—WIDTH OF THE BASILAR MEMBRANE AND AVERAGE CROSS-SECTIONAL AREA OF THE TWO INNER EAR CANALS.

Since the basilar membrane is long compared to its width, it is reasonable for calculation purposes to break it up into small vibrating units whose length and breadth are equal to the width b of the basilar membrane. The fact that this corresponds to a critical frequency band gives added strength to this point of view. There would then be about 140 such small vibrating elements along the length of the basilar membrane. As an approximation each little element will be considered to vibrate as a piston with an area of b^2 at each end. The forces driving each element are the pressure difference on the two sides of the membrane and the mutual forces exerted by adjacent elements. It will be assumed that these latter forces are negligible compared to Pb^2. When P is periodic, a steady state solution will be sought. One then can substitute $j\omega$, and $(j\omega)^2$ for the operators $\partial/\partial t$ and $\partial^2/\partial t^2$, respectively, wherever they occur in the equations to be developed.

Then if y and v are the displacement and velocity of the little element, and m its mass, and s its stiffness constant, and r its mechanical resistance, then

$$v = j\omega y = \cfrac{nPb^2}{j\left(m\omega - \cfrac{s}{\omega}\right) + r}. \qquad (14\text{--}10)$$

Let z be the distance from the stapes end to the position of the little vibrating element. Then all the quantities in equation (14–10) are functions of the position coordinate z except the frequency in radians ω and the number n. This number n is probably between 0.3 and 0.8. Both y and v vary from zero at the edges of the basilar membrane to a maximum near the center. Thus n is a number such that the displacements and velocities which are obtained by equation (14–10) are average ones. Then the displacement of liquid as the little element vibrates is given by $y \cdot b^2$. The length of the basilar membrane will be taken as 3.5 cm.

The problem, then, is to find m, s, r, and b from measurements which have been made, and then find P from a fundamental differential equation governing the motion.

First, consider the mass m. It is the radiant mass carried by the area b^2 plus the mass of the structures carried by this area (rods of corti, etc.). It is well known that the radiant mass for such a small vibrating element in water carried by both sides of the area is $0.85b^3$ if the area is circular having a diameter b. For the equivalent square area it would be somewhat greater than this, and it was taken as b^3. This is equivalent to saying that a volume of liquid extending out from the membrane a distance equal to only one-half the width of the membrane vibrates in phase with it. The basilar membrane itself, the rods of corti, and other structures carried by the basilar membrane have a thickness of about one half the width of the membrane. Also, it is assumed that the density of the structure is about 1.5 so that the mass of the little element itself is $0.75b^3$. Consequently,

$$m = 1.75b^3. \qquad (14\text{--}11)$$

It is important to notice that the vibration of the little element depends only upon the mass of the liquid which is within one or two-tenths of a millimeter of the surface of the membrane. So the extent of the liquid beyond this small distance does not influence the vibration except as it modifies P. In other words, the resonant characteristics are independent of the size and shape of the vessel in which the basilar membrane is immersed. This is in accord with Békésy's findings. The values of b vs. z shown in Fig. 154 were taken as the average values of

25 specimens as given by Wever.[2]   In Fig. 155, the values of m versus z obtained from (14–11) are plotted.

Next consider the stiffness constant s.   Until Békésy made his epochmaking experiments there was considerable speculation and controversy concerning the elastic properties of the basilar membrane.   Many have

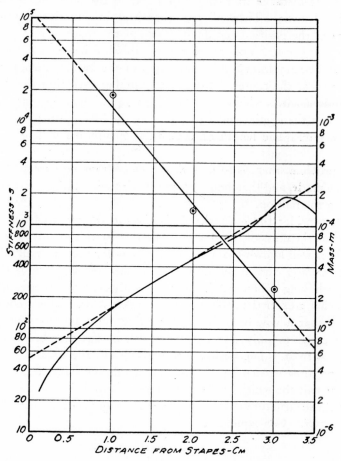

FIG. 155.—VALUES OF THE MASS m AND THE STIFFNESS CONSTANT s FOR THE BASILAR MEMBRANE VERSUS DISTANCE z FROM THE STAPES.

claimed that its structure was such that only small variations in the stiffness constant for different positions along its length were possible, and therefor the so-called resonance theory must be ruled out.

Békésy measured directly this stiffness constant.   He measured the deflection produced on a human basilar membrane by a hair probe.

[2] E. G. Wever, *Theory of Hearing*, John Wiley and Sons, Inc., New York, 1949, 100. p.

This probe was calibrated by noting that a hair fastened to its end started to bend at a definite applied force.   The magnitude of this force depended upon the length of the hair.   The deflection of the basilar membrane was measured with a calibrated microscope.   In this way the dynes force per centimeter of deflection, which is called the stiffness constant s, was measured at three positions along the membrane—namely, 10 mm, 20 mm, and 30 mm from the stapes end.   The values of s found were at

$$z = 10 \text{ mm} \qquad s = 1.8 \times 10^4$$

$$z = 20 \text{ mm} \qquad s = 1.4 \times 10^3$$

$$z = 30 \text{ mm} \qquad s = 2.5 \times 10^2$$

These values are also plotted in Fig. 155.   The total length of this basilar membrane in his sample was found to be 35 mm.

At the two ends the straight line chosen to fit the points is dotted, indicating an uncertainty.   It is to be noticed that to obtain the values plotted the force was applied over a small area near the center of the membrane.   When it was applied near the edge the deflection was smaller. For about one-half the width b of the basilar membrane the deflection per dyne was approximately constant.

Before considering the mechanical resistance let us consider the resonant frequency f_0 of each little element.   It is seen from equation (14–10) to be given by

$$2\pi f_0 = \omega_0 = \sqrt{\frac{s}{m}}. \tag{14–12}$$

The values of s and m are given in Fig. 155.   If one uses the straight lines given in the plot and represented by

$$s = 10^{5.07-0.94z} \tag{14–13}$$

and

$$m = 10^{-5.31+0.50z}, \tag{14–14}$$

then

$$f_0 = 25{,}000 \; 10^{-.72z}. \tag{14–15}$$

This, then, gives $f_0 = 25{,}000$ cycles per second at the stapes and 76 cycles per second at the helicotrema, which it will be seen gives good agreement with observed data.   This equation is represented by the straight line of Fig. 156.   A somewhat better fit of the data was obtained by using the solid line which departs somewhat from the straight line at the low frequencies.   The solid dots give the calculated position for maximum displacement of the basilar membrane.   This position is always shifted toward the stapes from the position for the resonant frequency.   The circles and crosses are two sets of experimental data by Békésy giving

the positions for maximum displacement.   In Fig. 126 there was shown
a comparison of these results with those obtained from pitch discrimination and masking data.

There is considerable uncertainty of the values of f_0 below 200 cycles
per second due to peculiar variations of the width of the basilar membrane
and consequently of its stiffness in this region.

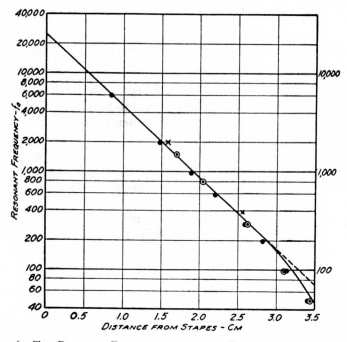

FIG. 156.—THE RESONANT FREQUENCY VERSUS THE DISTANCE FROM THE STAPES.

It should be emphasized that the position for these resonant frequencies remains the same regardless of the manner in which the sound
is conducted to the cochlea, that is, whether it is by bone conduction,
air conduction, through the stapes, or the round window, or both.

Next consider the mechanical resistance r.   Again we are indebted
to Békésy for values of this frictional resistance.   He found that the
logarithmic decrement was equal to 1.6 for all positions along the membrane less than $z = 2.85$ cm.   For positions nearer the helicotrema the
decrement increased.

If A_2 and A_1 are two successive amplitudes,

$$\log_e \frac{A_1}{A_2} = 1.6 = \frac{r}{2mf_0}$$

or

$$r = 0.5\,\omega_0 m, \tag{14-16}$$

which defines r for all positions z less than 2.85 cm.

One can compute the radiation resistance of the little element to be

$$r_r = \frac{\pi^2 f^2 b^4}{2c}$$

where f is the frequency of the impressed tone, and c the velocity of sound in water. This value of r lies between 10^{-4} and 10^{-6} for the audible range of frequencies. It will be seen to be negligible compared to the value given by equation (14–16). So the measured resistance does not arise from the radiation but probably from frictional sources within the membrane structure.

For positions nearer the helicotrema than $z = 2.85$ the increased resistance is no doubt due to the liquid moving back and forth in the helicotrema. I have made attempts[3] to estimate the amount of this increased resistance but a careful study of the analysis shows it to be faulty. In Table 45 are given values of $r/m\omega_0$ which can only be con-

TABLE 45

$f_0 =$	50	64	80	100	130	160	200	240	285	335
$z =$	3.5	3.4	3.3	3.2	3.1	3.0	2.9	2.8	2.7	2.6
$\dfrac{r}{m\omega_0} =$	1.0	.86	.72	.65	.60	.55	.5	.5	.5	.5

sidered intelligent guesses but they are useful in making calculations for the low frequencies. The values of $r/m\omega_0$ given in Table 45 may be considered typical but there is a great variation from sample to sample depending upon the dimensions involved.

Now if one substitutes the values of m and s in equation (14–10) there results for v and y

$$i\omega y = v = \frac{P}{j\omega b\,3.5}\left[1 - \frac{(f_0)^2}{(f)} - j\frac{(r)}{(m\omega_0)}\frac{f_0}{f}\right]^{-1} = \frac{P}{j\omega b\,3.5\,F}. \tag{14-10A}$$

It remains, then, to find the value of P at each position; then the value of v can be calculated for each position. To do this turns out to be rather complicated.

One can get a notion of what is taking place by the following consideration. First, let us assume that the canal walls and basilar membrane are unyielding, and the cross-section is uniform, and that the round window is a pressure release so that the pressure at this position

[3] H. Fletcher, *On the Dynamics of the Cochlea*, Journal of the Acoustical Society, Nov. 1, 1951.

falls to zero.   The equations representing this condition show that the amplitude of the acoustical pressure difference falls linearly from the oval window to the helicotrema for frequencies below 5000 cycles per second.   The situation is the same as for a stretched string fixed at one end and moved sinusoidally up and down at the other end.   As long as the string is short compared to the wave length being propagated the whole string moves, up and down in phase with the driving force.   For 10,000 cycles, however, for a 7 cm tube of water, the length of the tube is one-half wave length so resonances would occur giving rise to amplitudes much larger than the driving amplitude.

This pressure distribution builds up quickly (order of 10^{-5} seconds) because the walls and basilar membrane take time to yield, being of the order of 10^{-2} seconds for the 100-cycle position to 10^{-4} for the 10,000-cycle position.   The first time is the time for sound to travel 7 cm in water and the second time that for the little element to build up to two-thirds of its maximum amplitude.   So during this period of reaching the steady state the elements near the oval window build up to their maximum first, then successive elements build up as one goes from there toward the helicotrema.   This, then, produces a travelling wave along the basilar membrane very different from the acoustic wave going through the liquid and greatly modifies the initial pressure distribution.   The fundamental equation governing the motion of the liquid and membrane will now be developed.

The quantities S_1, u_1, p_1 will refer to the cross-sectional area, the fluid velocity parallel to the length of the canal, and acoustic pressure at the point z in the scala vestibuli.   Similarly, the letters S_2, u_2, and p_2 will refer to similar quantities in the scala typani.   Let ρ be the density of the liquid.

Consider a small box (see Fig. 153) which is Δz long and with the front at the position z having a cross-sectional area S_1 and with the back at the position $z + \Delta z$ having a cross-sectional area of $S_1 + (\partial S_1/\delta z)\Delta z$. The rate that the mass is changing in this little box is equal to the rate that the liquid flows through the front, minus the rate that it flows through the back, and minus the rate that it flows out of the bottom due to the bending of the basilar membrane.   The sides and top will be considered bounded by rigid surfaces which will not permit any displacement of liquid during the vibration cycle.   The difference in the rate between front and back is

$$- \rho\, \frac{\partial(S_1 u_1)}{\partial z}\, \Delta z.$$

The rate of coming in at the bottom is

$$- \rho v b \Delta z$$

where the velocity v is directed from the scala vestibuli to the scala tympani. The sum of these two must be equal to

$$\frac{\partial}{\partial t}(\rho S_1 \Delta z).$$

This, then leads to the equation of continuity

$$\frac{S_1}{\rho}\frac{\partial \rho}{\partial t} + \frac{\delta(S_1 u_1)}{\delta z} + vb = 0. \tag{14–17}$$

A similar equation exists for the scala typani with the subscripts changed from 1 to 2 and the sign of v changed from plus to minus.

The force driving this little box along the canal toward the helicotrema is

$$-\frac{\delta(S_1 p_1)}{\delta z}\Delta z.$$

This force is opposed by the inertia of the small mass in the box plus the frictional forces. It can be shown [4] that this leads to the following force equation:

$$-\frac{\delta(S_1 p_1)}{\partial z} = j\rho\omega S_1 \bar{u}_1 Q \tag{14–18}$$

where

$$Q = \left(\frac{1 - 2J_1(Ka)}{KaJ_0(Ka)}\right)^{-1} \tag{14–19}$$

where J_1 and J_0 are the well-known Bessels functions and K is determined by

$$K^2 = -j\frac{\rho\omega}{\eta} \tag{14–20}$$

and η is the coefficient of viscosity of the liquid and is equal to .02 for the ear fluid. It will be noticed that a bar is placed over the u_1 in equation (14–18). This means that it is an average value of u_1 taken over the cross-sectional area. It can be shown that when $S_1 f$ is small compared to unity

$$Q_1 = \frac{4}{3} - j\frac{08}{S_1 f} \tag{14–21}$$

and when $S_1 f$ is large compared to unity

$$Q_1 = 1 + \frac{.14}{\sqrt{S_1 f}}(1 + j). \tag{14–22}$$

[4] L. E. Kinsler and A. R. Frey, *Fundamentals of Acoustics*, John Wiley and Sons, Inc., New York, 1950, p. 240.

It is well known that in a fluid medium the acoustical pressure p_1 and density ρ are related by

$$\frac{\delta\rho}{\delta t} = \frac{j\omega}{c^2} p_1 \qquad (14\text{-}23)$$

where c is the velocity of sound in the liquid.

Equations (14-17), (14-18), and (14-19) can be combined into

$$\frac{1}{Q_1} \frac{\delta^2(S_1 p_1)}{\delta z^2} + k^2 S_1 p_1 - j\rho\omega bv \qquad (14\text{-}24)$$

where

$$k = \frac{\omega}{c}. \qquad (14\text{-}25)$$

A similar equation holds for the scala tympani, namely,

$$\frac{1}{Q_2} \frac{\delta^2 S_2 p_2}{\delta z^2} + k^2 S_2 p_2 + j\rho\omega bv. \qquad (14\text{-}26)$$

to solve this equation it will be assumed as good approximation that

$$S_1 = S_2 \doteq S = \frac{S_1 + S_2}{2} \qquad (14\text{-}27)$$

and that $Q_1 = Q_2$.

It is these values of S that are plotted in Fig. 154. It will be seen from Fig. 79 how well this approximation agrees with the anatomical facts. The dotted line in Fig. 154 was estimated to more nearly the value of S to use for values of z less than 0.3 cm.

Then if one subtracts equation (14-26) from (14-24) there results the following equation in SP:

$$\frac{1}{Q} \frac{\delta^2(SP)}{\partial z^2} + k^2(SP) - 2j\rho\omega bv. \qquad (14\text{-}28)$$

The density ρ may be taken as unity.

If one substitutes the value of v from equation (14-16), then

$$\frac{1}{Q} \frac{\delta^2(SP)}{\delta z^2} + \left(k^2 - \frac{1}{1.75\ SF} \right) (SP) = 0. \qquad (14\text{-}29)$$

It has already been assumed that we are dealing with a periodic driving force so

$$SP = \psi e^{j\omega t}.$$

The problem, then, is to find how ψ varies with z from the above differential equation and for various driving frequencies.

The wave constant k in water for 10,000 cycles per second is equal to 0.18. It is, of course, proportional to the frequency, so it is 0.0018 for 100 cycles per second.

The value of the reciprocal of $1.75\ SF$ becomes more than 100 in the region of resonance so k^2 may be considered negligible. This is an important conclusion for it means that for the waves travelling down the basilar membrane the fluid may be considered incompressible.

The values of Q for 50, 100, 200, and 600 cps are $1.28–j.18$, $1.2–j.12$, $1.1–j.10$, and $1.06–j.06$, respectively. In the range where Q differs appreciably from unity there is an uncertainty in the value of $r/m\omega_0$ greater than the departure of Q from unity. Therefore Q is taken as unity in the calculations.

The differential equation in ψ then becomes

$$\frac{d^2\psi}{dz^2} = \frac{\psi}{1.75\ SF}. \tag{14–30}$$

The quantities ψ, S and F are functions of z. This equation can be solved by numerical integration as follows.

Consider that the right-hand member $\psi \div 1.75\ SF$ remains constant over the interval from $z = z_1$ to $z_1 + \Delta z$ and equal to C_1. Then the solution of $(14–30)$ becomes

$$\psi = C_1\frac{z^2}{2} + C_2 z + C_3. \tag{14–31}$$

Substituting the value of Δz

$$z = z_1 + \Delta z$$

this equation reduces to

$$\psi = \left(C_3 + C_1\frac{z_1^2}{2}\right) + (C_2 + C_1 z_1)\Delta z$$
$$+ C_1\frac{\overline{\Delta z^2}}{2} = C_4 + C_5\Delta z + C_1\frac{\overline{\Delta z^2}}{2}. \tag{14–32}$$

In this equation C_4 and C_5 are arbitrary constants determined from the initial conditions that $\psi = \psi_1$ when $\Delta z = 0$ and $d\psi/dz = m_1$ when $\Delta z = 0$. The constant C_1, however, is not arbitrary but equal to the value of $\psi \div 1.75\ SF$ when $z = z_1$. These conditions determine

$$C_4 = \psi_1 \text{ and } C_5 = m_1.$$

So equation $(14–31)$ reduces to

$$\psi_2 = \psi_1 + m_1\Delta z + \frac{\psi_1}{1.75\ S_1 F_1}\frac{\overline{\Delta z^2}}{2} \tag{14–33}$$

where ψ_1 is the value at $z = z_1$ and ψ_2 is the value at $z = z_1 + \Delta z$. In general ψ and F are complex quantities, so let

$$\psi = A + jB \tag{14–34}$$

and

$$\frac{1}{1.75\ SF} = R + jx. \tag{14-35}$$

Then equation (14-33) breaks down into the two equations containing only real quantities

$$A_2 = A_1 + \frac{(\Delta A)}{(\Delta z)_1} \Delta z + (A_1R_1 - B_1\chi_1) \frac{\overline{\Delta z^2}}{2} \tag{14-36}$$

and

$$B_2 = B_1 + \frac{(\Delta B)}{(\Delta z)_1} \Delta z + (A_1\chi_1 + B_1R_1) \frac{\overline{\Delta z^2}}{2}. \tag{14-37}$$

The process of numerical integration, then, is to start with initial values of A_1, B_1, $(\Delta A/(\Delta z)_1$ and $(\Delta B)/(\Delta z)_1$. Then from these, calculate A_2 and B_2 from equations (14-36) and (14-37) for a small increment Δz. The new slopes at $z_1 + \Delta z$ will be given by

$$\frac{(\Delta A)}{(\Delta z)_2} = \frac{A_2 - A_1}{\Delta z} = \frac{(\Delta A)}{(\Delta z)_1} + (A_1R_1 - B_1\chi_1) \frac{\Delta z}{2} \tag{14-38}$$

and

$$\frac{(\Delta B)}{(\Delta z)_2} = \frac{B_2 - B_1}{\Delta z} = \frac{(\Delta B)}{(\Delta z)_1} + (A_1\chi_1 + B_1R_1) \frac{\Delta z}{2}. \tag{14-39}$$

These value of A_2, B_2, $(\Delta A)/(\Delta z)_2$, and $(\Delta B/\Delta z)_2$ can now be used as initial values and the process repeated.

Thus one proceeds from one end of the basilar membrane to the other by small steps and obtains A and B for each value of z, and thus determines magnitude and phase of the quantity SP. The results depend, of course, upon the boundary conditions at the two ends of the basilar membrane, which will now be considered.

At the stapes end the following condition must be satsified:

$$S_0P_0 = \psi_0 e^{j\omega t} = (A_0 + jB_0)e^{j\omega t}. \tag{14-40}$$

In other words, the acoustic pressure across the basilar membrane at the stapes end ($z = 0$) is given in amplitude and phase by

$$P_0 = \frac{1}{S_0} \sqrt{A_0^2 + B_0^2} \cos (\omega t + \Phi_0) \tag{14-41}$$

where the initial phase angle is given by

$$\tan \Phi_0 = \frac{B_0}{A_0}. \tag{14-42}$$

The calculation is started at the helicotrema end, and so Φ_0 does not come out zero, but its value can be used as a reference phase to which all the other calculated phases may be compared.

The value of the amplitude and phase of P at position z then is obtained from

$$P = \frac{1}{S} \sqrt{A^2 + B^2} \cos (\omega t + \Phi) \qquad (14\text{-}43)$$

where

$$\tan \Phi = \frac{B}{A}. \qquad (14\text{-}44)$$

So if one can find values of A and B at each position by the numerical integration one has the solution of the problem for the case when the initial driving pressure is P_0 as given by $(14\text{-}41)$.

At the helicotrema, the boundary condition that must be satisfied is determined from the fact that the pressure P_H across the membrane at this end must be the same as that driving the liquid back and forth through the helicotrema. The volume displacement V_1 of the liquid along the scala vestibuli at the position z is given by equation $(14\text{-}18)$. If

$$S_1 u_1 = \frac{\partial V_1}{\partial t}, \qquad (14\text{-}45)$$

then

$$-\frac{\delta(S_1 p_1)}{\delta z} = j\rho\omega Q \frac{\partial V_1}{\partial t}. \qquad (14\text{-}46)$$

A similar equation exists for the scala typani or

$$-\frac{\partial(S_2 p_2)}{\partial z} = j\rho\omega Q \frac{\partial V_2}{\partial t}. \qquad (14\text{-}47)$$

But near the helicotrema

$$\frac{\partial V_1}{\partial t} = -\frac{\partial V_2}{\partial t}, \qquad (14\text{-}48)$$

so that if equation $(14\text{-}47)$ is subtracted from $(14\text{-}46)$, then

$$-\frac{\partial(S_c P_c)}{\partial z} = 2 j\rho\omega Q_c \frac{\partial V_c}{\partial t} \qquad (14\text{-}49)$$

where the subscript c refers to quantities in the two canals. Now if the same equation $(14\text{-}18)$ is applied to the small helicotrema considered as a capillary tube

$$-\frac{\partial(S_H P_H)}{\partial z} = j\rho\omega Q_H \frac{\partial V_H}{\partial t} \qquad (14\text{-}50)$$

where S_H is the cross-section of the helicotrema, P_H the pressure along its length, and V_H the volume of liquid passing through it.

Since the rate of volume dleplacement along the canals is the same as through the helicotrema

$$- \frac{Q_H}{2Q_c} \frac{\partial(P_c S_c)}{\partial z} = \frac{\partial(S_H P_H)}{\partial z}. \tag{14-51}$$

For the short length of the helicotrema the quantity δz may be considered Δl the length of the helicotrema, and then the $\partial(S_H P_H)$ is the difference in $S_H P_H$ between its value on the scala vestibuli side from that on the scala typani side and consequently equal to $S_H P_c$. The quantity Q_H/Q_c is close to unity, so equation (14-51) reduces to

$$\frac{\delta(P_c S_c)}{\delta z} = - 2 \frac{S_H}{S_c \Delta l} (P_c S_c). \tag{14-52}$$

An estimate of S_H, S_c and Δl from anatomical measurements is $0.0025 \ \overline{cm^2}$, $0.006 \ \overline{cm^2}$ and -0.1 cm. Using these values, then, the boundary conditions become

$$\frac{\partial(A_1 + jB_1)}{\partial z} = - 8 \ (A_1 + jB_1) \tag{14-53}$$

where the subscript 1 refers to values at the helicotrema end of the basilar membrane. So the starting values of A_1, B_1, $(\Delta A)/(\Delta z)_1$, and $(\Delta B)/(\Delta z)_1$ must satisfy the conditions

$$\frac{(\Delta A)}{(\Delta z)_1} = - 8 \ A_1 \tag{14-54}$$

and

$$\frac{(\Delta B)}{(\Delta z)_1} = - 8 \ B_1. \tag{14-55}$$

It is convenient to start the calculation at the helicotrema end, in which case each step Δz is negative. For example, if one starts with

$$A_1 = 1, \ B_1 = 0 \quad \text{and} \quad \Delta z = - .05 \text{ cm},$$

then

$$\frac{(\Delta A)}{(\Delta z)_1} \Delta z = 0.4 \text{ and } \frac{(\Delta B)}{(\Delta z)_1} \Delta z = 0$$

and the calculation starts from these initial values. The arbitrary choice of $A_1 = 1$ and $B_1 = 0$ will result in calculated numerical values for A_0 and B_0 and Φ_0 which determine P_0 by equation (14-41) and the value of P at any position z corresponding to this initial pressure P_0 from equation (14-43). This, then, completes formally the solution of the problem of finding P. If this value is introduced into equation (14-16) one can find the values of v and y. The values of SP/SP_0 obtained from the calculated values of $\sqrt{A^2 + B^2} \div \sqrt{A_0^2 + B_0^2}$ are shown by the curves in Fig. 157.

The vertical arrows on these curves indicate the position where the little element of the basilar membrane will be at resonance for the frequency corresponding to each curve as indicated by the slanting arrows. The calculation of A and B from which one derives the ordinates of these curves is very long and tedious and no doubt errors have crept into the calculation, but the general shape of this family of curves is essentially correct. It should be noticed that the curves slope toward the resonant position and then go to negligibly small values at positions which are a few millimeters beyond this resonant position. Except for

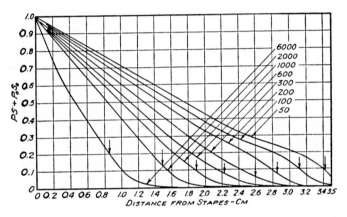

FIG. 157.—PRESSURE DISTRIBUTION ALONG THE BASILAR MEMBRANE FOR VARIOUS VALUES OF THE IMPRESSED FREQUENCY.

frequencies below 150 the pressure across the helicotrema is almost zero so there is no appreciable flow of liquid through the helicotrema for frequencies above 150 cycles per second.

To illustrate the type of values one obtains in the process of numerical integration the values when the frequency of the stimulating tone is 200 cps are given in Table 46.

It will be remembered that the integration starts at the helicotrema where $z = 3.5$ cm. The value of A starts at 0.01 here and then increases to 0.19, then decreases again to -2.0, and then again increases to the value 0.94, as one goes from the helicotrema to the stapes. Similarly, B goes from 0 to 0.9, and then decreases to -8.47.

Now if the value of P from equation (14–43) is introduced into (14–10A) one obtains for the displacement y of the basilar membrane

$$y = \frac{\sqrt{(A^2 + B^2)(R^2 + \chi^2)}}{2\omega^2 b} \cos (\omega t + \Phi + \theta - \pi) \qquad (14\text{–}56)$$

where the phase angle θ is given by

$$\tan \theta = \frac{\chi}{R} \qquad (14\text{-}57)$$

and Φ is given by (14–44).

This displacement y both in magnitude and phase corresponds to the values of P_0 obtained from the calculation outlined above and which depended upon the arbitrary values of A and B assumed for the position at the helicotrema. The arbitrariness will be removed if one takes relative values.

TABLE 46

VALUES FOR 200-CYCLE STIMULATING TONE

z	R	χ	θ	A	B	Φ	$\Phi+\theta$	$\bar{y}$ (normalized)	$\theta+\Phi-\theta_m-\Phi_m$
0			180°	.94	−8.47	264	444	.00	1.32 π
.5				+ .19	−7.00			.00	
1.0	− .07	.003	178	− .56	−5.54		435	.01	1.27 π
1.5	− .45	.04	177	−1.30	−4.04	252	429	.04	1.23 π
2.0	− 2.6	.3	173	−1.88	−2.19	229	402	.13	1.08 π
2.1	− 3.5		171	−1.91	−1.23	221	392	.15	1.02 π
2.2	− 4.5	.7	170	−1.95	−1.26	213	383	.18	.98 π
2.3	− 6.3	1.2	169	−1.89	− .76	202	371	.21	.92 π
2.4	−11	2.8	166	−2.01	− .24	187	353	.37	.81 π
2.5	−17	5.5	162	−1.74	.26	171	333	.44	.71 π
2.6	−26	12	155	−1.33	.70	152	307	.60	.55 π
2.7	−40	27	146	− .77	.90	130	276	.78	.38 π
2.8	−51	65	128	− .18	.84	102	230	.95	.13 π
2.84	−61	117	117	.00	.73	90	207	1.0	.00 π
2.92	0	136	90	.19	.44	68	158	.82	.27
3.0	58	115	63	.19	.22	50	113	.43	.47
3.1	82	83	45	.13	.09	34	78	.21	.72
3.2	87	61	35	.07	.03	22	57	.09	.83
3.3	88	49	29	.04	.01	13	42	.047	.92 π
3.4	86	40	25	.02	.00	6	31	.018	.98
3.5	83	34	22	.01	.00	0	22	.010	1.03

$b_m = 041$, $A_m = \infty$, $B_m = .73$, $R_m = -61$, $X_m = 117$, $\Phi_m = 90°$, $\theta_m = 117°$, $A_0 = .94$, $B_0 = -8.47$, $(\Delta A)/(\Delta z)_0 = -1.5$, $(\Delta B)/(\Delta z)_0 = 3.0$, $\alpha_0 = 116°$

First, consider the values of y relative to the maximum amplitude, that is, normalized so that the maximum amplitude is unity. Then

$$y \text{ (normalized)} = \frac{b_m}{b} \sqrt{\frac{(A^2 + B^2)(R^2 + \chi^2)}{(A_m^2 + B^2)(R_m^2 + \chi^2)}}$$

$$\times \cos(\omega t + \theta + \Phi - \theta_m - \Phi_m) \quad (14\text{-}58)$$

where m indicates the particular value corresponding to the position for maximum displacement. All of these values are given in Table 45 for the case when the frequency is 200 cycles per second, that is, $\omega = 1256$ radians per second. Such values were calculated for frequencies 50, 100, 200, 300, 600, 1000, 2000, and 6000 cycles per second. The resulting values of $P_0 S_0 \div PS$ have already been shown in Fig. 158. The calculated values of the amplitudes and phases of the displacement y obtained from (14-58) are shown by the curves of Fig. 158.

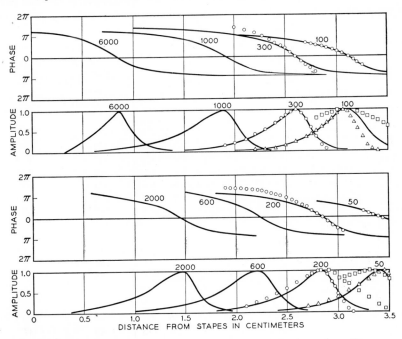

FIG. 158.—RELATIVE DISPLACEMENT AMPLITUDES AND PHASES OF THE BASILAR MEMBRANE FOR VARIOUS IMPRESSED FREQUENCIES.

By an ingenious and painstaking technique Békésy was able to view the displacements of the basilar membrane. He carefully cut away some of the bone surrounding the cochlea and placed a tiny window in the side wall. Then with a calibrated microscope he viewed the basilar membrane in stroboscopic light, when it was set into vibration by a tone impressed upon the eardrum. In this way he was able to measure the amplitudes and phases of the displacement at various positions. His results are shown in Fig. 158 by the points. The crosses and circles are all from one sample of ear. The two kinds of points are used so that the eye can follow the experimental curves. The squares represent results taken about two years earlier and upon a different ear.

It is seen that there is a good agreement between the calculated and observed results. Békésy took no data on phases for frequencies above 300 cycles per second. He also made measurements for 400, 800 and 1600 cycles per second corresponding to the series for the square points. They are not shown in Fig. 158 because no calculations were made at these frequencies but they fit very well between the calculated curves given.

One characteristic of these curves should be noted, namely, that they slope off more abruptly as one goes from the maximum toward the helicotrema or the low frequency side than when one goes toward the stapes or high frequency side. It will be remembered that this is also the general shape of the masking curves. It is due to the pressure P decreasing on one side and increasing on the other side of the maximum. Otherwise the curves would be much more symmetrical.

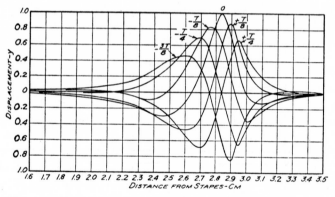

Fig. 159.—Relative Displacements of the Basilar Membrane for 200 Cycles per Second for Six Successive Times Separated by One-Eighth of a Period or in This Case by 1/1600 Seconds.

It must be remembered that these curves give the amplitudes of vibration but the membrane never takes the shape indicated. To find the actual shape of the membrane at any instant of time one must multiply the amplitude by the cosine factor of equation (14–58). This is illustrated for the case of 200 cycles per second in Fig. 159. The times are relative to the time when the maximum displacement of the membrane occurs.

Another displacement which may be compared to observed values is the volume of liquid displacement V_0 at the round window. This may be obtained as follows. First one must find an expression for V_0. Since the liquid of the inner ear may be considered incompressible the liquid displaced by the oval window is equal to that displaced at the round window but opposite in phase so that equation (14–18) applies or

$$- \frac{(\delta(SP))}{(\partial z)_{z=0}} = 2j\omega \frac{\partial V_0}{\partial t} = -2\omega^2 V_0. \qquad (14\text{–}59)$$

Or in terms of calculated quantities

$$V_0 = \frac{1}{2\omega^2}\left[\frac{(\Delta A)}{(\Delta z)_0} + j\frac{(\Delta B)}{(\Delta z)_0} \right]e^{j\omega t}. \qquad (14\text{–}60)$$

The volume displacement per dyne is then given by dividing (14–60) by (14–56) or

$$V_0 \text{ (per dyne)} = \frac{S_0}{2\omega^2}\sqrt{\frac{\frac{(\Delta A)^2}{(\Delta z)_0} + \frac{(\Delta B)^2}{(\Delta z)_0}}{A_0{}^2 + B_0{}^2}}\cos(\omega t + \alpha_0 - \Phi_0) \qquad (14\text{–}61)$$

where the phase angle α_0 is given by

$$\tan\alpha_0 = \frac{(\Delta B)}{(\Delta z)_0} \div \frac{(\Delta A)}{(\Delta z)_0} \qquad (14\text{–}62)$$

and Φ_0 is given by (14–42).

A comparison between the calculated values of V_0 per dyne and the experimental ones obtained by Békésy is shown in Fig. 160. The solid line is calculated and the circles observed. The agreement is excellent, better than one would expect knowing the error due to sampling. The value of S_0 which was used in the calculation happened to fit the particular ear on which Békésy made his measurements. The calculated phase $\alpha_0 - \theta_0$ varied from 0.84π to 0.92π, which agrees with Békésy's observed value of 0.9π, that is, V_0 lags P_0 by about 0.9π.

This volume displacement V_0 may also be compared to the displacement of the basilar membrane. Equations (14–56) and (14–60) when combined will give the volume displacement V_0 for a unit displacement of the basilar membrane or

$$\frac{V_0}{\text{cm}} = b\sqrt{\frac{\frac{(\Delta A)^2}{(\Delta z)_0} + \frac{(\Delta B)^2}{(\Delta z)_0}}{(A^2 + B^2)(R^2 + \chi^2)}}\cos(\omega t + \alpha_0 + \pi - \Phi_m - \theta_m). \qquad (14\text{–}63)$$

Békésy obtained experimental values of this ratio for the case where, for the frequency being used, the displacement of the basilar membrane was taken at the position where a maximum amplitude occurs. So in the calculation, values of A, B, R, χ and b are taken for this position. For 200 cycles per second these values are given at the bottom of Table 46. The calculated and observed values of V_0/cm are given in Table 47.

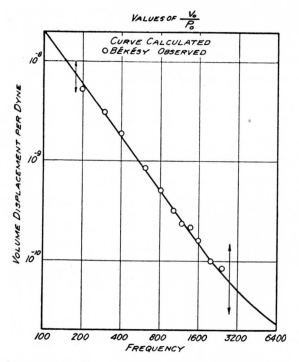

FIG. 160.—A COMPARISON OF OBSERVED AND CALCULATED VALUES OF THE LIQUID DIS-
PLACEMENT AT THE ROUND WINDOW DUE TO ONE DYNE PRESSURE ACROSS THE BASILAR
MEMBRANE AT THE STAPES END.

This is a rather discouraging result since for all the other quantities
the agreement between calculated and observed results is very good.
It is seen that the calculated values are about one-fifth of the observed
ones. The calculated values of the V_0/y_m may be in error as much as a
factor 2 but probably not more. This may arise from the initial slopes
$(\Delta A)/(\Delta z)_0$ and $(\Delta B)/(\Delta z)_0$, which are the final values after all the steps

TABLE 47

VALUES OF $\dfrac{V_0}{\bar{y}}$

f	Cal.	Obs.
100	2.4×10^{-3}	20×10^{-3}
200	1.4×10^{-3}	12×10^{-3}
300	3.1×10^{-3}	10×10^{-3}
600	2.0×10^{-3}	8×10^{-3}
1000	2.0×10^{-3}	6×10^{-3}
2000	1.0×10^{-3}	5×10^{-3}
6000	1.5×10^{-3}	—

in the integration process. Small errors along the way are therefore magnified in this quantity. The quantities y_m and V_0 are extremely small and the experimental difficulties very great in obtaining any values at all. So it is possible that the difference might be explained by observational and calculation errors although the difference seems rather large for this.

One can obtain V_0/cm from entirely different considerations. It was seen that V_0 can also be considered as the net displacement of fluid by the basilar membrane. Consequently,

$$V_0 = \int_0^{3.5} y b dz = y_m \int \frac{y}{y_m} b dz$$

or the volume displacement V_0 per cm of basilar membrane displacement at the maximum position is then given by

$$\frac{V_0}{\text{cm}} = \int_0^{3.5} \frac{y}{y_m} b \cos(\omega t + \beta) dz \qquad (14\text{–}64)$$

where

$$\beta = \Phi + \theta - \Phi_m - \theta_m. \qquad (14\text{–}65)$$

Equation (14–64) can be written

$$\frac{V_0}{\text{cm}} = \sqrt{A^2 + B^2} \cos\left[\omega t + \tan^{-1}\frac{(B)}{(A)}\right] \qquad (14\text{–}66)$$

where

$$A = \int_0^{3.5} \frac{y}{y_m} b \cos \beta dz \qquad (14\text{–}67)$$

and

$$B = \int_0^{3.5} \frac{y}{y_m} b \sin \beta dz. \qquad (14\text{–}68)$$

The values of y/y_m and β can be obtained from the curves of Fig. 158. Thus numerical values can be obtained for V_0/cm from (14–66). Such calculations were made for the 200 cycles per second. The value of $\sqrt{A^2 + B^2}$ was found to be 2.4×10^{-3}. If Békésy's experimental curves of y/y_m and β shown on Fig. 158 are used the value computed from (14–64) is found to be 2.1×10^{-3}. This seems to indicate that the observed values of V_0/cm are too high unless the volume displacement of the membrane is not the same as the volume displacement at the oval window.

It will be noticed from equation (14–64) that if one multiples the ordinates of the curves in Fig. 160 by b and then finds the net area under the resulting curves, the value of V_0/cm is obtained. In Fig. 161 the indicated points were obtained in this way. The time for a 200-cycle wave to travel from the stapes to the position where the maximum displacement of the basilar membrane occurs, namely, $z = 2.84$ cm, must be the time difference between maximum volume displacement and maximum basilar membrane displacement. Let t_1 be the time when the maximum displacement V_0 occurs and let t_2 be the time when maximum y_m occurs. From equation (14-60)

$$\omega t_1 + \alpha_0 = 0$$

and from (14-56)

$$\omega t_2 + \theta_m + \theta_m - \pi = 0.$$

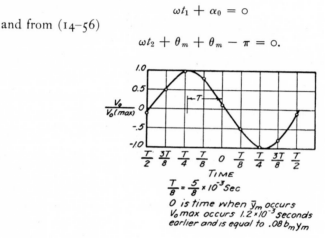

$$\frac{T}{8} = \frac{5}{8} \times 10^{-3} Sec$$

0 is time when $\bar{y}_m$ occurs
V_0 max occurs 1.2×10^{-3} seconds
earlier and is equal to $.08\, b_m y_m$

FIG. 161.—PLOT OF VOLUME DISPLACEMENT VERSUS TIME.

From these two equations the time difference τ becomes

$$t_2 - t_1 = \tau = \frac{\alpha_0 + \pi - \Phi_m - \theta_m}{\omega}. \qquad (14\text{-}69)$$

For example, for 200 cycles per second these values are given in Table 45 as $\alpha_0 = 116°$, $\Phi_m = 90°$, $\theta_m = 117°$ and $\omega = 360 \times 200$.

Therefore, $\tau = 1.2 \times 10^{-3}$ seconds. This is the time for a 200-cycle wave to ravel along the basilar membrane from the stapes end to a distance of 2.84 cm, which is the position for resonance for the 200 cycles per second tone. Similar calculations were made for the other frequencies and the results are shown by the curve in Fig. 162. The circles show Békésy's observed results. He observed the time from the instant the stapes was tapped until he could perceive that the membrane was beginning to move. The membrane was viewed through a microscope placed at various distances along the basilar membrane. Since the various frequencies are propagated at different speeds it is not evident at first why his observed result should agree with the ones calculated above. A tap on the stapes gives rise to a volume displacement V_0 having a large series of harmonics. The displacement at any position is principally due to the harmonic which has a frequency corresponding to the resonant frequency for this position. It is for this reason that the calculated and observed values of τ should agree. It is seen that the speed of travel of the wave is very much faster near the stapes, where the membrane is very stiff, and slows down very much near the helico-trema, where the stiffness of the membrane is very much reduced. For example, the average speed for the first 8 mm is 26 meters per second, while for the last 8 mm it is only 6 meters per second.

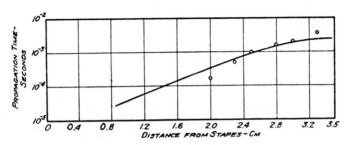

FIG. 162.—CALCULATED AND OBSERVED VALUES OF THE TRAVEL TIME OF A WAVE ALONG THE BASILAR MEMBRANE.

The value of the displacement y in centimeters for one dyne pressure in front of the eardrum can be calculated from the relations given above as follows. The maximum values of v and y are given approximately by (14–10A) when $f = f_0$ except for frequencies below 50 cycles per second, or

$$v_m = j\omega y_m = \frac{P_{\max}}{7\pi b f_0 \dfrac{(r)}{(m\omega_0)}}.$$

For 200 cycles per second and for higher frequencies it is seen (Table 44) that the value of $r/m\omega_0$ is 0.5. For 100 cycles per second it is 0.65 and for 50 and 25 cycles per second it is 1.0. For 25 cycles per second the maximum occurs at the last position at the helicotrema so $f = \frac{1}{2}f_0$ and

$$v = j\omega y = \frac{P_{\max}}{j\omega b \, 3.5 \, (1 - 4 - j2)}.$$

Then for calculation purposes one can use the formula

$$v_m = j\omega y_m = \frac{(SP)_{\max}}{S_0 P_0} \frac{P_0}{P_{ED}} \frac{S}{S_0} \frac{1}{3.5 \, \pi b f_0} P_{ED} \qquad (14\text{–}70)$$

for all cases and then multiply the results for 100 cycles per second by .50/.65; for 50 cycles per second by $\frac{1}{2}$; and for 25 cycles per second by $1/2\sqrt{13}$ or 0.14. It is seen that the velocity v is proportional to the acoustical pressure in front of the eardrum, but the factor of proportion-ality is a complicated function of the frequency. The first factor $(SP)_{\max}/S_0 P_0$ can be obtained from the curves in Fig. 158. It is the ordinate corresponding to each resonant position. The second factor P_0/P_{ED} is obtained from Fig. 152, and the third factor S/S_0 from Fig. 154. The values of b are also taken from Fig. 154. To show how these various factors vary with frequency they are shown in Table 48.

TABLE 48

	P_{ED} = One Dyne						Threshold Values		
f_0	$\dfrac{(SP)_m}{S_0 P_0}$	$\dfrac{P_0}{P_{ED}}$	$\dfrac{S_0}{S}$	b	v_1	y_1	P_T	v_T	y_T
25	.05	.003 est.	8	.04	$.15\times10^{-4}$	$.95\times10^{-7}$	5	$.75\times10^{-4}$	4.8×10^{-7}
50	.05	.01 est.	8	.04	$.9\times10^{-4}$	2.9×10^{-7}	.71	$.64\times10^{-4}$	2.0×10^{-7}
100	.06	.035	7	.047	2.3×10^{-4}	3.7×10^{-7}	.14	$.32\times10^{-4}$	$.51\times10^{-7}$
200	.07	.11	5.7	.042	4.8×10^{-4}	4.3×10^{-7}	.028	$.13\times10^{-4}$	$.10\times10^{-7}$
300	.07	.22	5.3	.038	6.5×10^{-4}	3.5×10^{-7}	.013	$.085\times10^{-4}$	$.045\times10^{-7}$
600	.08	.89	4.5	.032	15×10^{-4}	3.9×10^{-7}	.004	$.06\times10^{-4}$	$.016\times10^{-7}$
1000	.09	2.0	4.3	.028	28×10^{-4}	4.4×10^{-7}	.002	$.056\times10^{-4}$	$.0089\times10^{-7}$
2000	.13	4.5	4.1	.025	44×10^{-4}	3.5×10^{-7}	.0018	$.079\times10^{-4}$	$.0063\times10^{-7}$
6000	.20	6.3	3.6	.018	38×10^{-4}	1.0×10^{-7}	.0040	$.15\times10^{-4}$	$.0040\times10^{-7}$
10000	.24 est.	3.5	3.3	.015	15×10^{-4}	$.23\times10^{-7}$	.010	$.15\times10^{-4}$	$.0024\times10^{-7}$
18000	.30 est.	1.0	.7	.012	$.9\times10^{-4}$	$.08\times10^{-7}$	.2	$.18\times10^{-4}$	$.0016\times10^{-7}$

The first factor remains approximately constant for frequencies below 1000 cycles per second and then gradually increases from 0.1 to 0.3 at 18,000 cycles per second. The second factor has a very large variation with frequency from 0.003 at 25 cycles per second to 6.3 at 6000 cycles per second or 2000-fold. The third factor decreases to about 0.4 its value at 25 cycles per second for a frequency of 10,000 cycles per second. For higher frequencies it drops off sharply, being less than one-tenth at 18,000 cycles per second. The width of the basilar membrane decreases by a factor of 3 as one goes from 100 to 10,000 cycles per second. The values of the velocity v and displacement y for one dyne pressure on the eardrum are given in columns (6) and (7). It is seen that the displacement per dyne is approximately constant for frequencies from 25 to 2000 cycles per second. In this same range the velocity increases by a factor of 100.

It is interesting to find the velocity and displacement for acoustical pressures corresponding to the threshold of audibility. The pressures used for this purpose are obtained from the upper curve of Fig. 94, since the data at very low frequency are more accurate than for the other data. The values obtained for P_{ED} are given in column 8 and the corresponding values of v and y are given in columns 9 and 10. Now it is seen that the velocity is more nearly constant with change in frequency. This suggests that the nerve stimulation is dependent upon the velocity rather than the displacement.

It is interesting to note that the displacement y_T at 6000 cps of the basilar membrane is 4×10^{-10} cm. The diameter of a water molecule is about 2×10^{-8} cm, or about 50 times greater. This shows what extremely small displacements will excite the nerve endings of hearing.

Relation between Vibration and Nerve Stimulation on the Basilar Membrane

It will be remembered that near the threshold levels the stimulation of loudness per patch of nerves was approximately proportional to the square of the acoustic pressure and consequently to v^2 at any one frequency. So one might expect that except for frequencies below 300 cycles per second the vibrational energy per patch of nerves would be proportional to the stimulation, and indeed this turns out to be true, as will be shown. Below 300 cycles per second the nerve impulses are in synchronism with the vibration, most of the impulses starting when v is a maximum or minimum. Therefore, for a constant v, the number of nerve impulses per second is proportional to the driving frequency. Therefore, the total loudness can be written

$$N = K \frac{f}{300} \int_0^{100} v^2 dx = K \frac{f v_m^2}{300} \int_0^{100} \left(\frac{v}{v_m} \right)^2 dx. \qquad (14\text{--}71)$$

The values of v_m are given by (14–70) where the value of P_{ED} is the pressure level corresponding to the threshold of hearing. These values are given in the 9th column of Table 48.

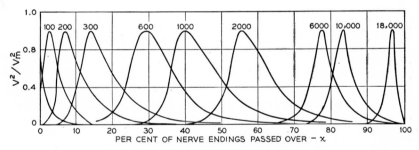

Fig. 163.—Plot of (v^2/v_1) versus x, the Percent of Nerve Endings from the Helicotrema to the Position x.

The value of the integral in (14–71) can be obtained as follows. The abscissas of Fig. 158 are changed from z to x by the relation in Fig. 125 and the corresponding ordinates are squared, giving the set of curves in Fig. 163. Except for frequencies below 300 cycles per second these curves represent the stimulation curves when the level of the stimulating tone is near the threshold level. The area under these curves gives the value of $\int_0^{100}(v/v_m)^2 dx$. The values for 25 cycles per second and 18,000 cycles per second were estimated. Throughout the middle range of frequencies these areas are approximately constant. At frequencies below 300 these areas decrease to values as low as one-tenth those in the middle range. This is largely due to the decrease in the density of the nerve endings near the helicotrema. Combining (14–70) with (14–71) one obtains a formula for computing the threshold pressure P_T, namely,

$$P_T = \frac{1}{v_1}\left(\frac{N}{K}\frac{300}{f}\right)^{\frac{1}{2}}\left[\int_0^{100}\left(\frac{v}{v_m}\right)^2 dx\right]^{-\frac{1}{2}}. \qquad (14\text{–}72)$$

where v_1 is the value of v_m for one dyne pressure and given in Table 48. At the threshold N/K is a constant for different frequencies but depends upon the manner of making the threshold measurements and the practice of the observers. To give the best fit of the data in the upper curve of Fig. 94 the value of N/K was taken as 10^{-9}. The values of P_T calculated and observed are given in the table. They are expressed as pressure

TABLE 49

f =	25	50	100	200	300	600	1000	2000	6000	10,000	18,000
Cal. Pressure Level =	88	71	54	44	37	30	23	20	24	32	60
Obs. Pressure Level =	88	71	57	43	37	27	21	19	26	33	60
Comparison with Sivian and White Data											
Cal. Pressure Level			41	31	24	17	10	7	11	19	
Obs. Pressure Level			44	30	22	12	8	6	14	19	

levels, that is, 20 log $P_T/.0002$. To compare with Sivian and White data, Fig. 92, 13 db was subtracted from the calculated values in line 2 to give the values in line 4. It is seen that equation (14–72) calculates the threshold pressures in front of the eardrum well within the observational error.

The curves of Fig. 163 deserve some more comments. Due to lack of nerve endings, the curves are crowded together at the helicotrema end ($x = 0$). Although the y vs z show a maximum for both 50 and 25 cycles per second, no such maximum is shown on y vs x curves. Even the peak for 100 cycles per second is uncertain; it may or may not be present, depending upon the dimensions of the particular ear.

Masking dara for my left ear were obtained for masker tones of 75, 125, 250, 500, and 1000 cps, and are shown by the curves in Fig. 164A and 164B. The dotted part of the curves is in the region where beats occur and therefore is not true masking. The solid bars give the sensation level

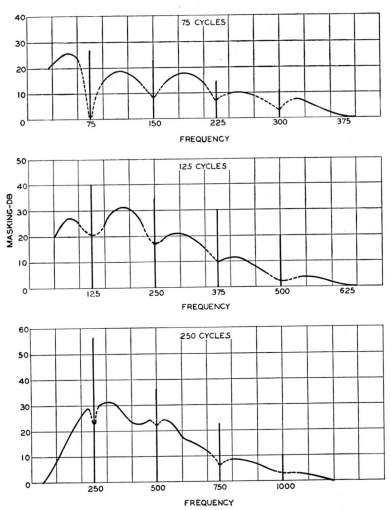

FIG. 164.—MASKING DATA FOR MASKING FREQUENCIES OF 75, 125, 250, 500 AND 1000 CPS.

of the subjective harmonics obtained by the best beat method. The first bar is the sensation level of the maskee tone. The sensation levels chosen for this masker tone were such that the intensity levels for the five tones were the same. It is obvious from the shape of these curves in Fig. 164

that the masking of one tone by another at frequencies of 100 cycles per second and lower is very complicated.   Also, the subjective harmonics are not included in the curves of Fig. 163.   However, a comparison of these curves with the masking curves of Figs. 164 and 165, shows they have the same general shape, but until more is known about the mechanism of masking, the detail of the masking curves cannot be calculated.

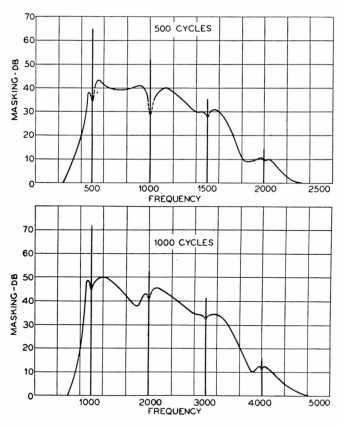

FIG. 165.—MASKING DATA FOR MASKING FREQUENCIES OF 75, 125, 250, 500 AND 1000 CPS.

Certainly the mechanism for detecting the presence of the maskee tone is very different when its frequency is near that of the masker tone, or any of its harmonics.

One might ask why the subjective harmonic tones did not appear in the experimental observations of Békésy.   The following Table 50 presents the case for a 600-cycles-per-second masker tone:

TABLE 50

		1	2	3	4
(1) Harmonic number	=	1	2	3	4
(2) Frequency	=	600	1200	1800	2400
(3) Pressure level of subjective harmonic	=	100	86	73	62
(4) db from one dyne = $20 \log P_{ED}$	=	26	12	-1	-12
(5) $20 \log \bar{y}_1 - 20 \log P_{ED}$	=	-102	-116	-113	-142
(6) Relative level	=	0	-14	-28	-40
(7) Relative level of 600 cps tone at positions for harmonics	=	0	-7	-12	-16
(8) Harmonics down from displacement curve	=	0	-7	-16	-24

It is evident that these harmonics will not add a detectable amount to the displacement.

The case for the evlocity v is different, however:

(9) $20 \log v_1$	=	-57	-50	-48	-48
(10) $20 \log v_1 - 20 \log P_E$	=	-31	-38	-49	-60
(11) Relative level	=	0	-7	-18	-28
(12) Harmonics down from velocity curve	=	0	0	-2	-4

The levels in line (11) are comparable to those in line (8) and therefore the harmonics should be easily detected, which accords with the facts. For example, when the first harmonic and the fundamental are in phase, the stimulation level at the position for the first harmonic should be increased about 6 db from that due to fundamental. This shows why the subjective harmonics cannot be seen under stroboscopic illumination but are easily detectable by the ear.

So it is seen that when tones are impressed upon the ear, space patterns similar to those of Fig. 163 are produced in the ear corresponding to a sinusoidal time pattern in the air.

Similarly, for every sound reaching the ear, a space stimulation pattern corresponding to the time pattern of the sound in the air is produced on the basilar membrane. This space pattern is transferred to the brain by a nerve cable containing about 3000 individual nerve fibers. This space pattern is dependent both upon the kind of sound and also upon the intensity with which it is applied to the ear.

Mechanism of Nerve Stimulation

Let us now consider more closely the mechanism of stimulating the nerves. Some of the nerve endings will be very sensitive while others will be very insensitive; others will have degrees of sensitivity scattered between these extremes. Let us take the stimulation level β at a point on the basilar membrane as the number of decibels that the velocity at that point is above the velocity of the membrane which would just stimulate the most sensitive fiber in a patch of auditory nerve endings

(one percent of total).   Then if the nerve endings in the ear have properties similar to those in the eye, the distribution of threshold values will
be as follows.   Let z be the fraction of fibers which have threshold
values below the stimulation level β; then

$$\beta + \beta_0 = 10 \log \frac{z^2}{1 - z}. \qquad (14\text{--}73)$$

The constant β_0 is the value of the right-hand member when z is the small
fraction of the nerves which have a maximum sensitivity.   As shown by
Hecht,[5] this relation holds for the nerve endings in the eye.

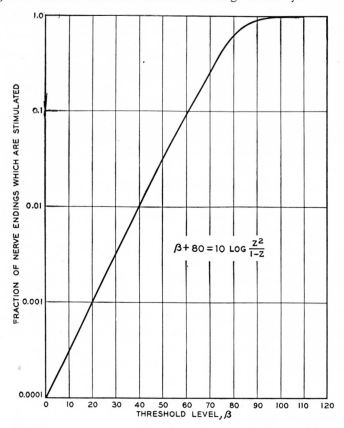

FIG. 166.—VARIATION OF THRESHOLD LEVELS OF A GROUP OF AUDITORY NERVE FIBERS.

The curve in Fig. 166 shows the relation given by (14–73).   It shows
the large range in sensitivity of the fibers, some starting to discharge at
levels 90 db lower than the most insensitive ones.

[5] Selig Hecht, *Light Sensitivity of Animals*, Optical Society of America Proceedings, *18*,
pages 264-286, 1929.

As the stimulation level goes above the threshold of a nerve ending, the firing of nerve impulses from that ending becomes more rapid. Let us consider this mechanism for a moment. We will assume that there are two opposing operations in the process of stimulating the nerves. The first, which may be called the active process, is dependent upon the magnitude of the motion and tends to create either a substance or energy which acts like a catalytic agent and produces a nerve discharge. The second, which may be called the reactive process, tends to destroy or annul the active process. For example, let us call the thing being created the discharger, which may be the energy of agitation of the element of the nerve ending or a fluid produced by some chemical process or some kind of electrical accumulation. The active process will tend to create this discharger at a rate depending upon the stimulating force and the reactive process will destroy the discharger at a rate depending upon the amount present. If the discharger is the amount of energy of vibration, then the action of frictional forces furnishes the reactive process. Let us call the amount of discharger present q. The amount of discharger depends upon the vibrational energy of the basilar membrane, which is $1/2\ mv^2$ for each element or

$$\frac{\delta q}{dt} = F(\tfrac{1}{2}\ mv^2) - bq \qquad (14\text{–}74)$$

where F represents the functional relationship between the vibrational energy and the rate the discharger is created. The rate at which the discharger is destroyed is proportional q or $-bq$, where b is a constant. It we make the assumption that

$$F(\tfrac{1}{2}mv^2) = av^2$$

it will simplify the calculations. After calculation is made, then one can look again at this assumption and see how the results will be modified if the general form is used.

For a periodic force produced by a pure tone

$$v = V \cos \omega t \qquad (14\text{–}75)$$

the solution of equation 14–74 is then

$$q = \frac{aV^2}{2b}\left[1 - e^{-bt} + \frac{b}{(2\omega)^2 + b^2}\ (b \cos 2\omega t + 2\omega \sin 2\omega t) \right]. \qquad (14\text{–}76)$$

Usually ω is so much larger than b that b can be neglected in comparison to ω. So $(14\text{–}76)$ becomes

$$q = \frac{aV^2}{2b}\left(1 - e^{-bt} + \frac{b}{2\omega} \sin 2\omega t \right). \qquad (14\text{–}67)$$

The amount of discharger present is proportional to the energy of agitation, inversely proportional to b, and directly proportional to the time factor in the parentheses.   This process continues until the threshold value of the nerve ending is reached, when a new process starts; a nerve discharge then takes place.   While this second process is going on, the equilibrium is upset so that the creation of the discharger stops.   This period of the stopping of the first process is the reaction time τ of the nerve ending.   After the reaction interval, the active process starts again.   At the high intensities the number of discharges is governed mostly by the reaction time, while at the low intensities, mainly by the time for the discharger to accumulate.

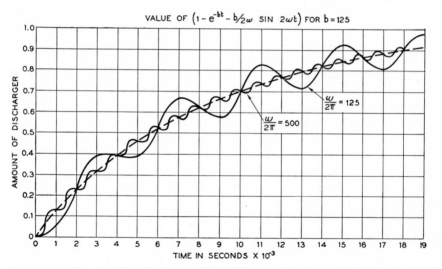

FIG. 167.—THE AMOUNT OF NERVE DISCHARGER VERSUS TIME.

To illustrate the form of this equation, the graphs of the time function in the parenthesis in 14–67 are shown in Fig. 167 when $b = 125$ and for the two cases when the frequencies are 125 and 500 cycles per second respectively.   Any fiber may obtain the requisite amount of q for a discharge either by having a large velocity V and a small time t or a small velocity V and long time t.   Consequently, for any given value of V the sensitive fibers will require only a short time to discharge and the insensitive ones a long time.   It is seen that for the 250-cycle tone q increases in the interval 0.001 to 0.003 second about 10-fold while in the same length interval 0.003 to 0.005 it remains practically constant. It is evident then that the number of discharges coming from a stimulated patch of nerve fibers which take place in the first interval will be very much greater than in the second interval.   Consequently, the bombardment of nerve discharges reaching the brain will have times of maximum intensity which are separated by intervals equal to half period of the oscillating body producing the stimulating sound. In other words, a time pattern of the changes taking place in the medium transmitting the sound wave is transmitted to the brain. Now if instead of $F(\frac{1}{2}mv^2)$ equal to av^2 the general expression is used the solution will be a sum of terms like those in (14–78) having multiple frequencies of ω and having coefficients outside the brackets which are proportional to v, v^2, v^3, etc. This will still leave the time factor generally the same. Since the sinusoidal terms will be small then all may be neglected and then (14–77) becomes

$$q = \frac{1}{b}(a_1V + a_2V^2 + a_3V^2 + \text{etc.})(1 - e^{-bt}). \qquad (14\text{–}77\text{A})$$

In passing to the brain, it follows the nerve tract shown in Fig. 168.

Although the nerve fibers are interrupted by synapse as indicated, where a restimulation is necessary, it seems reasonable to expect some sort of correlation between the rate that the nerve discharges are being received and the time pattern of the original wave. As the frequency of the stimulating tone becomes higher, the time pattern becomes less distinct since the ratio $b/2\omega$ becomes smaller. The case for 500 cycles is also shown in Fig. 167. The variation from the exponential lines for a 5000-cycle tone would be one-tenth that shown for the 500-cycle tone.

For a large value of V the nerve will discharge in a very short time and for small values it will take a longer time and may not discharge at all. Let V_1 be a value corresponding to a stimulation level β such that q will be at the threshold for a certain fiber when acted upon for a time long enough that e^{-bt} is negligible compared to unity, that is, so that the time factor in equation (14–77) has reached its maximum value. Let V_2 be any other velocity above V_1 corresponding to a level α which will give the same value of q in a time t. Then

$$\alpha - \beta = 10 \log \frac{1 + \dfrac{b}{2\omega}}{1 - e^{-bt} + \dfrac{b}{2\omega}\sin 2\omega t} \qquad (14\text{–}78)$$

$$\doteq -10 \log (1 - e^{-bt})$$

or

$$t = -\frac{1}{b}\log_e\left(1 - 10^{-\frac{a-\beta}{10}}\right). \qquad (14\text{–}79)$$

This derivation is based on the assumption that the dominant term in (14—77A) is a_2V^2.

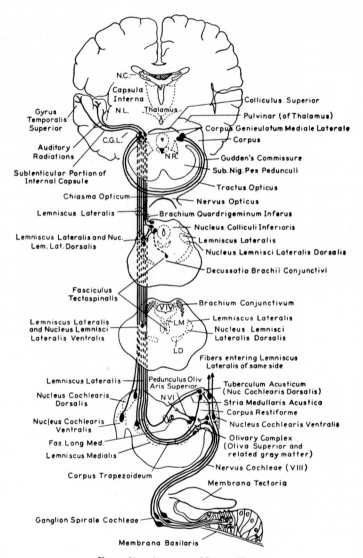

FIG. 168.—AUDITORY NERVE TRACT.

The value t in this expression is the time necessary for a nerve ending to be acted upon at a level which is $\alpha - \beta$ decibels above its threshold level, before it starts a nerve discharge. As mentioned above, the reaction time τ is the time necessary for the nerve to discharge and recuperate, thus being ready again for another stimulation. Hence the time $t - \tau$ is the time interval before the nerve is ready to start the process over again. At the end of this time interval the phase of vibration will not, in general, be the same as in the beginning.   However, on the average, we can neglect the term $b/\omega \sin \omega t$ when determining at each level the average rate of firing since it simply has the effect of making the time interval oscillate on either side of the value obtained when this term is omitted.   The rate so determined can then be applied to all frequencies and it depends only upon the stimulation level $(\alpha - \beta)$ as shown by (14–79). With this understanding the average rate of firing from a nerve which is stimulated at a level $(\alpha - \beta)$ decibels above its threshold is given by

$$r = \frac{1}{t - \tau}. \qquad (14\text{--}80)$$

For values of $\tau = 1/300$ second and $b = 50$ the values of r for different values of $\alpha - \beta$ are shown by the curve in Fig. 169.   That this represents

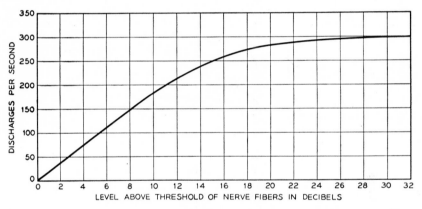

FIG. 169.—CALCULATED NUMBER OF DISCHARGES PER SECOND FROM A SINGLE NERVE FIBER AS THE STIMULATING LEVEL INCREASES ABOVE THE THRESHOLD OF STIMULATION.

the general character of the nerve stimulation is shown by comparing the curve in Fig. 169 to the experimental one shown in Fig. 81, which was observed from a cat's ear.

To get the total nerve discharges for a patch of nerve endings in terms of α, the stimulation level in decibels, one must add the effects of all the fibers having very greatly different sensitivities.   If N is the total nerve endings, then the number per patch is $N/100$.   The fraction of threshold levels lying between β and $\beta + d\beta$ is $(dz/d\beta)d\beta$.   Consequently, the total discharges $S(\alpha)$ coming from a patch of nerves stimulated at a level α is given by

$$S(\alpha) = \frac{N}{100} \int_0^\alpha r \frac{dz}{d\beta} d\beta = \frac{N}{100} \int_{z_0}^z rdz \qquad (14\text{--}81)$$

where z_0 corresponds to β_0 and in the curve of Fig. 166 it was taken as

10^{-4} corresponding to $\beta_0 = 80$ db.   The upper limit z corresponds to the ordinate in Fig. 166 when $\alpha = \beta$.   Using the values of r from Fig. 169 and taking N as 30,000, the values of $S(\alpha)$ were calculated to be those shown by the curve in Fig. 170.   It is seen that a patch of nerves has the

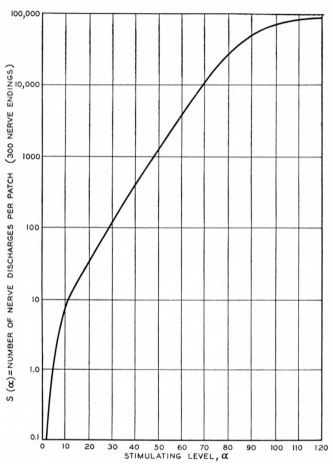

FIG. 170.—NERVE DISCHARGES PER PATCH OF NERVES
VERSUS THE STIMULATING LEVEL α.

possibility of changing the total discharge rates per second from 1 to 90,000 as the level changes from 5 to 120 db, a very remarkable capability.

The total rate R when any sound is vibrating the basilar membrane is then given by

$$R = \int_0^{100} S(\alpha) \, dx \qquad (14\text{--}82)$$

where α is the sensation level of each patch of the basilar above its threshold level.

This integral was found for the 1000 cycles per second tone. The ordinates of the curve for 1000 cycles in Fig. 158 were converted to deci-

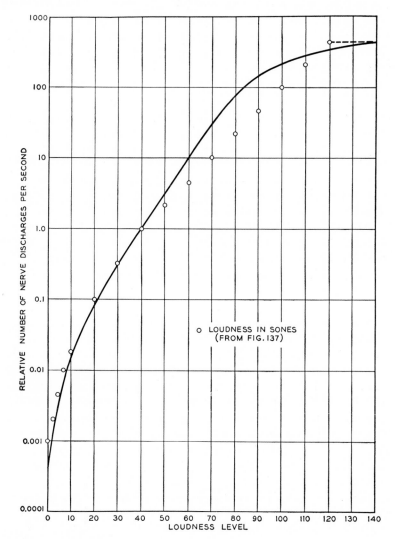

FIG. 171.—CALCULATED VALUES OF THE RELATION BETWEEN LOUDNESS AND LOUDNESS LEVEL.

bels and the maximum was given various values of decibels corresponding to relative loudness levels. A value of $v_{\max}$ corresponding to $\alpha = 6$

was taken as the zero loudness. The value of R was then caclulated for loudness levels from 0 to 120. These values were divided by the value corresponding to $L = 40$ so its relative value would be unity corresponding to a loudness of one sone. The other values are shown in Fig. 171. The circles are taken from the experimental curve of loudness versus loudness level shown in Fig. 137. There is good agreement at the low levels although the departures are rather large at 80 to 100 db levels.

However, I think one can say that this nerve mechanism gives a fairly good prediction for the loudness function. There is no doubt that the loudness reaches a maximum and should bend over as indicated by the theoretical curve. So it seems to me that the experimental data underyling this experimental curve should again receive careful evaluation and also new data obtained on these high level regions.

Comparison of Space-Time Pattern with Experimental Facts of Audition

The variation of the acuity of hearing with frequency has been satisfactorily explained. It was shown to be due principally to the poor transformer action of the middle ear.

It has been shown that loudness is closely associated with the total nerve discharges going to the brain. It is seen from Fig. 168 that the number of discharges per second from a single patch of nerve endings varies from 1 to 90,000 as the level goes from 5 to 120 db. For the 100 patches all stimulated together this range is 1 to 9,000,000 as the level changes from 0 to 120 db. It is thus seen that the mechanism outlined above provides ample range of the loudness and indeed gives a fairly good fit of the loudness function. When a tone is gradually increased in intensity from the threshold, it first stimulates a small patch; this grows in length and then other patches corresponding to the subjective harmonics are started until finally some nerve fibers along the entire length are stimulated. If the membrane vibrated the same for all tones, similar for example to the diaphragm of a high quality microphone, then the loudness for all tones should be the same for the same sensation level, which is contrary to the observed facts. It is the difference in form of vibration of the basilar membrane that accounts for the difference in loudness of tones having the same sensation level.

The functions calculated above have been based on the assumption that as the intensity of stimulation increases the rate of discharging the nerve also increases until the limit of 300 per second is reached. Experiments on nerves have shown that as the nerve is continually stimulated it is fatigued, after which the maximum rate is very much reduced. Consequently, if a tone of given frequency stimulates the ear for some time, then immediately after such stimulation the loudness of tone in the same frequency region will be reduced. This effect has been measured by Békésy.[6] His results indicate that changes in loudness as much as 30 db occur immediately after strong stimulations.

Similarly, the threshold of audibility should be shifted if taken immediately after such strong stimulations. Measurements have indicated that especially for low pitched tones such shifts amount to as much as 25 db and some shifts take place as long as two minutes after the stimulating tone is stopped. So the relations developed above can apply only when the nerves are not fatigued. Both of these effects show that the changes are greatest for the tones near the pitch of the stimulating tone and decrease to zero for tones far removed from the pitch of the stimulating tone. This, then is additional evidence that certain regions only along the basilar membrane are stimulated by a simple tone.

It has been seen that due to the introduction of more subjective harmonics and also due to the form of vibration having less sharp resonant peaks, the region of maximum stimulation is much broader for tones of low frequency than for those of high frequency when both have the same sensation level. For this reason, these low tones will send more nerve impulses to the brain and consequently will be louder.

Let us now see how the differential sensitivity for pitch and intensity fits into the picture. These two are closely related, for in each case it is a small change of the vibration form of the basilar membrane that can be detected, at least for the higher frequencies. Since Békésy obtained his experimental curves of the vibration form of the basilar membrane it has been argued that the peaks are not sharp enough to discriminate the small pitch changes which are observed. However, a careful analysis indicates that a change of 4 cycles could probably be detected. For example, if the instantaneous pattern for 200 cycles shown in Fig. 159 is replotted using the frequency corresponding to maximum response as abscissa and V^2, that is, the ordinate of Fig. 159 squared, then the curve obtained is that shown in Fig. 172. The dotted curve is the solid curve shifted 4 cycles. It seems reasonable to expect the one could detect this much change. The maximum has shifted over 10 nerve endings in this change. It has been seen that for all frequencies the change in the maximum represents approximately the same nerve ending stimulation change. For all frequencies below 100 cycles the maximum stimulation point is at the helicotrema. So pitch changes are not recognized by shifts in this maximum. However, the total pattern changes and also the valleys of nerve discharges produce a distinct time pattern going to the brain. So it is a combination of these two that enables one to recognize the pitch.

[6] G. V. Békésy, Physikalische Zeitschrift, vol. 30, pages 721-745, 1929.

When the stimulation intensity is increased the base of the stimulation pattern is widened and the stimulation at the peak is increased. It is a combination of these two that enables the ear to detect a change.

There then remains the facts of binaural audition and some of the more subtle psychological effects, such as "volume" and "brightness."

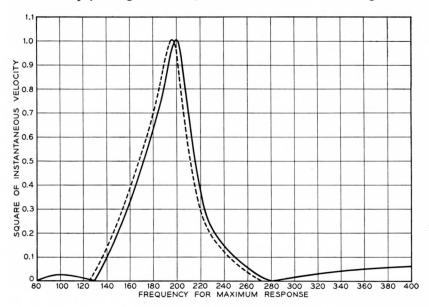

FIG. 172.—VELOCITY OF BASILAR MEMBRANE SQUARED VERSUS FREQUENCY FOR POSITION OF MAXIMUM RESPONSE.

In Fig. 173 a diagrammatic sketch of the auditory tract taken from Fig. 168 is shown. The circles represent places where some nerve fibers stop and others begin. These are scattered along the length of the nerve path. Some nerves have a continuous passage from the cochlea to the auditory brain center, while others may be interrupted three or four times by such synapse. As shown the nerves running from each ear are cross-connected at two points. More nerve fibers coming from the left ear terminate in the right side of the brain and vice versa.

So we see that according to the conceptions given above, when the left ear receives a tone then there should be two space patterns in the brain which are almost alike, one on the left side and one on the right. They are designated by the letter L. Similarly, a sound in the right ear produces the two patterns labelled R. If the nerve is interrupted at A, the left ear will be totally deaf. If, however, it is interrupted at B or C, only a slight diminution in hearing in either ear will occur. Cases of brain tumor have been found where it was necessary to remove one of the auditory brain centers and also a considerable portion around it, and still the patient recovered. Although it left one side of the body paralyzed, hearing tests on such a person indicated that the two ears had practically the same sensitivity as before the operation.

Although some of the nerve fibers from the two ears are placed near together for part of their length and terminate close together in the

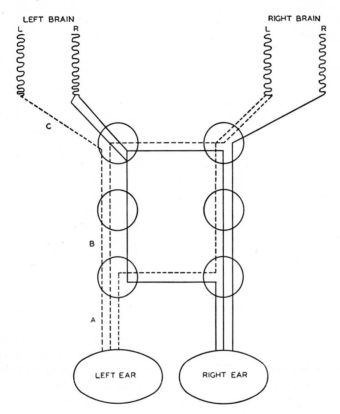

FIG. 173.—DIAGRAM OF THE AUDITORY NERVE TRACT.

periphery of the brain, there is little interference between them. This is shown by the experimental fact that a tone introduced in one ear will produce little masking to a sound introduced into the other one. Wegel and Lane showed that a tone to be masked in an opposite ear to that receiving the masking tone needed to be 1,000,000 more intense, that is, at a 60 db higher intensity level than if introduced in the same ear as the masking tone.

Also, binaural "objective" beats will not occur until the intensity of tone in one ear is at least 60 db above that in the other ear. Objective beats are distinguished from "subjective" beats by the following criteria. They can be readily heard by every observer and can be produced at all audible frequencies while the subjective beats can only be heard by about 80% of observers and only then when the frequencies are below 1000 cycles per second. The objective beats are undoubtedly produced by the more intense sound forcing the bones of the head into bivration so that the sound is conducted to the cochlea of the opposite ear. Consequently, such an intense tone produces the same effect as if it were attenuated and introduced directly into the same ear as the other tone.

The patterns from the two ears are laid down close in duplicate so that an accurate comparison can be made. Since the times of maximum stimulation have been shown to be directly correlated to the times of maximum displacement in the medium conducting the sound, the differences of phase which occur at the two ears will manifest themselves as phase differences in the times of maximum stimulation between L and R on both sides of the brain. In locating the direction of a source of sound both the differences in intensity and also the differences in phase are used. Due to a process of education, we have come to associate a definite direction of sound with this difference in the intensity of the stimulation between L and R and the times between the occurrence of maximum stimulation. It has been seen that the definiteness of this time pattern in the brain decreases with increasing frequency, which agrees with the fact that the location of the direction of a source of sound having frequencies higher than 1000 cycles is extremely difficult.

If tones having the same frequency and intensity are applied to the two ears and then the phase changed, it causes a sound image to rotate around the head. Such an effect is related to our experience of locating sounds, but it is a new experience since the usual change in intensity is missing, but most persons can make an adjustment for this absence of intensity change and assign a definite direction for the sound image. The changing of phase can be produced by making the tones in the two ears slightly different in frequency. Then the phenomenon known as subjective binaural beats is produced. As mentioned above, these beats cannot be heard for tones having high frequencies, which is in accordance with the theory outlined.

Summary

Summarizing, then, the pitch of a tone is determined both by the position of its maximum stimulation on the basilar membrane and also by the time pattern sent to the brain. The former is probably more important for the high tones and the latter for the low tones. The loudness is dependent upon the number of nerve impulses per second reaching the brain and possibly somewhat upon the extent of the stimulated patch.   The experience called by psychologists "volume" or "extension" is probably identified with the length of the stimulated patch on the basilar membrane.   This extension is carried to the brain and forms a portion of excited brain matter of a definite size.   It is, then, this size that determines our sensation of the volume of a tone.   The low pitched or complex tones have a large volume, while the very high pitched tones have a small one.

The time pattern in the air is converted into a space pattern on the basilar membrane.   The nerve endings are excited in such a way that this space pattern is transferred to the brain and produces two similar space patterns in the brain, one on the left and the other on the right side.   Enough of the time pattern in the air is sent to each of these stimulated patches to make time of maximum stimulation in each patch detectable.   So when listening to a sound with both ears, there are four space patterns in the brain produced, each carrying also some sort of time pattern.   It is a recognition of the changes in these patterns that accounts for all the phenomena of audition.

CHAPTER 15

METHODS OF MEASURING THE RECOGNITION ASPECT OF SPEECH[1]

There are several aspects to the perception of speech but the foremost is the process which enables one to recognize correctly and record the speech sounds which are spoken. This is the recognition aspect of perception. The method of measuring this aspect of perception is to have a speaker read aloud a certain number of speech sounds to a listener who writes what he thinks he hears. In order that the sounds may be used as they occur in ordinary talking, they must be grouped into syllables or words. A comparison of the sounds, syllables, or words recorded by the listener with those uttered by the speaker shows the fraction that is interpreted correctly. This fraction is called the articulation. It is syllable articulation S if the syllable is considered the unit—for example, "pat"—and sound articulation s if each individual speech sound is considered the unit—for example, "p," "a," and "t." In a similar way we may deal with the vowel articulation v or with the consonant articulation c. Various types of syllable lists have been used by various investigators.[2,3] A sample list of syllables of the consonant-vowel-consonant type is shown in Table 51. The carrier sentence shown in the second column is spoken before the "called" (i.e., spoken) syllable shown in the fourth column. In this sample test there were 6 vowel errors out of 66 spoken, 35 consonant errors out of 132, 41 speech sound errors out of 198, and 32 syllable errors out of 66. So the values of S, s, v, and c are those shown in Table 51.

In this book four extensive sets of articulation data designated I, II, III, and IV are considered. The first three sets were taken at the Bell Telephone Laboratories, I in the years 1919 to 1925, II in the years 1928 to 1929, and III in the years 1935 to 1937. The IV set was taken at the Psycho-Acoustic Laboratory at Harvard University during World War II.

To obtain a desirable precision[2] in the measurement of articulation, it is advisable to use at least five different voices and five listeners, at

[1] This chapter and Chapter 16 are taken directly from a paper by Fletcher and Galt. Journal Acoustical Society America, March, 1950.

[2] H. Fletcher and J. C. Steinberg, *Articulation Testing Methods*, Bell System Technical Journal, 8, 806, 1929.

least 25 values being averaged in some way to obtain a final value for the condition tested. Various types of weighting have been proposed and used but here only straight averages without weighting are used.

In set I of the articulation tests (conducted by J. B. Kelly) each list was composed of 80 syllables of the consonant-vowel-consonant type, 10 syllables of the consonant-vowel type, and 10 syllables of the vowel-consonant type. For these tests the syllable and sound articulations are

TABLE 51

Articulation Test Record

Date   3-16-28   Syllable articulation 0.515 = S
Title of test   Practice tests   Condition tested   1500~ low pass filter
Test no.   10   Observer   W.H.S.
List Nos.   5-9-37   Caller   E.B.

No.		Observed	Called	Observed	Called	Observed	Called
1	The first group is	ma'v	na'v	po'z	po't'h	kŏb √	kŏb
2	Can you hear	pōch √	pōch	nēz	nēzh	shēt'h	siz
3	I will now say	seng √	seng	jo'ch √	jo'ch	fūch √	fūch
4	As the fourth write	chūd √	chūd	t'ha'm √	t'ha'm	thōl √	thōl
5	Write down	run √	run	hab √	hab	pot'h √	pot'h
6	Did you understand	chiz	kiz	def	doth	wa'm √	wa'm
7	I continue with	foz	fozh	chech	chej	gūm	gūn
8	These sounds are	lo'l √	lo'l	lun	lon	nāsh	nāth
9	Try the combination	jās	zhāth	shāl √	shāl	vo'g √	vo'g
10	Please record	t'ha'th	t'ha'sh	muz √	muz	lung	long
11	Write the following	wūr √	wūr	lēd	bēd	diz	dizh
12	Now try	yāp √	yāp	wif √	wif	kak	tak
13	Thirteen will be	mad	maj	gōst √	gōst	t'ha'r	zha'r
14	You should observe	bēch	bēk	thāv	sāv	must √	must
15	Write clearly	gēm	dēm	kōf √	kōf	yo'd √	yo'd
16	Number 16 is	t'heb	veb	ra'g √	ra'g	jet √	jet
17	You may perceive	jok	jost	thip √	thip	rēp	rēj
18	I am about to say	gaf √	gaf	yar √	yar	t'hēp	hēp
19	Try to hear	hus √	hus	zhūt √	zhūt	yo'd √	chuv
20	Please write	hiv	thit'h	kūk	tūk	t'hef	t'hesh
21	Listen carefully to	tōg √	tōg	fung √	fung	bās √	bās
22	The last group is	sho't √	sho't	t'hev	vesh	t'ho'f	shaf

$v = 0.909$ $cvc = 0.491$
$c = 0.735$ $s^3 = 0.499$
$s = 0.793$

designated S_{23} and s_{23}, respectively, the subscript indicating that both two-sound syllables and three-sound syllables were used. The systems tested are designated I–A, I–B, I–C, etc., where A, B, or C represents added digits or letters or combination of these to differentiate the various systems that were tested at this time. In each of these tests only two talkers were used, a man and a woman, or in some instances two men, and seven or eight listeners. In the set II tests (conducted by W. B. Snow and A. Meyer) the lists were all of the consonant-vowel-consonant type. For these tests the syllable and sound articulations are designated S_3 and s_3, respectively, and the systems tested are designated II–A, II–B, II–C, etc. In these tests the crew of eight persons provided eight talkers, four men and four women, and eight listeners of whom four listened to each talker.   Each articulation test thus yielded a value which was the average of 32 talker-listener pairs.   In set III the lists were the same as for set II but a machine [3] was used for recording and calculating the average sound articulation, which is designated s_{3M}.   In all the other tests the syllables heard were written by the listeners but in set III the listeners did not write but punched keys.   This difference in technique is important as it yields slightly different values, and so the subscript M is added to s^3.   No values of syllable articulation S_{3M} were recorded because the machine was not so arranged.   The systems tested in set III are designated III–A, III–B, III–C, etc.   In tests III the crew consisted of from six to eight talkers and six to eight listeners, with 32 talker-listener pairs per test as in tests II.   In set IV, the tests made at Harvard University,[4] the lists were composed of consonant-vowel and vowel-

TABLE 52

GROUPS OF ARTICULATION TESTS WITH CORRESPONDING SYMBOLS FOR ARTICULATION

Designation of telephone systems	Dates of articulation tests	Tests made by	Received speech recorded by	Composition of syllables		Designation of average articulation	
				Consonants and vowels	Percent	Speech sounds	Syllables
I	(1919–1920) (1924–1925)	BTL	Writing	(CV (VC (CVC	10) 10) 80)	s_{23}	S_{23}
II	1928–1929	BTL	Writing	CVC	100	s_3	S_3
III	(1935–1936) (1936–1937)	BTL	Machine	CVC	100	s_{3M}	S_{3M}
H	1944–1945	Harvard Univ	Writing	(CV (VC	50) 50)	s_2	S_2

consonant syllables.   For these tests the syllable and sound articulations are here designated S_2 and s_2, respectively.   The systems tested are designated H–A, H–B, H–C, etc., the H indicating that the tests were made at Harvard University.   In these tests two male talkers and six male listeners were used.   Table 52 is a summary of these groups of articulation tests, together with the dates of the tests and the designations of the various articulation values.

The Relation Between Articulation Index and the Various Articulation Values

These various articulation values may be considered as probabilites. For example, the sound articulation s is the probability that a speech sound will be interpreted correctly and the syllable articulation S is the probability that a syllable will be interpreted correctly.   Similarly the

---

[3] T. G. Castner and C. W. Carter, *Developments in the Application of Articulation Testing*, Bell System Technical Journal, 12, 347, 1933; L. Y. Lacy, *Automatic Articulation Testing Apparatus*, Bell Lab. Record, 12, 276, 1934.

[4] OSDR Report No. 3802.

consonant articulation c and the vowel articulation v are, respectively, the probability that a consonant and the probability that a vowel will be interpreted correctly. If a syllable is composed of one consonant and one vowel, the probability that the syllable will be interpreted correctly is equal to the product cv.

From certain standpoints, the sound error $e = 1 - s$ may be regarded as a probability. This will be understood from the following considerations. As is well known, the speech sounds are transmitted from speaker to listener by waves having frequency components from about 100 cps to 8000 cps. Consider the frequency range divided into n frequency bands. It has been found experimentally that if e_1 is the sound articulation error when only the first band is used, e_2 when only the second band is used, and e_k when only the kth band is used, then when all bands are used simultaneously, the sound articulation error e is given by the following product:

$$e = e_1 e_2 \cdots e_k \cdots e_n. \qquad (15\text{--}1)$$

In other words, $e_1, e_2 \cdots e_k \cdots e_n$ act as probabilities. This relationship was deduced by J. Q. Stewart in 1921 from articulation data on band pass filters which could not be considered as very accurate but the concept proved to be a useful one. It will be shown that only small corrections to this fundamental equation are necessary to fit the various kinds of articulation tests. For example, if 10 errors out of 100 spoken sounds are made when only band 1 is used, and 20 errors are made when only band 2 is used, then when both bands 1 and 2 are used simultaneously, the error is $e = 0.1 \times 0.2 = 0.02$, or two errors will be made.

As before, let s = sound articulation corresponding to error e. Then $e = 1 - s$; $e_1 = 1 - s_1$; etc. Hence equation $(15\text{--}1)$ can be written thus:

$$1 - s = (1 - s_1)(1 - s_2) \cdots (1 - s_k) \cdots (1 - s_n)$$

from which the following relation is obtained:

$$\log(1 - s) = \sum_{1}^{n} \log(1 - s_k). \qquad (15\text{--}2)$$

If we regard $\log(1 - s_k)$ as a property of the kth frequency band which measures the contribution of this band, then equation $(15\text{--}2)$ states that the total contribution of the entire frequency band transmitted is equal to the sum of the contributions of the various partial frequency bands used singly. The term articulation index A has been used to designate such a simply additive measure of the contribution of a frequency band, and it is related to the quantity $\log(1 - s)$ by a factor of proportionality, as shown by the equation

$$A = -(Q/p)\log_{10}(1 - s). \qquad (15\text{--}3)$$

The quantity $\log_{10}(1 - s)$ is always negative when $s > 0$; and the two quantities Q and p which enter into the factor of proportionality are each taken as positive in sign. Thus a negative sign before the right-hand member of equation $(15–3)$ insures that the articulation index A will be positive in sign (if not zero).

The quantity Q in equation $(15–3)$ is a constant and will now be evaluated.

The quantity p is called the proficiency factor for it is dependent upon the proficiency of the particular talker-listener pair combination. It is sometimes called the practice factor. It may be divided into two factors—namely, p_T, the proficiency factor for the talker; and p_L, the proficiency factor for the listener. Then

$$p = p_T p_L, \qquad (15–4)$$

so if the talker speaks in a language unfamiliar to the listener $p_T = 0$ and so $p = 0$, and consequently s will be zero regardless of the value of the articulation index A. It is useful to divide p into these two factors when one desires to rate the proficiency of the talker and listener separately. For example, children in schools for the deaf can be rated on this scale. However, for calculating the articulation of telephone systems it is only necessary to know p. For a well-practiced and intelligent talker-listener pair the value p is taken arbitrarily equal to unity and Q is chosen so this is possible. Also the value for A for a flat response system having optimum amplification (that is, best for interpreting the speech sounds) is also taken arbitrarily equal to unity.[4a] It has been found experimentally that when such a pair with $p = 1.0$ make articulation tests over a system with $A = 1.0$, then s is found to be 0.985. Consequently, from equation $(15–3)$ the value of Q is found to be 0.55.

The 1935–1936 articulation crew of talkers and listeners was chosen as the crew for which the proficiency factor p shall be equal to unity. The average value of s for this crew corresponds to 0.985 for the flat response system at optimum amplification. Such a system will be called an ideal system and such a talker-listener pair a reference pair. For all other systems the value of A is between unity and zero and is a quantitative measure of the merit of the system for transmitting the speech sounds.

So when a talker uses a constant talking intensity level and a fixed transmission system transmits the speech sounds to a listener, then the articulation index A is constant and the two quantities, p the proficiency,

---

[4a] Although the present analysis of articulation phenomena assumes that the optimum telephone system is one having a uniform orthotelephonic response at all frequencies, other methods of analysis may make different assumptions. However, the writers know of no articulation observations which are sufficiently accurate to distinguish between these assumptions.

and s the sound articulation obtained, vary together in accordance with equation (15–3). For a system with adjustable gain the maximum articulation index depends only upon the system and is independent of talkers and listeners. In a paper[5] (not yet published) delivered before the Acoustical Society of America in 1945, W. A. Munson showed that an equation similar to equation (15–3) can be deduced from the statistical properties of speech and hearing.

As will be shown later, equation (15–3) fits the experimental data taken for systems III. Thus the equation

$$s_{3M} = 1 - 10^{-Ap/0.55} \qquad (15\text{–}5)$$

holds without modification for data taken on systems III. For the results of articulation tests on systems other than III, slight modifications of equation (15–5) are necessary. Before considering the experimental data which show what these modifications must be, it is necessary to consider the probability relationships between the various types of articulation.

Syllables of the type consonant-vowel-consonant were also used for systems II but the sounds heard were recorded by writing rather than by punching a key so that the listener had a chance to change some of the letters after they had been written if he thought an error had been made. One would expect the techniques used in testing systems II and III would yield approximately the same results. They do except for high values where the data show s_3 to be slightly greater than s_{3M} but definitely more than the observational error. The values of s_{23} are also slightly higher than s_{3M}.

Consider the probability relationships existing between the various articulation values. In a syllable of the type consonant-vowel-consonant the syllable articulation S_3 is related to the consonant articulation c and the vowel articulation v by the equation

$$S_3 = cvc. \qquad (15\text{–}6)$$

Since there are twice as many consonants as vowels in such lists,

$$s_3 = (2c + v)/3. \qquad (15\text{–}7)$$

If we define λ by the equation

$$\lambda = v/c \qquad (15\text{–}8)$$

then

$$S_3 = \lambda(3/\lambda + 2)^3 s_3^3. \qquad (15\text{–}9)$$

Similarly for the Harvard lists, which were of the type consonant-vowel

---

[5] W. A. Munson, *Relation between the Theory of Hearing and the Interpretation of Speech Sounds*, Journal Acoustical Society America, 17, 103A, 1945.

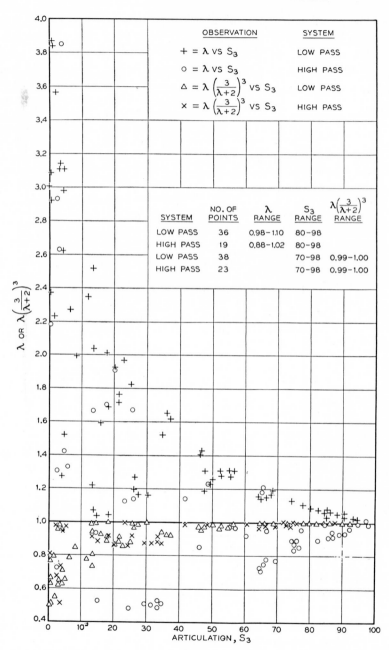

FIG. 174.—OBSERVED VALUES OF λ AND $\lambda(3/\lambda + 2)^3$ VERSUS SYLLABLE ARTICULATION S_3 FOR FILTER SYSTEMS.

and vowel-consonant, the value of S_2 is given by

$$S_2 = cv = \lambda(2/\lambda + 1)^2 s_2{}^2. \tag{15-10}$$

For the lists used in set I there were 80 of the consonant-vowel-consonant type and 10 of the vowel-consonant type and 10 of the consonant-vowel type so

$$S_{23} = \tfrac{1}{5}cv + \tfrac{4}{5}cvc \tag{15-11}$$

and

$$S_{23} = \tfrac{1}{5}\lambda(14/5\lambda + 9)^2 s_{23}{}^2 + \tfrac{4}{5}\lambda(14/5\lambda + 9)^3 s_{23}{}^3. \tag{15-12}$$

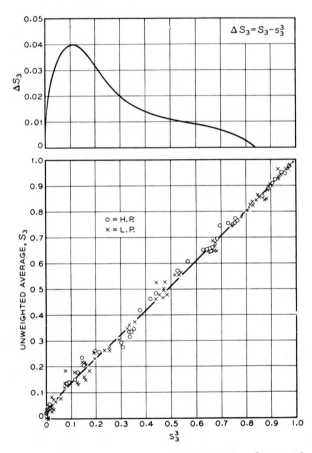

Fig. 175.—Unweighted Average Syllable Articulation S_3 and ΔS_3 versus Cube of Speech Sound Articulation $s_3{}^3$ for Filter Systems.

All of these probability relations are dependent upon the proposition that the probability of interpreting one sound is independent of the other sounds in the syllable. However, the data indicate that this is not strictly true so corrections for this lack of independence must be made.

These relations are dependent upon λ, which is known to vary through wide limits. For example, in Fig. 174 are shown all the data taken on filter systems II. The values of S_3 are shown as abscissas and the values of λ and $\lambda(3/\lambda + 2)^3$ as ordinates. The values of λ are scattered but most of the points for the high pass filter systems are below unity while those for the low pass filter systems are above unity. These varying values of λ make it seem hopeless to obtain unique relations between s_{3M}, S_3, s_3, S_2, s_{23}, and S_{23}. However, the case is not as bad as it looks for the factor $\lambda(3/\lambda + 2)^3$ varies only from unity to 0.9 as λ varies from

TABLE 53

MAXIMUM VALUES OF s_{3M} FOR IDEAL FILTER SYSTEMS

Cut-off frequency estimated from response curve	Estimated correction Δf	Ideal filter cut-off frequency f_c	Observed sound articulation s_{3M}
High pass filter systems			
520 c.p.s	45 c.p.s	565 c.p.s.	0.975
1000	25	1025	0.95
1410	15	1425	0.91
1410	15	1425	0.925
2510	10	2520	0.74
2510	10	2520	0.77
System III		285	0.981
Low pass filter systems			
1040	0	1040	0.68
1040	0	1040	0.705
1920	15	1905	0.875
1920	15	1905	0.875
2930	45	2885	0.94
4550	150	4400	0.973
System III		6500	0.981

0.6 to 1.75. It is seen to be unity for values of S_3 greater than 0.6. However, there are other influences—one referred to above being the lack of independence of one sound articulation upon the other two in the syllable—which have a greater effect than the effect of the departure of λ from unity. That this is true is shown by the curve in Fig. 175, which shows a plot of S_3 versus $s_3{}^3$ for all the set II filter data. According to equation (15–9) S_3 should always be less than $s_3{}^3$ but the curve through the data shows that S_3 is always either greater than or equal to $s_3{}^3$. Consequently one must rely upon the experimental data rather than these statistical relations but the latter are very useful because they hold except for small corrections which will now be considered. There is an influence, which we will call influence X, tending to make S_3 larger than $s_3{}^3$, which more than overcomes the effect of λ. It also affects the relation between s_{23} and S_{23} and s_2 and S_2.

Equation (15–5) is confirmed by experiments with filter systems from the series III tests, as now will be shown. An experimental curve of s_{3M} versus gain was obtained for each filter system and the maximum value of s_{3M} (corresponding to the optimum gain for interpretation) was determined from these curves. The values are given in Table 53.

Since the response of the filter systems only approached the ideal, certain small corrections to the cut-off frequencies were made as indicated in Table 53 in order to reduce the results to those which would be obtained if they were ideal. These corrections were first estimated from the lack of flatness of the response of the filter systems and the lack of steepness at the cut-off frequency. After the method of calculation here being developed was available, the estimates were made to agree with the calculated correction. These results are plotted in Fig. 176 by circles and dots and the two solid lines were considered to fit the points. The points corresponding to the $+$'a and $\times$'s will be discussed later. From this pair of solid-line curves one can obtain the function D which expresses at each frequency the importance of that frequency region for articulation index.

This function is defined by the equation

$$D = dA_f/df, \qquad (15\text{–}13)$$

where A_f is the maximum articulation index of an ideal filter system and f the frequency of cut-off. In other words, dA_f is the amount of articulation index carried by the small frequency band df in the frequency region between f and $f + df$ when the speech band is delivered to the ear at the optimum level for interpretation. For a low pass filter system with cut-off frequency f, then

$$A_f = \int_0^f D df. \qquad (15\text{–}14)$$

From equations (15–13) and (15–5) the expression for the function D becomes

$$D = (1/p) (0.239/1 - s_{3M}) (ds_{3M}/df). \qquad (15\text{–}15)$$

The values of s_{3M} corresponding to $p = 1.0$ are shown by the solid-line curves in Fig. 176. When the same curves are replotted using a linear scale of frequencies, the slopes of the curves give ds_{3M}/df, and so the function D is determined at each frequency. A plot of the values of D is shown in Fig. 177 by the curve $10^3 D(f)$ versus f. Also, the values of A_f from equation (15–14) are shown on this plot by the integral curve. Before drawing this final integral curve, three sets of data of the type shown in Fig. 176 were examined and the curve in Fig. 177 was

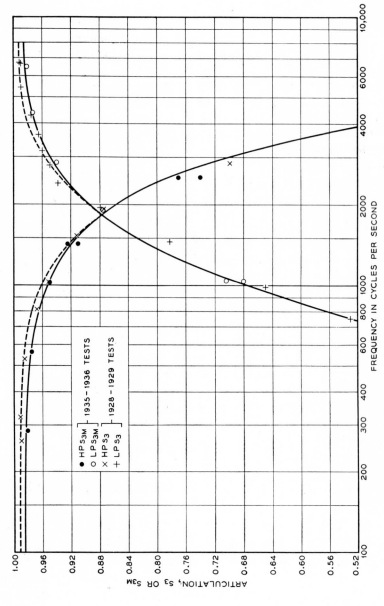

FIG. 176.—Speech Sound Articulation s_3 and s_{3M} versus Ideal Filter Cut-off Frequency.

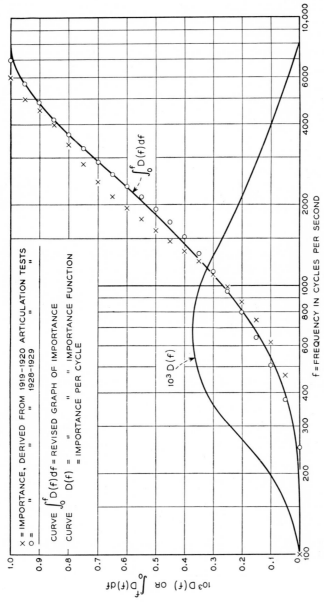

FIG. 177.—THE IMPORTANCE OF EACH FREQUENCY REGION FOR ARTICULATION OR INTELLIGIBILITY. (See also Table 53.)

chosen as giving the best fit for all of the facts known. The points indicated by circles in Fig. 177 define the earlier curve derived by Steinberg, Galt, and Anderson in 1937 and published in a paper by French and Steinberg.[3a] The points indicated by crosses define a still earlier curve obtained by Fletcher in 1921 and given in an unpublished memorandum.

Having the importance function D determined, the pair of curves for s_{3M} in Fig. 176 now can be computed from equation (15–5), with $p = 1.0$ so that

$$s_{3M} = 1 - 10^{-A_f/0.55} \qquad (15\text{--}16)$$

where A_f at each frequency is given by the integral curve in Fig. 177. The solid lines in Fig. 176 are such calculated curves. The agreement between the calculated curves and the observed points justifies the use of these curves in finding the derivative ds_{3M}/df from which the importance function D was obtained. Thus it is seen that equation (15–16) fits the set III data.

It will be realized that when the frequency importance function D has been integrated over a chosen frequency region from f_1 to f_2, the integral $\int_{f_1}^{f_2} Ddf$ is the same as the articulation index function, if the system is without noise and is composed of distortionless elements, and if it has an ideal uniform response at all frequencies with the over-all gain adjustment corresponding to maximum articulation for the ideal system. Consider a frequency such that the articulation of an ideal high pass filter system having this cut-off frequency is just equal to the articulation of an ideal low pass filter system having the same cut-off. These two systems having equal articulations must have equal values of the articulation index, each value being 0.5. The cut-off frequency of this pair of filters should agree with the intersection of the two curves in Fig. 176. The ordinate of the point of intersection is 0.876. When this value is substituted for s_{3M} in equation (15–16), the corresponding value of A_f is found to be 0.5 as it should be.

Because of the inherent lack of precision of articulation tests which form the experimental basis for the frequency importance function D, it is a matter of interest to discuss further the derivation of the function from this standpoint. Whether the function is derived by the method used in this paper or by the earlier procedure used in 1921 and also in 1937 and described by French and Steinberg,[3a] the basic data are of the same type and the first treatment of the data is the same. A series of articulation tests, over a wide range of gain adjustments, is made upon a high quality telephone system containing a filter of known cut-off fre-

[3a] N. R. French and J. C. Steinberg, *Factors Governing the Intelligibility of Speech Sounds*, Journal Acoustical Society of America, Vol. 19, page 90, 1947.

quency, and the results are shown as discrete points in a plot of articulation versus gain. Similar plots are made for various other cut-off frequencies. In any plot, each point shows the average of a certain number of values of articulation observed by each talker-listener combination. For example, in a plot of the set II tests of filtered systems each point shows the average of thirty-two talker-listener observations of the syllable articulation S_3. For points near the maximum articulation of a filter system the typical r.m.s. deviation σ of one observation from the average is about 0.02 to 0.05 when the suppressed frequency region is narrow, and about 0.07 to 0.15 when the suppressed region is wide. The values of $(1/n)^{\frac{1}{2}}\sigma$ for these points are typically from 0.005 to 0.025. These numbers are in terms of S_3, the maximum possible S_3 being 1.000. Through such an array of points a smooth curve is drawn, and the maximum ordinate of this curve is regarded as the maximum articulation for the cut-off frequency of the filter under test. Plots containing such arrays of points are shown in Figs. 197 and 199 for the set II filters, and in Figs. 196 and 198 for the set III filters. It must be remembered that the curves in these figures are not the curves just mentioned as having been drawn to represent the observed points. On the contrary, the curves in these figures were calculated using the functions adopted in the present paper, and hence their agreement or disagreement with the data in the regions of greatest articulation shows just how closely the curves in Fig. 177 represent the observed maxima. Although in each of these figures the response of the unfiltered system is included, the observed and calculated articulations are omitted to avoid crowding but can be found by comparison with Figs. 187 and 188.

When a smooth curve has been drawn to represent the array of points from articulation tests upon a filter with different adjustments of gain, it might be expected that the maximum ordinate of curve would be determined with an uncertainty comparable in magnitude with the quantity $(1/n^{\frac{1}{2}})\sigma$. In partial corroboration of this, it is found that repetitions of the set II filter tests at virtually the same gain, in the region of maximum articulation, generally yield values of S_3 which differ from the earlier values by an amount that does not exceed $(1/n)^{\frac{1}{2}}\sigma$. A few notable exceptions to this statement are found, which have raised the question whether or not in some instances other factors may have been operating—for example, some general gain or loss of proficiency on the part of the crew members.

The derivation of the importance function by the method used in this paper proceeds to assemble the maximum values found for the various filters, forming a succession of discrete points in a plot such as the points for the set III filters in Fig. 177. A curve is drawn to represent the points derived from low pass filters and another curve for high pass filters, the two curves being not independent but instead necessarily related because each represents the same function.   When both curves cannot be made to fit their respective sets of points, the fit of one curve or the other is sacrificed in the region of least precision.   Thus the integral function in Fig. 177 is made to depend more upon high pass filter observations in the low frequency region, and more upon low pass filter observations at the higher frequencies.

In order to derive a single integral curve from the results of three different sets of filter system articulation tests, there must be some basis for weighting the data.   The curve shown in Fig. 177 gives greatest weight to the set III data and least to the set I data, for the following reasons.   The number of voices used in these groups of tests was:

Set	Voices per test	Total voices
I	2	3
II	8	12
III	8	9

Thus the set I data were of limited relative value from this standpoint. Moreover, the responses of the set I systems were less well known, and there were fewer test from which the maximum could be determined in each plot of articulation versus gain.   The talking levels and circuit conditions in the set III tests were better controlled than in either of the other sets of tests, and the responses were better known.   The number of different gain adjustments used for each filter in set III was in general greater than in set II and much greater than in set I.   Thus the points in Fig. 176 representing maximum articulation values for the set III filter systems are regarded as more reliable than the corresponding maxima from set II and much more reliable than the maxima from set I (not shown in Fig. 176).

Having in mind these uncertainties associated with the data, an attempt has been made to re-draw the curves in Fig. 176 in such a way as to shift the intersection point as far to the right or to the left as the data would conceivably permit.   This study led to the conclusion that on the basis of the available articulation observations the intersection frequency in Fig. 176, and therefore the frequency in Fig. 177 at which $\int_0^f D df = 0.5$, could not justifiably be shifted either way by as much as 100 cps, and probably not by as much as 75 cps.   At higher frequencies the uncertainty in cps may be as great; at lower frequencies the uncertainty seems to be less than 50 cps.

Various writers have mentioned the resemblance between the curve $\int_0^f D df$ versus f (which involves the properties of both speech and hearing) and several other functions all of which are derived from tests of hearing or from a study of the ear.   The resemblances that exist among these other functions (which involve only the ear, and do not depend upon speech) have been known for some time. The relationship between the articulation index, or the frequency importance function for articulation, on the one hand, and the various functions of hearing, on the other hand, was recorded in 1939 in an unpublished memorandum by R. H. Galt. A general conclusion regarding the relationship between the importance of different frequency regions for articulation and the distribution of nerve endings on the basilar membrane was given in this memorandum from which the following is a quotation.[8]

"As a consequence of the spatial localization of tone stimulation on the basilar membrane, it seems that the number Δx of nerve endings associated with the frequency interval Δf must be at least approximately a simply additive quantity. For example, let there be one communication system which transmits only the band of frequencies from f_1 to f_2 and thus uses only a certain number N_1 of nerve endings for the purpose of recognizing speech sounds. Also let a second system transmit only the frequencies from f_2 to f_3 and thus use only a second group consisting of N_2 nerve endings. Then a third system transmitting the frequencies from f_1 to f_3 will use $(N_1 + N_2)$ nerve endings.

"Attention has already been called to the fact that the importance of a frequency interval for intelligibility is a simply additive function. That is,

$$\int_{f_1}^{f_2} D(f)df + \int_{f_2}^{f_3} D(f)df = \int_{f_1}^{f_3} D(f)df.$$

"It follows that a simple relationship might be expected to exist between these two functions, namely between the integral of the importance function and the position coordinate x, or between the importance function $D(f)$ and the slope dx/df of the curve x versus f (see Fig. 123). The relationship may be examined by plotting $\int_0^f D(f)df$ versus x, and it will be found that in the frequency region from about 700 or 800 cps to about 4500 cps the importance of any frequency interval for speech intelligibility is directly proportional to the number of nerve endings available. This relationship leads to the corollary that throughout the same region the available nerve endings are used uniformly by the spoken sounds of our language, in the conveying of intelligibility. Of course, this statement refers not to any one speech sound but to all the speech sounds in the aggregate."

The first relation between articulation and articulation index is that given by equation (15–5). The values of Ap and s_{bM} obtained by this equation are tabulated in Table 54 in columns 1 and 2. Although the

[8] Rogers H. Galt, *The Importance of Different Frequency Regions for Speech Intelligibility*, Journal Acoustical Society America, 20, 592A, 1948.

TABLE 54

RELATIONSHIP BETWEEN ARTICULATION AND ARTICULATION INDEX

$$s_{3M} = 1 - 10^{-A_\rho/0.55}$$

$$s_3 = s_{3M} + \Delta s_3 \qquad S_3 = s_3^2 + \Delta s_3$$
$$s_{23} = s_{3M} + \Delta s_{23} \qquad S_{23} = 0.8\,s_{23}^3 + 0.2\,s_{23}^2$$
$$s_2 = s_{3M} + \Delta s_2 \qquad S_2 = s_2^2$$

1 A_ρ	2 s_{3M}	3 Δs_3	4 s_3	5 ΔS_3	6 S_3	7 Δs_{23}	8 s_{23}	9 S_{23}	10 Δs_2	11 s_2	12 S_2	13 I
1.10	0.990	0.006	0.996	0	0.988	0.006	0.996	0.989	0	0.990	0.980	0.999
1.05	0.988	0.006	0.994	0	0.982	0.006	0.994	0.983	0	0.988	0.976	0.999
1.00	0.985	0.007	0.992	0	0.976	0.007	0.992	0.978	0	0.985	0.970	0.999
0.98	0.983	0.008	0.991	0	0.973	0.008	0.991	0.975	0	0.983	0.967	0.999
0.96	0.982	0.008	0.990	0	0.970	0.008	0.990	0.972	0	0.982	0.964	0.998
0.94	0.980	0.009	0.989	0	0.967	0.009	0.989	0.969	0	0.980	0.961	0.998
0.92	0.979	0.009	0.988	0	0.964	0.009	0.988	0.966	0	0.979	0.958	0.997
0.90	0.977	0.010	0.987	0	0.961	0.010	0.987	0.963	0.001	0.977	0.955	0.997
0.88	0.975	0.010	0.985	0	0.956	0.010	0.985	0.959	0.001	0.976	0.952	0.996
0.86	0.973	0.010	0.983	0	0.950	0.010	0.983	0.953	0.002	0.974	0.949	0.996
0.84	0.970	0.011	0.981	0	0.943	0.011	0.981	0.947	0.002	0.972	0.945	0.996
0.82	0.968	0.010	0.978	0	0.935	0.010	0.978	0.939	0.003	0.970	0.941	0.995
0.80	0.965	0.010	0.975	0	0.926	0.010	0.975	0.931	0.004	0.968	0.937	0.995
0.78	0.962	0.009	0.971	0	0.916	0.009	0.971	0.921	0.004	0.966	0.932	0.994
0.76	0.958	0.009	0.967	0	0.906	0.009	0.967	0.910	0.004	0.962	0.926	0.994
0.74	0.955	0.008	0.963	0	0.894	0.008	0.963	0.900	0.005	0.959	0.920	0.993
0.72	0.951	0.008	0.959	0	0.882	0.008	0.959	0.890	0.005	0.956	0.914	0.993
0.70	0.947	0.007	0.954	0	0.868	0.007	0.954	0.877	0.006	0.952	0.906	0.992
0.68	0.942	0.007	0.949	0	0.854	0.007	0.949	0.864	0.006	0.948	0.898	0.992
0.66	0.937	0.006	0.943	0	0.839	0.007	0.944	0.850	0.007	0.943	0.889	0.991
0.64	0.931	0.006	0.937	0	0.824	0.007	0.938	0.836	0.007	0.938	0.879	0.991
0.62	0.925	0.005	0.930	0.001	0.806	0.007	0.932	0.822	0.007	0.932	0.869	0.990
0.60	0.919	0.003	0.922	0.002	0.787	0.007	0.926	0.807	0.008	0.926	0.858	0.990
0.58	0.912	0.002	0.914	0.003	0.767	0.007	0.919	0.790	0.008	0.920	0.846	0.988
0.56	0.904	0.001	0.905	0.004	0.746	0.007	0.911	0.771	0.008	0.912	0.832	0.986
0.54	0.896	0	0.896	0.005	0.725	0.007	0.903	0.752	0.009	0.904	0.818	0.984
0.52	0.887	0	0.887	0.006	0.704	0.007	0.894	0.732	0.009	0.896	0.802	0.982
0.50	0.877	0	0.877	0.007	0.681	0.008	0.885	0.711	0.009	0.886	0.785	0.980
0.48	0.866	0	0.866	0.008	0.657	0.009	0.875	0.689	0.009	0.875	0.767	0.976

0.46	0.854	0	0.854	0.009	0.632	0.010	0.864	0.665	0.010	0.864	0.747	0.971
0.44	0.842	0	0.842	0.009	0.606	0.011	0.853	0.642	0.010	0.852	0.726	0.967
0.42	0.828	0	0.828	0.010	0.578	0.013	0.841	0.617	0.011	0.839	0.704	0.964
0.40	0.813	0	0.813	0.010	0.547	0.014	0.827	0.589	0.011	0.824	0.679	0.960
0.38	0.796	0	0.796	0.011	0.515	0.015	0.811	0.558	0.012	0.808	0.653	0.954
0.36	0.778	0	0.778	0.012	0.483	0.016	0.794	0.527	0.012	0.790	0.625	0.948
0.34	0.759	0	0.759	0.013	0.450	0.018	0.777	0.497	0.013	0.772	0.596	0.940
0.32	0.738	0	0.738	0.014	0.416	0.022	0.760	0.467	0.013	0.751	0.564	0.932
0.30	0.715	0	0.715	0.016	0.382	0.027	0.742	0.437	0.014	0.729	0.531	0.925
0.28	0.690	0°0	0.690	0.018	0.347	0.033	0.723	0.407	0.014	0.704	0.496	0.91
0.26	0.663	0	0.663	0.021	0.312	0.041	0.704	0.378	0.015	0.678	0.460	0.90
0.24	0.634	0	0.634	0.024	0.279	0.049	0.683	0.348	0.015	0.649	0.422	0.87
0.22	0.602	0	0.602	0.029	0.247	0.059	0.661	0.318	0.016	0.618	0.382	0.84
0.20	0.567	0	0.567	0.034	0.216	0.071	0.638	0.289	0.018	0.585	0.342	0.80
0.18	0.529	0	0.529	0.038	0.186	0.085	0.614	0.261	0.023	0.552	0.304	0.76
0.16	0.488	0	0.488	0.040	0.156	0.101	0.589	0.233	0.031	0.519	0.269	0.67
0.14	0.444	0	0.444	0.039	0.127	0.118	0.562	0.205	0.040	0.484	0.234	0.57
0.12	0.395	0	0.395	0.036	0.098	0.137	0.532	0.177	0.051	0.446	0.199	0.46
0.10	0.342	0	0.342	0.031	0.071	0.155	0.497	0.148	0.063	0.405	0.164	0.39
0.08	0.285	0	0.285	0.026	0.049	0.172	0.457	0.118	0.074	0.359	0.129	0.29
0.06	0.222	0	0.222	0.020	0.031	0.186	0.408	0.088	0.083	0.305	0.093	0.22
0.04	0.154	0	0.154	0.014	0.018	0.194	0.348	0.058	0.088	0.242	0.058	0.16
0.02	0.080	0	0.080	0.007	0.008	0.183	0.263	0.028	0.072	0.152	0.023	0.08
0.00	0.000	0	0.000	0.000	0.000	0.000	0.000	0.000	0.000	0.000	0.000	0.000

value of A never exceeds unity, the value of Ap may be higher for very expert talker-listener combinations. Therefore values of Ap from o to 1.1 are tabulated. Data similar to those shown in Table 53 for s_{3M} were also available for s_3 and are shown in Table 55. A plot of these data

TABLE 55

MAXIMUM VALUES OF s_3 FOR IDEAL FILTER SYSTEMS

Cut-off frequency estimated from response curve	Estimated correction Δf	Ideal filter cut-off frequency f_c	Observed sound articulation s_3
High pass filter systems			
250 c.p.s.	70 c.p.s.	320 c.p.s.	0.991
485	45	530	0.986
775	35	810	0.968
1000	30	1030	0.952
1500	25	1525	0.912
1900	15	1915	0.874
2850	15	2865	0.699
System II		260	0.990
Low pass filter systems			
755	0	755	0.53
1000	10	990	0.65
1480	20	1460	0.782
1980	30	1950	0.879
2440	40	2400	0.938
2850	50	2800	0.949
3250	65	3185	0.960
3700	75	3625	0.965
4400	100	4300	0.975
5600	160	5440	0.989
7000	250	6750	0.991
System II		6750	0.990

is shown in Fig. 176 by the $+$'s and x's. The dashed curve was considered to fit the observed points. Below the intersection point the solid curve was considered to fit the points for s_{3M} and also those for s_3 within the experimental error.

The difference between corresponding ordinates of the curves s_3 and s_{3M} in Fig. 176 is designated Δs_3 and is given in Table 54 in column 3. Since s_3 cannot be greater than unity, Δs_3 must approach zero as s_3 and s_{3M} approach unity. The addition of the numbers in columns 2 and 3 gives the numbers in column 4, which are the values of s_3 in the terms of Ap in the first column.

The relation between the syllable articulation S_3 and $s_3{}^3$ is obtained from the experimental data shown by discrete points in Fig. 175 which were obtained from articulation tests on a large variety of filter systems. The curve through the points was taken as fitting the experimental relation between S_3 and $s_3{}^3$. Above S_3 equal to 0.65 the value of S_3 will be seen to be accurately equal to $s_3{}^3$. Below this value S_3 is always greater than $s_3{}^3$ by an amount which will be designated ΔS_3.   The values of ΔS_3 chosen are defined by the curve but it is evident from the scatter of the points that this is only an average.   These values are given on an enlarged scale at the top of Fig. 175 and are recorded in column 5 of Table 54.   These values are added to the values of $s_3{}^3$ to give the values of S_3 recorded in column 6.   It is important to notice that these relations are accurate for values of Ap above 0.5 but can be considered as only approximate for values below 0.5.   Thus differences in this region between calculated and observed articulations will be expected to be of the same order as the scatter of the points in Fig. 175.

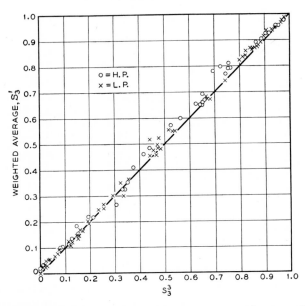

FIG. 178.—WEIGHTED AVERAGE SYLLABLE ARTICULATION S_3' VERSUS CUBE OF SPEECH SOUND ARTICULATION $s_3{}^3$ FOR FILTER SYSTEMS.

In order to take care of the skewness of the distribution of articulation values near zero and also near 100 percent, in the finding of an average of a group of values observed by different talker-listener pairs, a method of weighting these values was proposed in a paper[2] cited previously. Such weighted values were available for the systems II.   In Fig. 178 a plot of the values of such weighted average $S_{3(\text{weighted average})}$ versus $s_3{}^3$ is shown.   These weighted average articulations are taken from the same tests as the unweighted averages plotted in Fig. 175.   A comparison between Figs. 175 and 178 indicates that $S_{3(\text{weighted average})}$ is more nearly equal to $s_3{}^3$ than is S_3 for the lower values, but for the higher values S_3

is closer to the values of $s_3{}^3$ than is $S_{3(\text{weighted average})}$.   As stated above, all the values used in this paper are unweighted averages.

An examination of the corresponding values of S_{23} and s_{23} for systems I showed that equation (15–12) with λ equal to 1.0 held accurately over the entire range, or

$$S_{23} = 0.2s_{23}{}^3 + 0.8s_{23}{}^3. \qquad (15\text{--}17)$$

The data in Table 56 confirm this relation.   Two sets of data were taken upon the following four types of systems: (1) Approximately flat response system—HQ, (2) low pass filter systems—LP, (3) high pass filter systems—HP, and (4) band pass filter systems—BP.   Curves

TABLE 56

<small>RELATION BETWEEN SYLLABLE AND SOUND ARTICULATIONS FOR SYSTEMS I</small>

S_{23}	HQ	HP	LP	S_{23} BP	Average	$s_{23}{}^2$	$s_{23}{}^3$	$0.2s_{23}{}^2$ $+0.8s_{23}{}^3$
0.02				0.23	0.23	0.053	0.013	0.021
0.05				0.32	0.32	0.102	0.033	0.047
0.1	0.43			0.415	0.422	0.178	0.075	0.096
0.15	0.513		0.51	0.488	0.514	0.264	0.136	0.162
0.2	0.571		0.547	0.55	0.556	0.309	0.172	0.199
0.3	0.660		0.638	0.642	0.647	0.419	0.271	0.300
0.4	0.73		0.712	0.717	0.720	0.518	0.373	0.402
0.5	0.786		0.774	0.778	0.779	0.607	0.473	0.500
0.6	0.837	0.82	0.828	0.831	0.829	0.687	0.570	0.594
0.7	0.881	0.878	0.878	0.878	0.879	0.773	0.679	0.698
0.8	0.924	0.922	0.922	0.922	0.923	0.852	0.786	0.799
0.9	0.963	0.964	0.962	0.963	0.963	0.927	0.893	0.900
0.95	0.981	0.981	0.981	0.981	0.981	0.967	0.944	0.948

showing the relation between s_{23} and S_{23} were drawn through all of the points for each of these types of systems.   Values corresponding to each of the values of S_{23} shown in column 1 of Table 56 were taken from such sets of curves and are shown in columns 2–5, with the average for the four types of systems given in column 6.   The values of S_{23} calculated from the values of s_{23} given in column 6 by equation (15–17) are given in the last column.   A comparison of the first and last columns shows that formula (15–17) holds accurately not only for the region above $S_{23} = 0.65$ but also for the entire range of values.   This is a surprising result in view of the relation between S_3 and s_3 in this region.   The influence X referred to seems to just balance the effect of λ varying widely from unity.

Therefore, if we know the relation between s_{23} and s_{3M}, the values of s_{23} and S_{23} can be expressed in terms of Ap.

The values of s_{23} will be given in terms of $s_{3M} + \Delta s_{23}$.   From the statistical relationship shown by Fig. 175, it would be expected that the values of Δs_{23} would be equal to Δs_3 in the region above $Ap = 0.65$; they were so considered and are given in column 7 of Table 54.   The articulation data justify this assumption. In the lower range there are no experimental data giving a direct comparison between s_{23} and s_{3M} and thus giving Δs_{23} directly. So the values of Δs_{23} were chosen to give the best fit of the articulation data on a wide range of different systems. The values adopted are shown in column 7. These values of Δs_{23} are added to the values of s_{3M} to give the values of s_{23} given in column 8. The values of S_{23} are then calculated from these values of s_{23} by equation (15–17) and recorded in column 9.

In a similar way s_2 was obtained from s_{3M} by the addition of a correction term Δs_2. Since no values of s_2 were available to us we chose values of Δs_2 so that the articulation data given in terms of S_2 would best fit the calculated results. It is seen that these corrections are very small except for low values of s_2. In this region it is seen that Δs_2 is about $\frac{1}{2}\Delta s_{23}$. The values of Δs_2 are given in column 10. These values are added to s_{3M} to give the values of s_3 recorded in column 11. The values of S_2 are computed from these values of s_2 by the equation

$$S_2 = s_2{}^2 \qquad\qquad (15\text{–}18)$$

and the values recorded in column 12.

When sentences are used as a unit for testing the articulation the percent of sentences correctly understood has been called the intelligibility and indicated by the letter I. It is probable that the intelligibility is more directly related to the thing which it is desired to measure than is articulation. However, it is a much more difficult quantity to measure. It is evident that, due to memory effects, a set of sentences can be used with the same personnel only a very few times. Also, the psychological factors become more prominent when using sentences than when using simple syllables.

However, a set of simple interrogative and imperative sentences was compiled so as to obtain the approximate relation between the articulation as determined by the standard lists and the intelligibility as determined by the simple test sentences. In making up these test sentences the list was designed to test the observer's acuteness of perception and to minimize demands upon his intelligence. The questions are of a self-evident nature, the answers being frequently implied in the questions. They vary in length from about five to twelve or more words, each sentence containing four or five "thought" words. These "thought" words must be correctly received in order to understand the idea of the sentence. Various topics covered by ordinary conversation are represented, including personal experiences and points of interest in politics, science, and commerce. An effort was made to eliminate duplicate ideas. In only a few instances were the ideas repeated and in those cases the manner of expressing them was varied. In this manner forty-nine lists of fifty sentences each were compiled.   A sample of one of these lists is shown below.

Intelligibility List

List I

1. Name a prominent millionaire of the country.
2. How large is the sun compared with the earth?
3. Why are flagpoles surmounted by lightning rods?
4. Give the abbreviations for January and February.
5. Name the tree on which bananas grow.
6. How often does the century plant bloom?
7. What description can you give of the bottom of the ocean?
8. Explain the difference between a hill and a mountain.
9. What is the chief purpose of industrial strikes?
10. Describe the shoes of the native Hollander.
11. Name some uses to which electricity is put.
12. What would cause the air to escape from a bicycle tire?
13. Where is more grain raised, in the East or the West?
14. Tell what is meant by an Indian Reservation.
15. For what invention is Thomas Edison noted?
16. Name a state which has no seacoast.
17. Write the Roman numeral ten.
18. Explain the difference between export and import.
19. Explain why a corked bottle floats.
20. What substance is a good conductor of electricity?
21. Explain why Indians were afraid of firearms.
22. Explain the purpose of fire drills.
23. At what time do ocean waves become dangerous?
24. What medicine would you take to remedy indigestion?
25. What knowledge is covered by the study of astronomy?
26. Name a good restaurant in this vicinity.
27. What is the importance of large windows in stores?
28. Explain why a giraffe eats the foliage of trees.
29. How are the pages of a magazine held together?
30. Explain why the name string-bean is appropriate.
31. Name a nearby city in which there is a shipyard.
32. Name a fruit which grows in bunches.
33. Which of our Presidents went to South Africa?
34. Why are wire springs used in beds?
35. Why are books bound in stiff covers?
36. Why did the home people conserve food during the war?
37. Name an insect that has a hard shell.
38. What symbol on the United States money stands for liberty?

39. What weapons did the Indians use in warfare?
40. In what kind of weather does milk sour?
41. What streets in this city have Dutch names?
42. How does turning a ship's wheel steer the ship?
43. What nation aided us in the Revolutionary War?
44. What are some personal characteristics of the people of Japan?
45. What candy is black and good for colds?
46. Name a famous Indian Tribe.
47. Why is this building lighted by reflected light?
48. Why are most lighthouses situated on rocks?
49. Give some ingredients used in soap.
50. Why is a house built of stone superior to others?

In order to obtain an experimental relationship between the intelligibility and the syllable articulation, tests were made on eight transmission systems which gave syllable articulations varying from 5 percent

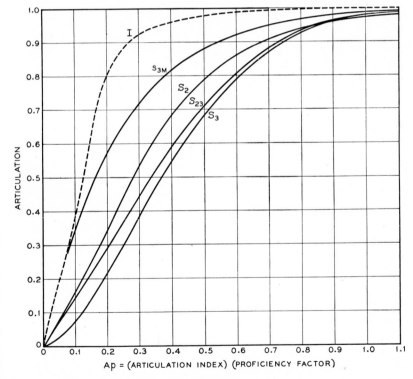

Fig. 179.—Relation between Various Measures of Articulation and the Articulation Index. The symbols for articulation are explained in Table I. The symbol I denotes sentence intelligibility.

to 98 percent.   Six observers were used in the work and 1800 sentences were used to determine the intelligibility for each condition.   Similarly, 1800 syllables were used to determine the articulation for each condition. The results obtained from these tests are shown by the dotted line in Fig. 179.   After a testing crew has had some practice at listening to sentences and syllables, it becomes more efficient in recognizing the speech sounds. However, the data indicated that within the observational error the improvement is such that the points will still remain on the curve; that is, if the articulation shows an improvement of from 5 to 10 percent the intelligibility will show an improvement of from 20 to 38 percent as shown by the curve.   This is consistent with practice coefficient relations discussed above.   It will be seen that for articulations of less than 20 percent a change of 10 percent in articulation is equivalent to a change of approximately 40 percent in the intelligibility, while an equal articulation change for distortions above 80 percent corresponds to less than 1 percent change in the intelligibility.   For this reason these test sentences are useful for testing systems having very large distortions but are of little value for testing ordinary transmission systems.

From these relations then the value of the intelligibility I and can be related to Ap.   It was from this curve that the values of I shown in column 13 of Table 54 were obtained.

So in Table 54 are contained the required relations between Ap, s_{3M}, s_3, S_3, s_{23}, S_{23}, s_2, S_2 and I.   Several of these relations are shown by the curves of Fig. 179.

Before setting up methods of calculating A from the physical characteristics of the telephone system and noise conditions at the listener's ear, the methods of defining the response of the system, the speech intensity level of the talker, and the acuity level of the listener will be discussed, and how these together with the proficiency p were applied to the talkers and listeners and systems used in this investigation.

CHAPTER 16

SPECIFICATION OF THE TELEPHONE SYSTEM RESPONSES, LISTENER ACUITIES, AND PROFICIENCIES OF TALKER LISTENER PAIRS

The methods of measuring the response characteristics of the various telephone systems used in this investigation will first be discussed.

The Responses of the Telephone Systems

With the exception of three systems having carbon microphones, every articulation test system included here consisted of linear elements. Condenser microphones were used. The receivers were dynamic type earphones except in the 1919–1925 tests, when simple bipolar structures were used having special air damping.

The performance of any telephone system is here expressed in terms of its orthotelephonic response characteristic, which at each frequency is equal to the difference in db between the transmission supplied by the telephone system and that supplied by the orthotelephonic reference system.[1] This reference system consists of the air path between a talker and a listener, using one ear, who faces the talker in an otherwise free acoustic field at a distance of one meter between the lips of the talker and the aural axis of the listener.

In plotting each response versus frequency characteristic for a chosen adjustment of the amplifier gain, the adjustment has been designated arbitrarily as gain $\alpha = 0$ db. The observed values of articulation have been plotted against the appropriate values of α.

In answer to the questions, how were these responses obtained? and how reliable are they?, a few remarks will be made regarding the three groups of telephone systems tested for articulation at the Bell Telephone Laboratories. For the fourth group, tested at Harvard University, reference should be made to publications by Egan and Wiener.

The earliest of these groups of articulation tests was made in 1919–1920, when response determinations were in a relatively early stage of development. As compared with later tests, these responses

[1] A. H. Inglis, *Transmission Features of the New Telephone Sets*, Bell System Technical Journal, 17, 374, 1938.

are known with less certainty, especially at the higher frequencies. Over-all single frequency measurements (not published) were made by F. W. McKown in such a way as to compare the transmission of the telephone system with that of a one-half inch air path between an artificial voice and an artificial ear, the reference system at that time being the air path employed when a talker speaks from a distance of one-half inch directly into the ear of a listener.

As a check upon the measurements at single frequencies, an over-all comparison was made between the high quality system and the one-half inch air path using a talker and listener. Two voices were used and five listeners. The comparison test involved selecting the gain adjustment of the system that caused the two specimens of speech (which were of nearly identical quality) to sound equally loud. For five talker-listener pairs the gain for equal loudness of speech was lower than the gain based on single frequency tests by the following amounts:

$$1, \ 0, \ 3.5, \ 3.5, \ 2.5 \ \text{db;} \quad \text{average} = 2 \ \text{db.}$$

The single frequency responses have been used in the present study and have been converted to responses of the orthotelephonic type. The conversion was accomplished by adding two increments required by the change in the reference air path. The first increment takes account of the decrease in the acoustic pressure of received speech waves [2] under reference conditions when the distance measured from the lips to the ear is increased from one-half inch to one meter less the semi-diameter of the head. The second increment allows for the decrease in pressure at the ear caused when the listener turns through 90 degrees so as to face the speaker.[3,4] Finally, on the basis of limited and uncertain evidence, the single frequency response characteristics have been extended to the region above 4500 or 5000 cps as shown by broken lines in the plots of the 1919–1920 responses. For the 1919–1920 high quality system, here termed system I, the response is shown in Fig. 186.

The 1919–1920 high quality system was also used in the 1924–1925 articulation tests involving interfering pure tones, shown in Figs. 207, 208, and 209.

For the two later groups (II and III) of articulation tests made at the Bell Telephone Laboratories, each over-all response may be regarded as obtained by adding together three responses measured separately,

---

[2] H. K. Dunn and D. W. Farnsworth, *Exploration of Pressure Field Around the Human Head During Speech*, Journal Acoustical Society America, 10, 184, 1939.

[3] L. J. Sivian and S. D. White, *On Minimum Audible Sound Fields*, Journal Acoustical Society America, 4, 288, 1933.

[4] F. M. Wiener, *On the Diffraction of a Progressive Sound Wave by the Human Head*, Journal Acoustical Society America, 19, 143, 1947.

namely, the real voice response of the microphone, the electrical response of the circuit, and the real ear response of the receiver. Actually, the basic over-all response from the experimental standpoint was that of the 1935–1936 high quality system. From it the other over-all responses for this group are derived by adding to the high quality response the responses of the inserted networks together with small differences, if any, in the microphones and receivers as measured by coupler calibrations. Similarly, the over-all response of the 1928–1929 high quality system in Fig. 187 has been derived from that of the 1935–1936 system in Fig. 188 by adding coupler differences together with an increment (measured by C. W. Carter) which allows for a change of housing of the condenser microphone; other 1928–1929 over-all responses are then obtained by adding the responses of networks.

The experimental procedure followed in making real voice measurements of the 1935–1936 condenser microphone, and in making real ear measurements of the receiver, need not be given in detail because adequate accounts of the methods have been described in the literature on the subject.[5] In regard to the precision of the response measurements, it is presumed that the performance of the electrical circuits was known to within close limits, so that comments need be made only concerning the real voice and real ear measurements.

The over-all response given in Fig. 188 for the 1935–1936 high quality system is the mean of two independent determinations of this response. Each determination contained a measurement of the real voice response of the microphone and of the real ear response of the receiver, involving many difference in the technique of measurement and in the personnel of the testing crews.

The precision of a set of measurements of the real voice response of a microphone will be illustrated by the first determination used here, from data obtained by H. K. Dunn. Five voices were employed, and the spectrum below 8000 cps was divided into eleven octave or half-octave bands. The response was measured for every voice for each of the eleven bands. The r.m.s. deviation of the response for one voice from the mean of the responses for the five voices was obtained for each frequency band, and the average value of this deviation for the eleven bands was found to be 1.2 db, the maximum value for any band being 2.3 db and the minimum 0.4 db.

The precision of a set of measurements of the real ear response of a receiver will be illustrated for the first of the two determinations used here. This response was the average of four values of response—one

[5] F. F. Romanow, *Methods of measuring the Performance of Hearing Aids*, Journal Acoustical Society America, 13, 294, 1942.

value obtained by S. D. White using threshold observations made by a crew of eight listeners, and three values obtained by W. Koenig and H. J. Michael from three sets of loudness balances made by a different crew of seven listeners. At each frequency, the response obtained by one listener using two or more trials was regarded as one observation; thus there were eight (or seven) observations in each test, and the r.m.s. deviation of a single observation from the mean was found. These deviations are in general smaller for the intermediate frequencies from 600 cps to 2000 cps than for the extremes, and tend in the aggregate to be from 3 to 6 db, with a maximum of 8 db and a minimum of 1.1 db. At most frequencies the set of threshold observations scattered somewhat more widely than the best two of the three sets of loudness balances. The four mean values obtained from the four sets of data were averaged at each frequency to obtain the response here referred to as the first determination of the receiver response. Each group of four mean values thus averaged was in general spread over a range of 2 to 5 db.

The first determination of the over-all response of the high quality telephone system tested in 1935–1936 was obtained by adding the microphone and receiver responses, of which the precision has just been indicated, together with the response of the electric circuit. The second determination of the over-all response was the result of other measurements, one difference being that the real voice response of the microphone was measured by W. Koenig using bands of width 200 cps throughout the spectrum. Either of the two determinations generally differed from the final average by less than 1 db below 1000 cps and by less than 3 db above 1000 cps.

The responses of the 1936–1937 telephone systems in Figs. 193–195, 210–211 were derived from real voice (band width 200 cps) and real ear measurements made under the direction of W. Koenig and P. V. Dimock. Several units of each type of carbon microphone were tested, and the average or typical response was adopted. Each "hybrid" microphone (designated as HY in figures) consisted of the mechanical elements of the corresponding type of carbon microphone, but with the carbon granules either removed (transmitter types 323 and 625) or retained but not connected electrically (type 395), and including a small condenser microphone, so as to provide essentially a linear instrument which resembled the carbon instrument in geometry and motional characteristics.

The noise employed in certain of the tests represented in Figs. 194, 195, 210, and 211 was introduced electrically into the circuit from a phonograph record of typical room noise. The plotted spectrum levels are the levels of a field equivalent to the noise reaching the ear from the receiver.

Acuity of Hearing of the Listeners

The available information concerning the acuity of hearing of the listeners in the articulation tests will be summarized in the present section of this paper. The information is not sufficient to permit the assigning of different measures to the different crews, but is sufficient to justify the adopting of a definite acuity at each frequency, which acuity is regarded as characteristic of each of the testing crews.

The assumption that the average acuity of hearing was the same for each crew is made plausible by the fact that every crew member was a selected young adult, and that each crew contained from six to nine listeners so that the effects of small random individual peculiarities would tend to cancel out in the averages of observed articulations. In the 1919–1920 group of articulation tests, antedating the audiometer, the requirement to be satisfied by candidates in order that they might be accepted as listeners was that their performance must not be abnormal in a series of rehearsal tests upon the high quality system with different gain adjustments. The members of the 1928–1932 and 1935–1937 articulation crews were selected on the basis of having normal audiograms, with some attention given also to their interest in the work and to their alertness and general facility of performance in rehearsal tests. At Harvard University the acuity of the observers was described as follows: "All of the crew members had satisfactorily normal hearing." It is understood that the candidates for the Harvard articulation crew were accepted only if the audiograms were normal.

In order to assign a useful measure to the acuity of hearing of the typical listener in the articulation tests, it should be understood that for any person having a definite ability to hear, there may be widely different measures of acuity depending upon the technique and circumstances of making the measurements and upon the skill of the listener developed through experience in observing thresholds and in making other auditory observations. For the purposes of the present study, two different measures of acuity are required in order to answer the two following questions. First, at each frequency what was the minimum audible pressure as measured through the use of a refined technique in an extremely quiet place, the listener being experienced in observing thresholds and having his ears well rested against auditory fatigue? Second, at each frequency what was the hearing loss of the same listener measured by an audiometer with standard technique, the listener being inexperienced in observing thresholds and taking only ordinary precautions against noise and auditory fatigue? The first of these measures of acuity is significant in considering the effect upon articulation of a noise having a known intensity or masking spectrum. The second measure is significant in comparing the articulation observed by the test crews with that which would be observed by a different listener who is not skilled in observing thresholds but has an audiogram measured in the customary manner.

The first of the two expressions for the acuity of the typical articulation test listener has been based upon the binaural zero loudness contour [6] of the American Standards Association. This contour corresponds to the thresholds of observers who are somewhat more acute than the average young adult having normal hearing. From various threshold tests made by W. A. Munson, it was concluded by the present writers that in the frequency region more important for speech perception the binaural field threshold level for a typical experienced young listener is generally from 1.5 to 3 db above the zero loudness contour level. In the present work this difference has been arbitrarily adopted as 2.5 db at every frequency. Thus a curve was drawn parallel to the A.S.A. zero loudness

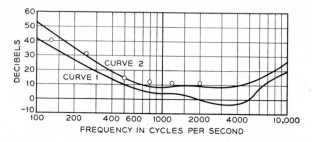

FIG. 180.—MINIMUM AUDIBLE PRESSURE LEVELS FOR TYPICAL LISTENER OF THE ARTICULATION TEST CREWS, IN DECIBELS FROM 0.0002 DYNE/CM². CURVE 1 = MONAURAL MINIMUM AUDIBLE FIELD. CURVE 2 = MONAURAL MINIMUM AUDIBLE PRESSURE LEVEL UNDER EARPHONE. POINTS = OBSERVATIONS FOR 1919–1920 CREW.

contour but above it by 2.5 db to represent the free field intensity levels of pure tones at the threshold of audibility for two-ear listening, for the typical listener of the articulation test crews. From this curve for two ears, the corresponding free field intensity levels at threshold for one-ear listening have been found by adding the difference (1 ear − 2 ears) given by French and Steinberg.

The curve thus derived is plotted as curve 1 in Fig. 180. This curve shows the free field intensity level of a pure tone which is just audible to a typical member of the articulation test crews facing the source and listening with one ear, the intensity being measured with the observer absent. The technique for observing the thresholds indicated by this curve is a refined technique similar to the procedures followed by W. A. Munson in threshold observations connected with studies of loudness and

[6] *American Standard for Noise Measurement*, Journal Acoustical Society America, 14, 109, 1942.

masking. Two different procedures have been described. By one technique [7] the tone level is lowered near the threshold by successive steps of 1 db until a reversal occurs—that is, until the tone becomes inaudible. Then the tone level is raised by steps of 1 db until a second reversal occurs, the tone becoming audible. The entire procedure is repeated until the reversal points are definitely located. The average of the levels corresponding to the ascending and descending reversal points is accepted as the threshold intensity level. By the second technique [8] the observer watches a signal light and by pressing a button indicates whether or not he hears a tone which is presented for a duration time of 1 second while the light is on, at intervals of 5 seconds. The tone level is controlled by a machine which selects at random one of seven levels available in steps of 2 db. Each level is presented five times. When the results of the test have been plotted to show at each level the number of times the tone was heard, and when a smooth curve has been drawn, one point on the curve indicates the level at which the tone is heard in 50 percent of the presentations, which level is accepted as the threshold level.

Another curve, closely related to the M.A.F. pressure level shown by curve 1 in Fig. 180, has been drawn to represent the minimum audible pressure level (M.A.P.) under an earphone receiver cap. In order to draw this second curve we have again started by raising the binaural zero loudness contour by 2.5 db to obtain the binaural M.A.F. of the articulation test crews. To this M.A.F. has been added the difference between the monaural M.A.P. and the binaural M.A.F. from Sivian and White.[12] The resulting M.A.P. for the articulation test crews is shown by curve 2 in Fig. 180. The corresponding technique for observing thresholds is a refined technique of the types described for curve 1.

To compare the measured acuity of the 1919–1920 articulation test crew with the acuity adopted as typical for all the crews, certain discrete points have been added to Fig. 180 for frequencies from 130 to 2000 cps. These points were derived from measurements of the acuity of hearing of articulation crew members. In these tests a single frequency e.m.f. was applied by an oscillator connected in place of the microphone of the high quality system. The voltage was found which caused the tone to be at threshold for an observer listening in the customary manner to the sound from the receiver when the system gain was adjusted to give unity reproduction as described in the section of this paper dealing with responses. This voltage was expressed as an equivalent pressure applied to the microphone, the conversion being made by means of the ther-

[7] H. Fletcher and W. A. Munson, *Loudness, Its Definition, Measurement and Calculation*, Journal Acoustical Society America, 5, 90, 1933.

[8] J. C. Steinberg and W. A. Munson, *Deviations in the Loudness Judgments of 100 People*, Journal Acoustical Society America, 8, 71, 1936.

mophonic calibration of the microphone. The pressure so found for the different members of the crew were averaged at each frequency and the corresponding average pressure level was plotted as a discrete point in Fig. 180. The agreement between these points and the corresponding ordinates of curve 2 is regarded as sufficiently close to justify the adoption of the curves in Fig. 180 to represent the acuity of hearing of the 1919–1920 articulation crew.

The two curves in Fig. 180 together describe the first of the two desired measures of the acuity of the listeners in the articulation test crews—namely, the acuity as it would have been measured by use of a refined technique, the listeners being experienced observers. Another desired measure of the acuity of the same listeners is shown in Table 57.

TABLE 57

AUDIOGRAM OF TYPICAL ARTICULATION CREW LISTENER BEFORE TRAINING

(1) Frequency c.p.s.	(2) Audiogram hearing loss — Observed using 2A audiometer db	(3) Audiogram hearing loss — Proposed standard audiometer db	(4) Minimum audible pressure level under earphone — From column 2 per search tube calibration db	(5) Minimum audible pressure level under earphone — From curve 2 Fig. 8 db	(6) Difference Column 4– Column 5 db
125 or 128	−3.4	−4.9	44.1	46.7	−2.6
250 or 256	−1.0	−7.0	38.3	29.2	9.1
500 or 512	−0.9	−6.0	28.1	14.1	14.0
1000 or 1024	−5.0	−4.5	17.6	8.3	9.3
2000 or 2048	−4.0	−2.2	19.6	9.0	10.6
4000 or 4096	−0.7	−4.4	20.0	9.6	10.4
8000 or 8192	0.0	−3.1	25.9	21.2	4.7
Weighted average loss for speech $\beta_u=$	−4.0	−3.9			

This table expresses the acuity of the typical listener in the articulation crews when the members of the crews had little or no previous experience in auditory testing. The acuity is given by two audiograms corresponding to the use, respectively, of the 2A audiometer and of the proposed A.S.A. standard audiometer. The origin of these audiograms, and the meaning of the other columns in Table 57, will now be explained.

For each of the twenty persons who acted as listeners in the 1928–1929 and 1935–1936 articulation tests, an audiogram is available which was measured by aid of the 2A audiometer using customary technique. In twelve instances the audiogram was taken either just before or shortly after the individual was employed by the Bell Telephone Laboratories. In the remaining eight instances, the person had been in the employment for from one-half to three years, but probably had not received training in auditory work to the degree represented by the later work in the articulation test crews.

Of the twenty listeners just mentioned seven took part in the loudness and masking tests during which threshold observations were made by the refined techniques previously described. In addition, for four other members of the loudness and masking crews there are audiograms taken either just before or shortly after the individual was employed by the Laboratories. So for twenty-four young adults who acted as listeners in the various crews and tests, audiograms are available which express the acuity of each listener when almost or quite inexperienced in auditory observations, each audiogram having been measured by the 2A audiometer with customary technique. The total of twenty-four persons thus considered together will be referred to as the group of 24.

At each frequency the average was found of the 24 values of hearing loss measured for these persons by means of the 2A audiometer. For each person the hearing loss of only one ear was used in finding these averages, namely the loss for the ear used customarily when listening with one earphone as in the articulation tests. The average hearing loss thus obtained at each frequency (the median, at 8192 cps has been entered in column 2 of Table 57, and together these values constitute an audiogram which has been adopted as the 2A audiometer audiogram of the typical listener of the articulation test crews at a time when each listener had little or no experience in making auditory observations. This audiogram corresponds to the use of a dial attenuation step of 5 db and to the selection of that value of hearing loss which is indicated by the dial at the lowest setting at which the tone is definitely heard.

Typically the average value of hearing loss in column 2 of Table 57 represents 24 observations distributed over a range of 15 to 25 db. Typically the root-mean-square deviation of one observation from the mean is about 5 db. The greatest value of the r.m.s. deviation is 6.9 db, for the observations at 8192 cps. For this frequency column 2 shows the median instead of the mean hearing loss.

The values shown in column 3 of Table 57 were derived from those in column 2 by aid of the differences between the tone pressure levels supplied by the two audiometers at zero dial setting. These values of hearing loss in column 3 together constitute the audiogram of the typical listener of the articulation test crew as measured by aid of the proposed A.S.A. standard audiometer using standard technique, the audiogram referring to a time when the listeners had little or no experience.

Column 4 of Table 57 shows at each frequency the pressure level under the cap of the earphone of the 2A audiometer for the dial setting indicated by column 2. These pressure levels are derived from the search tube pressures measured by W. A. Munson and reported by Steinberg and Gardner.[9]   To compare with these levels in column 4, column 5 shows at each of the 2A audiometer frequencies the M.A.P. level from curve 2 in Fig. 180   The difference between columns 4 and 5 of Table 57 is shown in column 6 and will be discussed briefly.

From the manner of deriving columns 4 and 5 of Table VI it is seen that these two columns show two values of M.A.P. for the same listener and therefore one might expect them to be approximately equal instead of unequal by the rather large differences shown in column 6.   However, these differences can be explained in the following manner.   Column 4 shows the M.A.P. when the threshold adjustment is the lowest audiometer dial setting at which the tone is definitely heard.   If the audiometer step had been much smaller than 5 db, these threshold levels would have been lower on the average by about one-half step or 2.5 db.   The differences in column 6 would then have been smaller by 2.5 db (except at the lowest frequency).   Moreover, the audiogram from which column 4 was derived applies to the typical listener when inexperienced, whereas column 5 applies to the listener when experienced.   From a comparison of audiograms before and after obtaining experience in auditory observations, for eight members of the group of 24, it is concluded that a fair value for the average apparent decrease in hearing loss as measured by the audiometer is 4 or 5 db.   This is in reasonably good agreement with a difference of about 6 db found by Steinberg and Munson[17] between the threshold levels at 1000 cps for a group of inexperienced observers and a group of experienced observers.   Thus experience in auditory testing may be regarded as accounting for about 5 db of the difference shown in column 6 of Table 57.

After accounting as just indicated for about $2.5 + 5 = 7.5$ db of the total difference shown in column 6 at each frequency, there remains a residue of difference which may be attributed to the effect of using dissimilar techniques in the two sets of observations from which columns 4 and 5 were derived.   Neglecting the two extreme frequencies, namely 128 and 8192 cps, this residual difference ascribed to technique amounts to about 3 db on the average, which is regarded as a reasonable value.   Thus it is concluded that the acuity of the inexperienced listener represented by the audiograms in column 2 and 3 of Table 57 is consistent with the acuity of the same person as an experienced listener represented by the curves in Fig. 180.

In the last line of Table 57, and in columns 2 and 3, the weighted average hearing loss for speech is entered as approximately or exactly equal to

---

[9] J. C. Steinberg and M. B. Gardner, *On the Auditory Significance of the Term Hearing Loss*, Journal Acoustical Society of America, 11, 276, 1940, Fig. 9.   If the recent probe tube results obtained by the Bureau of Standards are used the differences in the last column of Table 57 are much smaller.

— 4 db.   The manner of obtaining this weighted average from the single frequency observations is explained in Appendix 2.

Talking Levels and Proficiency Factors of the Articulation Crews

For a listener having a definite acuity of hearing and using a telephone system of chosen physical characteristics, the received speech has an intelligibility which depends upon the acoustic spectrum level produced at each frequency by the talker.   Therefore we need to know these spectrum levels for the various crews involved in the basic articulation tests.

The talking level is an over-all measure of the acoustic level and is here defined to be the long-time average intensity level of speech at a point one meter directly in front of the talker's lips in a free acoustic field and is designated β_t.   The long-time average intensity is the average taken over a length of time sufficient to include the typical pauses between syllables and words.   The measurements of talking levels of the various articulation test crews involve the use of actual test syllables with the introductory phrases, or an approximate phonetic equivalent.

Measurement was not made of the spectrum level versus frequency curves for each of the talkers used in the articulation tests, but data are available for certain of these talkers and for other talkers who are considered typical of those used in the tests.   These data, averaged, and smoothed, are given in Table 81 of Appendix 1 in the column headed B_s.

TABLE 58

TALKING LEVELS AND PROFICIENCY FACTORS FOR VARIOUS GROUPS
OF ARTICULATION TESTS

Date of tests	Acoustic talking level of crew measured or estimated	Proficiency factor p
1919–1920	*69 db from 10^{-16} watt/cm²	0.88 to 1.0
1924–1925	*68 to 70	0.95 to 1.05
1928–1929	69	1.0
1935–1936	68.5 to 69.5	1.0
1936–1937	66 to 67.5	1.0
{ 1944–1945 (Harvard) }	70	1.0

* = estimated.

The talking level β_t corresponding to this spectrum level B_s is $\beta_t = 68$ db from 10^{-16} watt/cm², which has been chosen as typical of conversational speech.   Tests made upon talkers using the telephone indicate that for about 95 percent of them the talking level may be anywhere from 55 to 75 db.   It will be seen from Table 58 that the average talking level for any one of the various articulation test crews varied by not more than 2 db from this 68-db value.   Therefore, it was considered that the spectrum level curves were raised or lowered uniformly by the difference between 68 and the observed talking levels.   The values given in Table 58 are those used in the calculations of articulation versus gain to be described.

If the shape of the spectrum level curve for a talker departs radically from that shown in Table 81, for example as in whispered speech, then in order to calculate articulation by the present method it is necessary to treat the case differently from any considered here.   However, it is presumed that the departures in db at each frequency of such a spectrum level curve from the typical one may be treated as a corresponding change in the response curve of the transmission system.

Table 58 includes also the values of the proficiency factor p for the various articulation crews.   These values were obtained from the articulation tests in the following manner.   As already stated, the proficiency factor $p = 1.0$ was arbitrarily made to apply to the 1935–1936 testing crew in the tests of the high quality and filtered systems by choosing the value of Q in equation (15–3) equal to 0.55.   The same proficiency factor was used for the other 1935–1936 systems.

In Fig. 176 a pair of curves was drawn to represent the maximum values of observed sound articulation s_{3M} for the low pass and high pass filters, respectively, in the 1935–1936 tests.   In the same plot another pair of curves represents the corresponding quantity s_3 for the 1928–1929 filtered systems.   At the intersection point of each pair of curves the sound articulation is the same and hence the values of articulation index for the low pass and the high pass filtered systems must be equal to each other so that $A = 0.5$ for each of these systems.   The intersection point is seen to be the same for the two pairs of curves.   It follows that for a system having the index $A = 0.5$ the 1928–1929 crew obtained the same value of sound articulation as did the 1935–1936 crew.   For this reason the proficiency factor $p = 1.0$ was applied also to the 1928–1929 crew and is so shown in Table 58.

Although the proficiency factor $p = 1.0$ has here been applied to all of the 1928–1929 systems, there is some evidence that for two or three of the filtered systems the crew was relatively low in training.

For any particular testing crew it may happen that articulation data for noiseless filtered systems are not available to the extent required for a plot of the type of Fig. 176.   In such a case the proficiency factor is chosen to fit the articulation values observed by the crew using one of the systems, preferably the system having highest observed articulations, and then this value of the factor is applied to all the other systems tested by the same crew.   For example, this procedure has been followed in considering the fourth major group of articulation tests, which were made at Harvard University with due regard to the requirement that when conditions are changed, proficiency tests must be made until the training reaches the previous stable level. The value $p = 1.0$, which has been used here for all of the tests of group IV as well as for those of groups II and III, represents apparently a typical degree of proficiency for a testing crew composed of selected normal young adults who are well trained and have an incentive to give attention to their work.

An examination of the results of the 1919–1920 articulation tests yields definite evidence of an increase in proficiency on the part of the testing crew during this long series of tests. This is shown by the observed values of articulation for the high quality system for values of gain near the optimum, as plotted in Fig. 186, where the maximum observed value of articulation was between 0.94 and 0.95 in November, 1919, but had risen to become 0.95 to 0.96 in January, 1920, and reached 0.975 in April, 1920. To make the calculated articulations for this high quality system agree approximately with observed articulations at optimum gain, the proficiency factor $p = 0.88$ has been adopted for November, 1919, $p = 0.98$ for January, 1920, and $p = 1.0$ for February to December, 1920. Between these tests of the high quality system, many resonant systems and filtered systems were tested, so for these systems the proficiency factor has been arranged on the chronological basis derived from the tests upon the high quality system as just explained. Thus the resonant systems represented in Fig. 205 which were tested in early December, 1919 were assigned the value $p = 0.9$; and for the resonant systems in Fig. 206 which were tested in late December, 1919 and early January, 1920, the assigned value was $p = 0.94$.

The test represented in Figs. 207 and 208 were made in 1924, and those in Fig. 209 were made in 1925. The group I high quality system was used in these tests, without and with various interfering single frequency tones admitted at the received levels indicated in the plots. For each of these figures the value of the practice factor has been assigned so as to make calculated articulations agree with those observed, for the high quality system with no noise and with optimum gain.

From the standpoint of talking level, it is convenient to discuss the four groups of articulation tests in the reverse of the chronological order.

During the Harvard tests, the talker endeavored to keep his talking level uniform through hearing his own voice and watching a VU-meter, monitoring undistorted speech, which had been calibrated by comparison with a square law integrator used under free field conditions. The talking level in these tests was reported by Egan and Wiener[4] above as 70 db.

The articulation tests made at the Bell Telephone Laboratories in 1935–1936 involved the use of automatic equipment which has been described in published articles,[3] above including two volume indicators monitoring, respectively, the undistorted speech output of the microphone and the input to the receivers necessarily following the distorting network, if any. The first of these instruments gave a visual signal. The second instrument gave a printed record of the average speech wave level actually applied to the receivers, thus including the small variations in average level which occurred in spite of the attempt of the talker to maintain a uniform over-all talking level through hearing his own voice and watching the visual signal.

When the response of a system is known from talker to volume indicator, the reading of the volume indicator may be used in calculating the acoustic talking level. From such calculations for the high quality system, the 1935–1936 talking levels in Table 58 were derived, with an uncertainty of about ± 1 db.

In the 1936–1937 articulation tests of systems having either a carbon microphone or the corresponding linear "hybrid" microphone, the acoustic speech wave was applied to the microphone by an artificial voice forming a part of the caller's control circuit.[3] The human talker spoke into the high quality microphone of the caller's control circuit. As the response of the entire system from human talker to recording volume indicator was known, the acoustic talking level could be calculated. The average talking level so calculated varied from about 66 to about 68 db for the different systems which were tested. Another measure of the talking level of this crew was made using a calibrated condenser microphone under approximately free field conditions, resulting in the value 66.5 db which has been used here for all of these systems.

During the Harvard articulation tests every talker attempted to speak at the same over-all level. Likewise in the 1935–1936 tests the same over-all level was attempted by every talker, and the records indicate that such uniformity was attained on the average to within a fraction of 1 db. Consequently the average talking level and also the average received speech level is a relatively precise quantity for any one of these tests. The technique was somewhat different in the 1928–1929 tests. By preliminary trials each talker established his or her natural voice level and thereafter tried to talk uniformly at that level, hearing his own voice and watching a volume indicator which monitored the undistorted speech. The average volume indicator reading for every talker was recorded in writing for each test, the spread of such readings with respect to the average for all eight talkers being frequently greater than ± 6 db.

Although the volume indicator readings for the eight talkers differed considerably among themselves in the 1928–1929 articulation tests, the average of the eight readings for a test rarely differed by more than 1.5 db from the grand average for all the tests. While these differences may correspond to actual differences in the average acoustic talking level, they have here been used as shifts applied to the over-all gain setting so that the data could be plotted as though obtained with a uniform talking level. The grand average volume indicator reading was used together with the response from talker to volume indicator in calculating the average acoustic talking level for the entire group of tests.   The response entering into this calculation included the average over-all efficiency of the various condenser microphones employed in the tests.   Because this average efficiency was not so accurately known as in the later tests, it was thought desirable to supplement the calculation just mentioned by a second calculation based upon threshold observations of speech delivered by a system whose response characteristics are known.   As will be seen later, equation (15–22) gives the value of the talking level in terms of a weighted average of the response $\bar{R}_1$ and the gain α_0 necessary to deliver the speech so it will be at the threshold of hearing for the reference crew listeners.   This second calculation used the 1928–1929 observations of the gain adjustment which caused speech to be at the threshold of audibility when heard over the high quality system.   The two calculations were in satisfactory agreement and together resulted in the talking level 69 db in Table 58, with an uncertainty probably less than ± 2 db.

CHAPTER 17

METHODS OF CALCULATING ARTICULATION SCORES

In this chapter methods will be developed which enable one to calculate the articulation score of any specified talker-listener pair using any specified transmission system. The first step in this process is to determine the articulation index A of the telephone system being used.

The articulation index depends upon (1) the response characteristic R versus f for the system; (2) the over-all gain α from this response curve; (3) the noise conditions at the listener's ear; and (4) other special types of distortion such as overloading, room reverberation, etc.

It has been found that A can be calculated as the product of four factors: the articulation growth factor V, the ear desensitizing factor E, the maximum articulation index factor F, and the special distortion factor H, or

$$A = V \cdot E \cdot F \cdot H. \tag{17-1}$$

A formula such as equation (17-1), which is empirical, can be made to fit the complex set of experimental data because one has considerable latitude in choosing the variables for determining each factor. The separation into factors of this type is useful for engineering purposes because it makes clear the effect upon A of changing the two important variables, namely, the shape of the response curve and the amplification or attenuation in the system.

The first factor V shows how A grows as the gain α in the system increases and it depends upon the effective gain x_V, which will be defined later.

The second factor E is dependent upon the level of the speech above the threshold level in the absence of noise—that is, the stimulation level in the listener's ear. It is unity when this level is below 68 db and gradually decreases as the level increases above this value.

The third factor F is dependent only upon the shape of the response curve. It is unity when the response curve is flat, and is between zero and unity for any other shape.

The fourth factor H is unity except when special types of distortion are present such as overloading, carbon microphone distortion, and when high intensity noise is present.

The Effective Gain x_V

For any telephone system, the factor V in equation (17–1) grows from zero to the maximum value unity as the received speech level rises from the threshold level for audibility to some higher level. When the telephone system is an ideal flat response system, or an ideal filter system, the gain must be increased by 68 db in order that V may rise from zero to unity, and for such an ideal system the factor V may be expressed as a function solely of the level of the received speech above threshold. For many other types of system, however, V cannot be so simply expressed. In general, it has been found necessary to define a quantity called the *effective gain* x_V, which may be regarded as the *effective* level of the received speech above threshold, so that when x_V is known the value of V is determined. The effective gain is defined in terms of the following quantities: the actual gain α of the system, the response characteristic R versus f from which α is measured, the talking level β_t, and the hearing loss β_H of the listener. The following equation defines this effective gain.

$$x_v = \alpha + \beta_t - \beta_H - 12 + \bar{R}_1 - \phi\gamma(\bar{R}_1 - \bar{R}_4). \qquad (17\text{–}2)$$

The first term α is the actual gain in db in the system from the responses shown on the plot of R versus f. The talking level β_t has been defined. The value β_H is the listener's hearing loss for speech. It was found that the average intensity level of undistorted speech was $\beta_H + 12$ db when at the threshold for a listener having a hearing loss β_H. For the typical listeners in our tests $\beta_H = -4$ so that for all the articulation test crews $\beta_H + 12 = 8$. Therefore, the level of the speech above threshold as it was uttered is $\beta_t - \beta_H - 12$.

The values $\bar{R}_1$ and $\bar{R}_4$ are weighted average values of the response R. The method of deriving them will be explained later.

The coefficient ϕ depends directly upon x_V and becomes zero when x_V is zero and is equal to unity when x_V is 40 db or greater.

The coefficient γ depends upon the shape of the response curve and lies between zero and 1.4.

It will be seen that for an ideal system where $\bar{R}_1 = \bar{R}_4 = R$, the value of x_V becomes

$$x_V = (\beta_t - \beta_H - 12) + (\alpha + R). \qquad (17\text{–}3)$$

The first term is the level above threshold level of the speech as uttered and the second term is the amplification given to the speech by the system. In other words, the value of x_V for an ideal flat response system is the db above threshold level of the speech at the listener's ear. When x_V is equal to zero, then ϕ in equation (17–2) is also equal to zero. Let α_0 be the amplification under these conditions; it is the db gain necessary to bring the speech delivered by the system to the threshold level of the listeners. Then, by equation (17–2),

$$\alpha_0 = \beta_H + 12 - \beta_t - \bar{R}_1. \qquad (17\text{–}4)$$

The value 12 was obtained from threshold measurements of speech using an approximately flat response system. Experimental values of α_0 were obtained for systems II and III (response curves shown in Figs. 187 and 188 for talkers having $\beta_t = 69$ db and listeners having $\beta_H = -4$ db, and values of $\bar{R}_1$ calculated from the response curves. It was found that these values satisfied equation (17–4) when the constant was 12 db.

It should be emphasized that for the crews used in the articulation tests reported in this paper $\beta_H = -4$ db so for these crews

$$\alpha_0 = 8 - \beta_t - \bar{R}_1.$$

For the tests made at Harvard the value of β_H could depart considerably from -4 db without affecting the calculated results since the threshold levels were determined by the noise. Equation (17–4) is very important because it enables one to calculate the gain α_0 required to reach the threshold level of hearing, that is the gain at which speech is just detectable as determined by the technique described in Appendix 1. This gain α_0 is regarded in the present paper as the foot of the articulation versus gain curve, neglecting any articulation scoring which in an actual test may occur through correct guesses even when no speech sounds are heard.

In order to use equation (17–4) one must know how to calculate $\bar{R}_1$. Loudness studies have shown that near threshold levels $\bar{R}_1$ can be obtained by the equation

$$10^{\bar{R}_1/10} = \int_0^\infty G_1 10^{R/10} df. \qquad (17\text{–}5)$$

The value $10^{R/10} df$ is proportional to the speech power carried by the frequency band df. Thus $10^{\bar{R}_1/10}$ is a weighted average value of the speech power. The value of the weighting factor G_1 depends both upon the hearing and upon the speech characteristics. But it can be determined directly from threshold measurements of speech as follows.

Let α_0 be the amplification in an ideal system which delivers speech to the ear at the threshold level. If an ideal low pass filter is introduced having a cut-off frequency f_c, then the amplification must be increased $\Delta\alpha$ above α_0 for the speech to be again at the threshold level. Then, as shown in Appendix 1,

$$\int_0^{f_c} G_1 df = 10^{-\Delta\alpha/10}. \qquad (17\text{–}6)$$

Similarly for high pass filter systems

$$\int_{f_c}^{\infty} G_1 df = 10^{-\Delta\alpha/10}. \qquad (17\text{-}7)$$

From experimentally determined values of $\Delta\alpha$ the curve for $\int_0^f G_1 df$ in Fig. 181 was determined as outlined in Appendix 1. The values of G_1

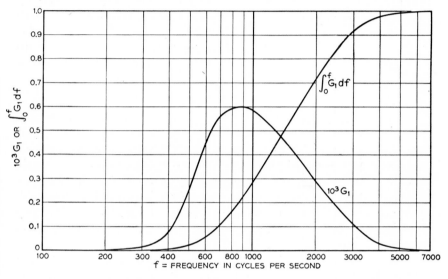

FIG. 181.—THE FUNCTIONS G_1 AND $\int_0^f G_1 df$. G_1 IS THE FREQUENCY WEIGHTING FACTOR FOR LOUDNESS, WHEN SPEECH IS AT THE THRESHOLD OF AUDIBILITY. (See also Fig. 50 and Table 59.)

were obtained from the slope of this curve when plotted with both coordinate scales linear as in Fig. 222.

Consider system II–RN–1060 which has a non-uniform response shown in Fig. 182, and let $\bar{R}_1$ be the calculated value as given by equation (17–5) and indicated in the figure. Also consider an ideal system having a uniform response equal to $\bar{R}_1$. Then the attenuation in db to bring the received speech to the threshold level will be the same in both the ideal and the peaked systems. At levels near the threshold the speech delivered in each system will sound equally loud.

However, when gains of more than 40 db above the threshold level are introduced in each system, the speech delivered in each case will no longer sound equally loud; the speech from the ideal flat response system will be the louder. Now it might be expected that when the loudness of the speech in both cases is the same, the effective gain would be approximately the same. If this is true, then at these levels $\phi = 1.0$ and γ is approximately equal to unity (see equation (17–2)) so that

$$x_V = \bar{R}_4 + \alpha + (\beta_t - \beta_H - 12)$$

and system II–RN–1060 must have a weighted average response equal to $\bar{R}_4$ instead of $\bar{R}_1$ to make the two effective gains equal. However, we know from our loudness measurements upon speech (see Appendix 1) that at these higher levels one must take a weighted average of the fourth root of the speech power to obtain equality of loudness, or

$$10^{\bar{R}_4/40} = \int_0^\infty G_4 10^{R/40} df. \qquad (17\text{–}8)$$

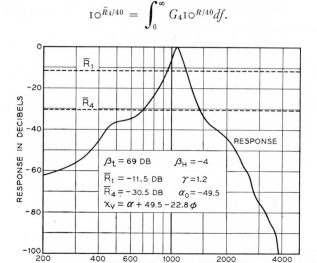

FIG. 182.—RESPONSE OF RESONANT SYSTEM II–RN–1060, WITH WEIGHTED AVERAGES $\bar{R}_1$ AND $\bar{R}_4$ AND VALUES OF γ, α_0 AND x_V.

It is shown in Appendix 1 that G_4 is related to G_1 through the properties of speech and hearing, so that

$$G_4 = G_1^{\frac{1}{4}} 10^{-3\kappa/40} \quad \text{(constant)} \qquad (17\text{–}9)$$

where κ is the critical band width in db and the constant is determined by the condition that

$$\int_0^\infty G_4 df = 1.0. \qquad (17\text{–}10)$$

Values of G_4 thus determined are given in Table 81 of Appendix 1. The values of $\int_0^f G_1 df$ and $\int_0^f G_4 df$ are given in Tables 59 and 60. The tables are arranged so that the frequency f is given for each 0.01 increase in the integral since this form is most useful for calculation. To evaluate equation (17–5) one plots $\int_0^f G_1 df$ as abscissas and $10^{R/10}$ as ordinates, then the area under such a plot is the required value of the integral. It is seen that an average value of $10^{R/10}$ taken at the one hundred different frequencies given in Table 59 gives a very good approximation to this value. For most systems it is sufficiently accurate to use only the twenty

TABLE 59

Values of f versus $\int_0^f G_1 df$. (See also Figs. 181 and 222.)

$\int_0^f G_1 df$	0.005	0.015	0.025	0.035	0.045	0.055	0.065	0.075	0.085	0.095
0.00	400	470	510	540	570	600	620	640	660	680
0.10	700	715	730	750	770	785	800	820	835	850
0.20	870	885	900	920	935	950	965	980	1000	1015
0.30	1035	1050	1070	1085	1105	1120	1140	1160	1175	1195
0.40	1210	1230	1250	1270	1290	1320	1340	1360	1380	1400
0.50	1420	1450	1470	1490	1520	1540	1560	1590	1610	1630
0.60	1660	1690	1710	1740	1770	1800	1830	1860	1890	1930
0.70	1960	1990	2020	2060	2090	2130	2170	2210	2250	2300
0.80	2340	2380	2430	2480	2530	2590	2640	2700	2760	2830
0.90	2910	3000	3100	3200	3330	3490	3560	3930	4420	5400

TABLE 60

Values of f versus $\int_0^f G_4 df$

$\int_0^f G_4 df$	0.005	0.015	0.025	0.035	0.045	0.055	0.065	0.075	0.085	0.095
0.00	180	250	320	370	410	440	470	500	530	555
0.10	580	605	630	655	680	705	730	750	775	800
0.20	825	845	870	895	920	945	965	990	1015	1040
0.30	1065	1095	1120	1145	1175	1200	1230	1260	1290	1320
0.40	1350	1380	1410	1440	1470	1505	1535	1570	1605	1640
0.50	1680	1720	1760	1800	1840	1880	1920	1960	2000	2040
0.60	2090	2140	2190	2240	2290	2340	2390	2440	2500	2550
0.70	2610	2670	2740	2810	2880	2950	3020	3090	3160	3250
0.80	3340	3430	3520	3620	3720	3830	3950	4080	4210	4350
0.90	4510	4690	4890	5100	5350	5660	6060	6600	7430	9600

frequencies in italics. The other frequencies are used only where R is changing rapidly with frequency. The calculation of $\bar{R}_4$ is made in a similar manner using Table 60. The value of $\bar{R}_4$ for system II–RN–1060 is shown in Fig. 182. A flat response system having this response $\bar{R}_4$ will deliver speech which at the higher levels sounds equally loud to that received from system II–RN–1060.

Equation (17–2) for the effective gain x_2 can be weitten

$$x_V = \alpha - \alpha_0 - \phi\gamma(\bar{R}_1 - \bar{R}_4) \qquad (17\text{--}11)$$

the value of α_0 being that in equation (17–4). This shows that for systems where γ is equal to zero (ideal filter systems) and for systems where $\bar{R}_1 = \bar{R}_4$ (ideal flat response systems) the effective gain is equal to $\alpha - \alpha_0$ or the db above threshold level. For older systems the effective gain is always less than $\alpha - \alpha_0$ by the amount $\phi\gamma(\bar{R}_1 - \bar{R}_4)$. For some systems the articulation growth curve approximately follows the speech loudness growth curve for a considerable range of levels above the threshold level of received speech, but this statement is not true for telephone systems in general.

It remains, then, to determine ϕ and γ before the value of the effective gain x_V can be calculated for any system. Before doing this it is necessary to determine V, E, and F because these functions are involved in the determination of ϕ and γ.

Determination of V and E

The articulation growth factor V and the ear desensitizing factor E are determined in the following manner from articulation data on three different systems designated I–III, for which the responses are given in Figs. 186–188.

TABLE 61

Articulation versus Gain for Ideal System

(1) $\alpha - \alpha_0$ or x_V or x_E	(2) S_{23}	(3) S_3	(4) s_{3M}	(5) A	(6) V	(7) E
0	0	0	0	0	0	1.0
5	0.073	0.024	0.189	0.05	0.05	1.0
10	0.163	0.084	0.367	0.11	0.11	1.0
15	0.289	0.216	0.567	0.20	0.20	1.0
20	0.437	0.382	0.715	0.30	0.30	1.0
25	0.604	0.563	0.821	0.41	0.41	1.0
30	0.752	0.725	0.896	0.54	0.54	1.0
35	0.850	0.839	0.937	0.66	0.66	1.0
40	0.905	0.900	0.957	0.75	0.75	1.0
45	0.943	0.939	0.969	0.83	0.83	1.0
50	0.961	0.959	0.976	0.89	0.89	1.0
55	0.975	0.967	0.980	0.94	0.94	1.0
60	0.975	0.973	0.983	0.98	0.98	1.0
65	0.978	0.976	0.985	1.0	1.0	1.0
70	0.978	0.976	0.985	1.0	1.0	1.0
75	0.976	0.974	0.984	0.99	1.0	0.99
80	0.975	0.973	0.983	0.98	1.0	0.98
85	0.972	0.970	0.982	0.96	1.0	0.96
90	0.967	0.965	0.980	0.93	1.0	0.93
95	0.963	0.961	0.977	0.90	1.0	0.90
100	0.956	0.953	0.974	0.87	1.0	0.87
105	0.950	0.946	0.972	0.85	1.0	0.85
110	0.943	0.939	0.969	0.83	1.0	0.83
115	0.935	0.930	0.966	0.81	1.0	0.81
120	0.926	0.921	0.963	0.79	1.0	0.79

It is seen that these systems had only an approximately flat response so certain small corrections, to be discussed later, are applied to obtain results corresponding to an ideal flat response system. The final results are given in Table 61.

For the ideal system, $\bar{R}_1 = \bar{R}_4 = 0$ so that by equation (17–11) $x_V = \alpha - \alpha_0$. Thus in Table 61 the level above threshold $\alpha - \alpha_0$ and the effective gain x_V are both given by column 1.   So also is the argument x_E of the function E, as will be explained.

In columns 2–4 are given the articulation values S_{23}, S_3 and s_{3M} corresponding to the values of $\alpha - \alpha_0$ in column 1.   For each of these articulations the value of the articulation index A has been found by the relations in Table 54 and Fig. 179.   The average of the three such values of articulation index, for each value of $\alpha - \alpha_0$, is given in column 5.

For the ideal system the factors F and H are each equal to unity. So for Table 61, by equation (17–1)

$$A = VE.$$

Thus for each value of A in column 5 we must find a value of V and of E such that the product VE is equal to A.   By an arbitrary choice, the factor E has been taken as unity for all values of $\alpha - \alpha_0$ from 0 to 68 db, and the factor V has been taken as unity for $\alpha - \alpha_0 \geq 68$ db.   Thus the values of V and E in columns 6 and 7 were obtained.

It is considered that V becomes less for values of $\alpha - \alpha_0$ below 68 db because more and more of the components of speech drop below the threshold of hearing as the level is lowered until all the speech components are below the threshold when $\alpha - \alpha_0$ becomes equal to zero.   Therefore, the value of V is determined in terms of x_V by Table 61 or

$$V = V(x_V).$$

Above $\alpha - \alpha_0 = 68$ db another cause is operating to reduce the articulation as the gain is increased, namely, the sounds become so loud that the ear is fatigued by the loud sounds and cannot differentiate as accurately the succeeding softer sounds.   Consequently, E is considered to be dependent upon the db above the threshold level when no noise is present. This corresponds to the stimulation level of the nerves of hearing.   When noise is present this level is slightly increased but is raised only 3 db when the db above threshold for the noise and the speech are equal.   For these reasons it is considered sufficiently accurate to regard E as dependent upon $\alpha - \alpha_0$ only, where α_0 in this case is the gain adjustment for threshold for the condition of no noise in the system.   Thus E is the same for systems in the quiet or for any amount of noise.   Therefore,

$$x_E = \alpha - \alpha_0 \qquad (17\text{–}12)$$

and

$$E = E(x_E)$$

so for this ideal system $x_V = x_E = \alpha - \alpha_0$ but this is not true for other systems.   The function E is considered unity for values of x_E from 0 to 68 db but determined by the values in Table 61 above 68 db.   The corresponding values of x_E and E are given in columns 1 and 7 of Table 61.

It should be realized that the decrease in the factor E, as the received speech level is increased above the level $\alpha - \alpha_0 = 68$ db, has been determined largely by the earliest group of articulation tests. The later tests cited here, upon relatively flat response systems, did not reach sufficiently high levels to confirm or deny these results. Some more recent articulation tests have been interpreted as indicating that for some observers there is little or no decrease in articulation at high received speech levels. However, the use of the factor E as given in Table 61, with a droop at high levels, has resulted in a better over-all fit of calculated articulations upon observed articulations for all the systems tested than would have been obtained by the present method without such a function.

Maximum Articulation Factor F

The effect of a change of amplification upon the calculated articulation index of a telephone system is accomplished through the factors V and E, and sometimes through the factor H, in equation (17–1). The factor F is not dependent upon the gain of the system, hence this factor sets a limit which the articulation index cannot exceed but which it can equal if each of the other factors has the value unity.

When the gain α of the system is adjusted so that the effective gain x_V is equal to 68 db, then as has already been explained the factor V is equal to unity. Let this particular gain be designated as α_F. This is the gain that gives the condition for calculating F. To express the value of α_F, it is evident that at such levels ϕ is equal to unity so that from equation (17–11)

$$\alpha_F = \alpha_0 + 68 + \gamma(\bar{R}_1 - \bar{R}_4). \qquad (17\text{–}13)$$

The factor F depends upon the relative response at the various frequency regions. Its value is given by the equation

$$F = \int_0^\infty D \cdot W \cdot df \qquad (17\text{–}14)$$

where D is such a function of frequency that the product $D df$ is equal to the element dA of articulation index carried by the frequency region between f and $f + df$ when this region is at the optimum level for speech interpretation. This function D is the frequency importance function for articulation which was defined by equation (15–6) and has the values given in Fig. 177.

The factor W which multiples the function D in equation (17–14) is a quantity having any value from zero to unity. This factor W determines the reduction of dA due to the interval df being sent to the ear at levels below the optimum level for speech interpretation. Ideally

W would be determined from articulation tests of a system which could be so altered that the received level of any chosen frequency interval could be set at any desired value, with no change in other frequency regions except an over-all adjustment for the optimum.

The factor W should not be confused with the factor V which ideally is determined from articulation tests of a flat response system having only such gain adjustments that all frequencies are raised or lowered equally.

Although the phenomena which control the factor W are different from those which control the factor V, the same range of magnitudes (namely 68 db) has been assigned to the two arguments upon which these two factors respectively depend, as the range which corresponds to the change of the factors from zero to unity. Thus W is a function of x_W such that $W = 1.0$ when $x_W = 0$ db, and $W = 0$ when $x_W = 68$ db. However, the growth of W from zero to unity as x_W changes is not the same as that of V as x_V changes.

The manner in which x_W is defined, and the relationship between W and x_W will now be described.

Let $\bar{R}$ be defined thus:

$$\bar{R} = \tfrac{1}{2}(\bar{R}_1 + \bar{R}_4), \qquad (17\text{--}15)$$

where $\bar{R}_1$ and $\bar{R}_4$ are as before the weighted average values of the response, using weightings which are appropriate respectively for very low received speech levels and for levels 50 db or more above threshold. Thus $\bar{R}$ is a sort of weighted average response for the whole range of levels.

It has been found satisfactory to assume that W has the value unity whenever $R \geq \bar{R}$, and that W becomes less than unity as R becomes less than $\bar{R}$. When R decreases to a critical value R_c, W becomes zero and remains zero when the response is decreased further.

The variable x_W which determines W is defined by the equation

$$x_W = 68(\bar{R} - R)/(\bar{R} - R_c). \qquad (17\text{--}16)$$

The form of this equation was chosen so that when $R = \bar{R}$, $x_W = 0$ db and when $R = R_c$, $x_W = 68$ db. The difference $\bar{R} - R_c$ turns out be equal to 68 db for the greater part of the frequency range. For this reason the constant 68 has been introduced into equation (17–16) so that for the greater part of the frequency range x_W becomes equal to $\bar{R} - R$, simplifying the calculation.

The value of W is taken equal to unity for $R \geq \bar{R}$, that is when x_W is zero or negative; and W is taken equal to zero for $x_W \geq 68$ db. It remains to find the form of W as a function of x_W, and also to find R_c as a function of frequency.

First, consider R_c. Measurements upon typical undistorted speech which is at the optimum level for interpretation, namely 68 db above the threshold level, show that the level Z_F of each critical band (in db above threshold) is that given in Fig. 183. The values were calculated

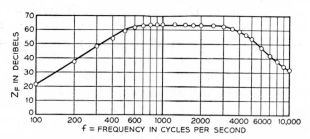

FIG. 183.—LEVEL Z_F OF EACH CRITICAL BAND OF UNDISTORTED SPEECH IN DECIBELS ABOVE THRESHOLD, WHEN THE SPEECH IS AT THE OPTIMUM LEVEL FOR INTERPRETATION.

from equation (17–23) given below. It is seen that from 700 to 3000 cps this level for each critical band is 63 db, which is 5 db less than that for speech as a whole. Thus it follows that statistically about three or four bands are cooperating together at one time to increase the effective level at threshold about 5 db over that of each band acting separately. It is thus seen that each band must be at least 5 db below its threshold level before it ceases to contribute toward the articulation index. Therefore, the value of R_c is given by

$$\bar{R} - R_c = Z_F + 5. \qquad (17\text{–}17)$$

Consequently, the values of $\bar{R} - R_c$ are 5 db greater than the ordinates of Fig. 81. So it is seen that equation (17–16) reduces to

$$x_W = 68(\bar{R} - R)/(Z_F + 5) \qquad (17\text{–}18)$$

TABLE 62

$W(x_W)$ VERSUS x_W

z	0	1	2	3	4	5	6	7	8	9	Difference
0	1.0	0.997	0.994	0.990	0.985	0.980	0.973	0.966	0.958	0.950	0.007
10	0.940	0.930	0.920	0.910	0.899	0.887	0.874	0.860	0.846	0.832	0.012
20	0.818	0.804	0.789	0.774	0.759	0.744	0.728	0.712	0.695	0.678	0.017
30	0.660	0.642	0.623	0.603	0.582	0.561	0.539	0.516	0.492	0.467	0.022
40	0.441	0.415	0.390	0.365	0.340	0.315	0.291	0.267	0.244	0.222	0.022
50	0.202	0.183	0.165	0.148	0.132	0.118	0.104	0.091	0.080	0.070	0.013
60	0.060	0.050	0.040	0.030	0.022	0.015	0.010	0.005	0.000		0.010

The values of W which correspond to values of x_W between 0 and 68 were determined empirically from the articulation data and are given in Table 62.

The Effect Upon the F Factor Due to the Masking of One Speech Sound by another

The masking effects of one speech sound by another are of two kinds. The first kind is due to the fatigue effect upon hearing lasting after the stimulus is gone. It principal effect is in the same band of frequencies as that for the stimulating speech sounds, but it also has an effect, although much smaller, upon adjacent bands. This effect is presumably taken care of by the V and E factors. The second kind of effect is due to the masking action of one component of a speech sound upon a second component in a different frequency band. In this case both components are sounding simultaneously. It is estimated that about one-third of the fundamental speech sounds are essentially in one frequency region and consequently need no correction for simultaneous masking. It is assumed that these are the unvoiced sounds and the long vowels ū (too), ō (toe), ȯ (not) and à (father). The other two-thirds of the total speech sounds are assumed to have two or more important components. For this second group we will now calculate this second kind of masking. If B is the spectrum level of the noise, κ the critical band width in db, and β_0 the threshold level for pure tones, then the experiments on masking by thermal noise show that the masking M is equal to the level Z in db above threshold for the critical bands and can be computed correctly by the formula

$$M = Z = B + \kappa - \beta_0 \qquad\qquad (17\text{-}19)$$

except for the following conditions: (1) Except when dZ/df (absolute value) exceeds critical values which depend upon the frequency range and masking level; (2) except for very narrow frequency bands; (3) except for sharply resonant peaks for B; and (4) except for values near the threshold. The quantity Z is always taken equal to the value on the right-hand side of this equation. But M is equal to Z only with the exceptions noted.

These exceptions seem complicated but the following simplifications can be made without too much sacrifice in accuracy. The last restriction for values near the threshold can be removed because, for the condition for calculating F, these low levels never occur for frequencies that cause masking. Due to the statistical nature of speech it will be only a fraction of the time that speech energy will lie in a very narrow band or in a sharply resonant peak. Since masking occurs principally when voiced sounds are used, we can consider the components for the voices of men and women as spaced 180 cycles apart as an average. Consequently, in a frequency region where the Z versus $\log f$ curve has a peak, the curve is regarded as flat over a band 180 cycles wide and the ordinate is taken to be the average ordinate over the 180-cycle band. The same also applies to filters having band widths less than 180 cycles, although their case is academic, since there are no articulation data on such narrow band systems. Let a curve of Z versus log f be plotted and the peaks corrected as above. Then whenever the positive slope of the curve thus plotted is greater than 80 db per octave, the masking curve is higher by an amount ΔZ than the Z curve calculated by equation (17–19). One obtains a good approximation for the masking curve sloping toward the low frequency side of the curve by proceeding as follows. Let the point where the Z curve begins to have a slope greater than 80 db per octave be (f,y) where f is the frequency and y the ordinate on the masking curve. Draw a straight line from (f,y) to $(0.7f, y - 40)$. Then from this last point to $(0.5f, y - 60)$ and then to $(0.35f, y - 70)$, and so on, halving the slope each half-octave as we go to the lower frequencies. The slope of the first half-octave is always 40 db per half-octave and does not change with different values of y. This geometrical construction also fits approximately the masking curve produced by a pure tone. This constructed series of straight lines will be referred to as the speech masking curve on the low frequency side.

On the high frequency side of a point on the Z versus log f curve the critical slope σ depends upon the ordinate y of this curve; but the curve M versus log f may be represented approximately by a single tangent line. This tangent line is drawn at the point where the slope of the Z versus log f curve exceeds the slope σ and the tangent continues with this critical slope σ. The masking data indicate that the following simple relation holds approximately, namely,

$$\sigma = 75 - Z_T/2 \qquad (17\text{--}20)$$

where Z_T is the value of Z computed from equation (17–19) at the point where the tangent is drawn, and σ is expressed in db per octave.

If these relations are applied to speech, then a curve will be derived which will be the db above threshold for each critical band of speech. This will also be the masking curve except where the slope exceeds the critical values discussed above. For speech transmitted through a system with response R and gain α from talkers having a talking level β_t, the spectrum level at the listener's ear is given by

$$B = B_s + \Delta B_s + R + \alpha + (\beta_t - 68) \qquad (17\text{--}21)$$

where B_s is the average spectrum level for speech at one meter's distance from the lips of the speaker having a talking level of 68 db. The quantity ΔB_s is the peak level above B_s. (See Appendix 1.)

When the typical articulation crew member was listening to speech, the threshold level β_0' for each critical band was somewhat higher than the pure tone threshold level β_0, in the region of lower frequencies, so that $\beta_0' = \beta_0 + \Delta\beta_0$. Here β_0' is the r.m.s. pressure level of one of the more intense speech sounds. The values of β_0 and β_0' are given in Table 81 in Appendix 1. In general, for a listener with hearing loss β_H who is listening to speech, the threshold level $\beta_0' + \beta_H + 4$ must replace the level β_0 in equation (17–19). Also for the case for calculating F the amplification α in equation (17–21) becomes α_F, given by equation (17–14). Consequently, when the system has this gain α_F the db above threshold Z_s of each critical band of received speech is given by

$$Z_s = B_s + \Delta B_s + R + \alpha_F + (\beta_t - 68) + \kappa - (\beta_0' + \beta_H + 4). \quad (17\text{–}22)$$

Let the value of Z_s for a flat response system be designated Z_F when the received speech is at the optimum for interpretation. For such a system

$$\bar{R}_1 = \bar{R}_4 = R = 0$$

and

$$\alpha_0 = \beta_H + 12 - \beta_t$$

and

$$\alpha_F = \alpha_0 + 68$$

and consequently

$$Z_F = B_s + \Delta B_s + \kappa - \beta_0' + 8. \quad (17\text{–}21)$$

This is the equation from which the values in Fig. 183 were taken. The values of B_s, ΔB_s, κ and β_0' are given in Table 81, Appendix 1. It is seen that Z_F is independent of both β_t and β_H since the amplification is always adjusted so that the received speech is at 68 db above the threshold of the listener. It gives the level above threshold of each critical band of speech when the received undistorted speech is at the optimum level for interpretation. The values of Z_F are also tabulated versus frequency in Table 81 of Appendix 1.

Substituting this value of Z_F and the value of α_F from equation (17–13), equation (17–22) becomes

$$Z_s = Z_F + R - \bar{R}_1 + \gamma(\bar{R}_1 - \bar{R}_4). \quad (17\text{–}24)$$

Let the point on the Z_s versus $\log f$ curve where the slope starts to exceed the critical slope be designated (Z_T, f_T). Also let R_T be the ordinate corresponding to f_T on the response curve R versus $\log f$. Then the value of Z_s becomes Z_T when $R = R_T$ so that equation (17–24) reduces to

$$Z_T = Z_F + R_T - \bar{R}_1 + \gamma(\bar{R}_1 - \bar{R}_4). \quad (17\text{–}25)$$

If this is substituted in equation (17–20), the desired formula for calculating σ is obtained or

$$\sigma = 75 - \tfrac{1}{2}[Z_F + R_T - \bar{R}_1 + \gamma(\bar{R}_1 - \bar{R}_4)] \quad (17\text{–}26)$$

which is the slope in db per octave for the speech masking tangent line for the high frequency side. Let y be the ordinate either of the speech masking curve on the low frequency side or of the speech masking tangent constructed as just outlined. Then the increment

$$\Delta Z = y - Z_s \qquad (17\text{--}27)$$

gives the number of db that the threshold level of any critical band of speech is raised due to the masking of one component of a speech sound by another component. Consequently, under these circumstances the critical value $\bar{R} - R_c$ becomes, instead of equation (17–17),

$$\bar{R} - R_c = Z_F + 5 + \Delta Z. \qquad (17\text{--}28)$$

The work involved in constructing the Z_s versus $\log f$ curve to find the values of ΔZ can be avoided and ΔZ determined directly from the R versus $\log f$ curve by noting the following relationships.

If Z_s from equation (17–24) is substituted in equation (17–27), then

$$\Delta Z = y - Z_F - R - \gamma(\bar{R}_1 - \bar{R}_4) + \bar{R}_1.$$

Now shift the Z_s versus $\log f$ curve and the corresponding masking curves downward by an amount $63 + \gamma(\bar{R}_1 - \bar{R}_4) - \bar{R}_1$ and let y' designate the ordinate of the shifted masking curves. Then

$$\Delta Z = y' - R + 63 - Z_F = \Delta R + 63 - Z_F \qquad (17\text{--}29)$$

where ΔR is the difference between the ordinate of the shifted masking curves and the corresponding ordinate of the response curve. Consequently, the value of ΔZ can be determined from equation (17–29) if one knows how to construct the shifted masking curves on the R versus $\log f$ plot. Let y_T be the ordinate of the beginning point of such shifted masking curves for the frequency f_T. At this point $\Delta Z = 0$ so from equation (17–29)

$$y_T = R_T - (63 - Z_F). \qquad (17\text{--}30)$$

So from 700 to 3000 cps where $Z_F = 63$ db the ordinate y_T is on the response curve and equal to R_T. At frequencies beyond these limits the starting point of the masking lines is below the response curve by the amount $63 - Z_F$ at the frequency f_T. One can usually determine f_T from inspection of the R versus $\log f$ curve. It is the point where the response curve drops very suddenly as for a partial suppression filter system or at the frequency corresponding to the average ordinate over 180 cycles in the peak response for a resonant system.

Calculation of the F Factor

To calculate the F factor, one proceeds as follows. Examine slopes of the response curve under consideration. One can usually estimate whether the corresponding Z_s curve will or will not exceed the critical slope σ. If not, then no tangent curves need be drawn and equation (17–18) applies.

This is the case for many of the systems with which one deals. For filter systems and sharply resonant systems the value of σ is calculated and the tangent lines are drawn to determine ΔZ and from this by aid of equation (17–28) the value of $\bar{R} - R_c$ is calculated. Then by equation (17–16) the value of x_W is given by

$$x_W = 68(\bar{R} - R)/[Z_F + 5 - (\Delta R + 63 - Z_F)] = r(\bar{R} - R) \quad (17\text{–}31)$$

where the quantity r is defined by the equation

$$r = 68/[Z_F + 5 - (\Delta R + 63 - Z_F)]. \quad (17\text{–}31a)$$

Values of $W(x_W)$ for each value of x_W are obtained from Table 62. Then to calculate F one obtains the value of $\bar{R}$ from equation (17–15) and the values of D from Fig. 177. To obtain the integral indicated by equation (17–14) giving the value of F, one plots $\int_0^f Ddf$ as abscissa and $W(x_W)$ as ordinate. The area under such a curve is the required value of the integral. In general this area can be evaluated more simply by taking an average W at frequencies corresponding to equal intervals of $\int_0^f Ddf$.

TABLE 63

VALUES OF f VERSUS $\int_0^f Ddf$ FROM CURVE IN FIG. 177

$\int_0^f Ddf$	0.005	0.015	0.025	0.035	0.045	0.055	0.065	0.075	0.085	0.095
0.00	200	260	310	350	385	415	470	470	500	530
0.10	555	585	610	635	660	685	715	740	770	800
0.20	825	855	880	910	935	965	990	1020	1050	1080
0.30	1110	1140	1170	1200	1230	1270	1300	1330	1370	1410
0.40	1440	1480	1520	1550	1590	1640	1680	1720	1760	1810
0.50	1850	1900	1950	1990	2040	2090	2140	2200	2250	2300
0.60	2360	2410	2470	2530	2580	2640	2700	2770	2830	2890
0.70	2960	3020	3090	3160	3230	3310	3390	3480	3560	3640
0.80	3730	3820	3920	4020	4120	4230	4350	4480	4610	4740
0.90	4890	5050	5220	5400	5610	5800	6060	6370	6750	7300

In Table 63 frequencies corresponding to 100 intervals of $\int_0^f Ddf$ are given. Usually the twenty frequencies shown in Table 63 in italics are sufficient except near a sharp cut-off in the response curve, where for accuracy the one percent intervals should be taken.

This, then, gives the value of F designated F_M for the two-thirds of the speech sounds which involve masking of one component by another. Another calculation is made without masking curves, $\bar{R} - R_c$ being given by equation (17–17); the value so calculated is designated F_0. This value corresponds to the one-third of speech sounds which are in the first class. The value of F to use in equation (17–1) is, then,

$$F = \tfrac{2}{3}F_M + \tfrac{1}{3}F_0. \tag{17-32}$$

Determination of the Functions ϕ and γ

We now return to the problem of calculating ϕ and γ, referred to at the end of Section 7. In Fig. 184 the articulation data shown by discrete points were obtained from tests of two telephone systems designated

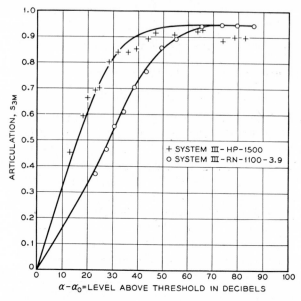

FIG. 184.—ARTICULATION VERSUS LEVEL OF RECEIVED SPEECH ABOVE THRESHOLD, FOR A RESONANT SYSTEM AND A FILTER SYSTEM HAVING APPROXIMATELY EQUAL MAXIMA OF ARTICULATION.

respectively as III–RN–1100–3.9 and III–HP–1500. The circles correspond to the resonant system and the crosses to the filter system. An attempt was made to choose a resonant system and a filter system having approximately the same value of F; but it is seen that the maximum articulation for the filter system is somewhat lower than that for the resonant system. Its maximum was the closest one for which articulation data were available. The solid line through the crosses is calculated for an ideal filter system having the same value of Fp, namely $Fp = 0.704$, as for the resonant system.

For the ideal filter system the value of V is approximately equal to that for an ideal flat response system at the same level above threshold, in accordance with the statement included in the first paragraph of Section 7. In this case γ is nearly equal to zero so that, for the filter, equation $(17\text{--}11)$ becomes

$$\alpha - \alpha_0 = x_V$$

whereas for the resonant system, γ is not zero, hence

$$\alpha - \alpha_0 = x_V + \phi\gamma(\bar{R}_1 - \bar{R}_4).$$

Thus for these two systems the same value x_V of the effective gain corresponds to values of $\alpha - \alpha_0$ which are not equal.

The two systems which have been chosen were composed of parts that introduced no peculiar types of distortion. Moreover, we shall consider only values of $\alpha - \alpha_0$ which are less than 55 db. It follows that in equation $(17\text{--}1)$ the factors E and H are each equal to unity, and therefore

$$Ap = VFp.$$

The two systems have been chosen so that the value of Fp is the same for each. It follows that for these two systems equal values of Ap correspond to equal values of V. Consequently, equal values of articulation correspond to equal values x_V of the effective gain.

Comparing the two curves in Fig. 184, two points having equal values of articulation are displaced by an amount $\Delta\alpha$ which is the difference between $\alpha - \alpha_0$ for the resonant system and $\alpha - \alpha_0$ for the filter system, for the same x_V. Hence

$$\Delta\alpha = \phi\gamma(\bar{R}_1 - \bar{R}_4).$$

Values of $\phi\gamma(\bar{R}_1 - \bar{R}_4)$ were obtained in this manner from the displacement $\Delta\alpha$. The value of $\bar{R}_1$ and of $\bar{R}_4$ were calculated by aid of equations $(17\text{--}5)$ and $(17\text{--}8)$ from the response characteristic of the reso-

TABLE 64

VALUES OF $\Delta\alpha$ FOR DETERMINING ϕ

$x_V = \alpha - \alpha_0 = 0$	5	10	15	20	25	30	35	40	50
$\Delta\alpha = 0$	5	10	12.5	14.2	16	17	17	17	17
$\phi\gamma = 0$	0.37	0.74	0.92	1.04	1.17	1.25	1.25	1 25	1.25
$\phi = \phi\gamma \div 1.25 = 0$	0.29	0.59	0.74	0.83	0.94	1.0	1.0	1.0	1.0
Adopted values of $\phi = 0$	0.22	0.45	0.65	0.85	0.93	0.97	0.99	1.0	1.0

nant system III–RN–1100–3.9 given in Fig. 202. It was found that $\bar{R}_1 - \bar{R}_4 = 13.6$ db. Consequently,

$$\phi\gamma = \Delta\alpha/13.6.$$

The experimental values of $\Delta\alpha$ obtained from the curves in Fig. 184 are shown in Table 64.   If the maximum value of γ is taken as 1.25 for this resonant system, then the values of ϕ obtained from these data are given in the fourth row.   It will be seen later that γ for this system is 1.25. After similar calculations with other resonant systems, the values of ϕ given in the last row were adopted.

As stated above, the factor γ is dependent upon the shape of the response curve.   It is found to be more intimately related to the curve W versus $\int_0^f Ddf$, which is obtained from the response curve.   In Fig. 185

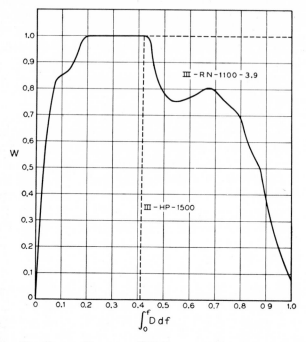

are shown two such curves for systems III–RN–1100–39. and III–HP– 1500, whose response curves are given in Figs. 202 and 198.   It will be remembered that the areas under each of these curves give the corresponding values of F.   Now if we define another quantity n by the equation

$$n = \int_0^\infty W' \cdot D \cdot df$$

where W' is any function of x_W such that W' is less than or equal to W for all values of x_W, then the ratio

$$x_\gamma = n/F = \int_0^\infty W' \cdot D \cdot df \bigg/ \int_0^\infty W \cdot D \cdot df$$

is a variable which is closely correlated with the shape factor γ. For a flat system or a filter system $x_\gamma = 1.0$ and for all other systems x_γ will be less than unity, being least for very resonant systems. After a choice of W' is made, x_γ can be related to γ by the experimental results on systems having a wide variety of response curve shapes.

About the most simple form of W' is $W' = 1.0$ for $x_W \geqq 0$ and $W' = 0$ for all other values of x_W. Then for system III–RN–1100–3.9 the value of n is equal to the area in Fig. 185 included under the curve between abscissas 0.20 and 0.43, while for system III–HP–1500 the value of n is almost equal to F. Thus the value of x_γ, for the first system is $0.23/F = 0.307$ and for the second system it is almost unity.

This method of calculating n was tried and the corresponding x_γ was related to γ and the resulting calculations gave a fairly good agreement with the observed results. After studying these results it was evident that a somewhat better choice for W' is

$$W' = 10(W - 0.9)$$

with the condition that $W' = 0$ when $W \leqq 0.9$. So this value of W' was adopted. The value of n corresponding to this choice for system III–RN–110–3.9 is equal to 0.27 instead of 0.23, which is larger than for the previous choice of W' since the area in Fig. 185 corresponding to it includes the same area as before plus two small triangular areas on either side. For system III–HP–1500 the value of n is still approximately equal to unity.

Thus the value of x_γ will be given by

$$x_\gamma = 10 \int_{f_1}^{f_2} (W - .9) \cdot D \cdot df \bigg/ \int_0^\infty W \cdot D \cdot df = n/F \qquad (17\text{--}33)$$

where f_1 and f_2 are the two frequencies where $W = 0.9$ so that the summation covers only the values of W greater than this value.

Since there will be two values of F and n when masking lines are necessary, the equation for calculating x_γ becomes

$$x_\gamma = \tfrac{1}{2}(n_0/F_0 + n_M/F_M) \qquad (17\text{--}34)$$

where n_0/F_0 is the value of equation (17–33) when the argument x_W of W is

$$68(\bar{R} - R)/Z_F + 5$$

and n_M/F_M is the value of equation (17–33) when x_W is equal to

$$68(\bar{R} - R)/[Z_F + 5 - (\Delta R + 63 - Z_F)].$$

In the twenty-band method of calculation the process of getting n_0 and n_M is very simple. From each value of W greater than 0.9 one subtracts 0.9, and then takes one-half the sum to get n. One might have combined n_0/F_0 and n_M/F_M by some other method than by taking an arithmetical average but this simple method of combination was found satisfactory.

Then the value of γ can be related to x_γ by a functional relationship indicated by

$$\gamma = \psi(x_\gamma)$$

where the form of ψ is found from experiment. It was taken as zero for $x_\gamma = 1.0$ and equal to 1.20 for small values of x_γ. The values between these limits were determined empirically from the articulation data and are shown in Table 65. This relation was tried and found to give a

TABLE 65

VALUES OF ψ VERSUS x_γ

x_γ	0	0.1	0.2	0.3	0.4	0.5	0.6	0.7	0.8	0.9
3	1.20	1.20	1.20	1.20	1.20	1.20	1.198	1.196	1.194	1.192
4	1.185	1.176	1.167	1.158	1.149	1.140	1.128	1.114	1.097	1.083
5	1.070	1.060	1.045	1.030	1.010	0.990	0.970	0.940	0.905	0.870
6	0.840	0.805	0.770	0.740	0.710	0.685	0.655	0.625	0.595	0.560
7	0.530	0.500	0.475	0.445	0.415	0.390	0.360	0.335	0.310	0.285
8	0.265	0.240	0.215	0.185	0.155	0.130	0.110	0.090	0.070	0.055
9	0.045	0.035	0.025	0.015	0.008	0.003	0	0	0	0

fairly good fit for all the data but an even better fit is obtained by adding a small correction term $x_\gamma \sum \Delta$ to ψ as follows.

$$\gamma = \psi(x_\gamma) + x_\gamma \sum \Delta. \qquad (17\text{--}35)$$

It was found that high pass filter systems grow more rapidly to their maximum articulation as the gain is increased than do the low pass filter systems. This is what one would expect since the speech sounds are distributed over a smaller range of levels in the higher range of frequencies than at the lower range. For this reason the correction term $x_\gamma \sum \Delta$ is negative for the higher range of frequencies and positive for the lower range. For resonant systems it was found that this correction factor must be much smaller than for ideal filter systems. This is brought about by multiplying the correction term by x_γ since for ideal filters $x_\gamma = 1$ and for resonant systems it is usually less than 0.4.

A number of methods of calculating this correction term were tried but none of them gave better results than the following simple one. Let Δ for each frequency be defined by the empirically determined values given in Table 66. Then

$$\sum \Delta = 20 \int_{f_1}^{f_2} \Delta \cdot D \cdot df + 20 \int_{f_3}^{f_4} \Delta \cdot D \cdot df, \text{ etc.,}$$

where the limits are those corresponding to $W = 0.99$. In the twenty-band method of computation this consists of adding the above Δ's together using only those bands where $W \geqq 0.99$. This sum is designated $\Sigma \Delta$.

TABLE 66

VALUES OF f AND Δ

$f=$	310	470	610	740	880	1020	1170	1330	1520	1720
$\Delta=$	−0.03	−0.01	0.01	0.03	0.04	0.04	0.03	0.02	0.00	−0.02
$f=$	1950	2200	2470	2770	3090	3480	3920	4480	5520	6370
$\Delta=$	−0.04	−0.05	−0.06	−0.06	−0.05	−0.04	−0.02	0.00	0.01	0.03

Determination of Articulation Data for an Ideal System from Data on Systems I, II and III

As stated in Section 8 these three relatively flat systems were not ideal, the response curves for them being given in Figs. 186–188. From these response curves the values of $\bar{R}_1$, $\bar{R}_4$, F_0, F_M, and γ were calculated and are given in Table 67.

TABLE 67

CONSTANTS FOR SYSTEMS I, II, AND III

System	$\bar{R}_1$	$\bar{R}_4$	F_0	F_M	n_0	n_M	$\Sigma\Delta$	γ
I	0	−2.0	0.974	0.938	0.849	0.849	−0.06	0.006
II	−1.2	−2.8	0.987	0.987	0.870	0.870	−0.04	0.032
III	−2.5	−4.8	0.980	0.980	0.798	0.798	−0.05	0.181

$$\alpha - \alpha_0 = x_V + \phi\gamma(\bar{R}_1 - \bar{R}_4)$$

It is seen from the values in this table and from the formula at the bottom (see equation (17–11)) that the term $\phi\gamma(\bar{R}_1 - \bar{R}_4)$ for systems I and II is always less than 0.1 db for all values of ϕ so that x_V and $\alpha - \alpha_0$ can be considered equal for these two systems. The values of x_V in steps of 5 db are written in the first column of Table 65, which gives the steps taken in deriving the values of A versus x_V for the ideal system. The corresponding values of articulation S_{23} and S_3 were read from the experimental curves drawn through the observed points showing the relationship between $\alpha - \alpha_0$ and S_{23} or S_3 and are recorded in columns 3 and 6 of Table 68. For system III the values of $\phi_\gamma(\bar{R}_1 - \bar{R}_4)$ are not negligible and are added to x_V to give $\alpha - \alpha_0$ The resulting values of $\alpha - \alpha_0$ are given in column 8. The corresponding observed articulation values of s_{3M} are given in column 9. The values of articulation index for each value of articulation were found from Table 54 and tabulated in columns 4, 7, and 10. These values were divided by maximum articulation values for each system to obtain the values in columns 11–13.

TABLE 68

DERIVATION OF ARTICULATION INDEX A VERSUS EFFECTIVE GAIN x_V FOR AN IDEAL FLAT RESPONSE SYSTEM

(1) x_V	(2) $\alpha - \alpha_0$	(3) S_{23}	(4) A_{23}	(5) $\alpha - \alpha_0$	(6) S_3	(7) A_3	(8) $\alpha - \alpha_0$	(9) S_{3M}	(10) A_{3M}	(11) A_{23}/A_m	(12) A_3/A_m	(13) A_{3M}/A_m	(14) A Average	(15) A Adopted
0	0	0	0	0	0	0	0	0	0	0	0	0	0	0
5	5	0.078	0.053	5	0.016	0.035	5.1	0.183	0.049	0.054	0.036	0.051	0.047	0.05
10	10	0.180	0.121	10	0.057	0.087	10.2	0.362	0.106	0.123	0.090	0.112	0.108	0.11
15	15	0.318	0.221	15	0.142	0.149	15.3	0.544	0.188	0.225	0.160	0.198	0.194	0.20
20	20	0.472	0.323	20	0.305	0.257	20.3	0.698	0.286	0.330	0.268	0.301	0.300	0.30
25	25	0.615	0.418	25	0.491	0.365	25.4	0.822	0.411	0.427	0.380	0.433	0.413	0.41
30	30	0.731	0.521	30	0.685	0.505	30.4	0.897	0.542	0.532	0.525	0.570	0.542	0.54
35	35	0.817	0.614	35	0.820	0.637	35.4	0.935	0.655	0.627	0.664	0.690	0.660	0.66
40	40	0.880	0.707	40	0.892	0.736	40.4	0.953	0.730	0.722	0.766	0.767	0.752	0.75
45	45	0.922	0.783	45	0.927	0.802	45.4	0.967	0.810	0.800	0.836	0.853	0.830	0.83
50	50	0.949	0.847	50	0.949	0.858	50.4	0.972	0.85	0.863	0.894	0.895	0.884	0.89
55	55	0.964	0.905	55	0.961	0.900	55.4	0.977	0.90	0.924	0.940	0.947	0.937	0.94
60	60	0.971	0.955	60	0.967	0.940	60.4	0.980	0.94	0.975	0.980	0.990	0.982	0.98
65	65	0.975	0.980	65	0.969	0.955	65.4	0.981	0.95	1.000	0.995	1.000	0.998	1.00
70	70	0.975	0.980	70	0.970	0.960	70.4	0.981	0.95	1.000	1.000	1.000	1.000	1.00
75	75	0.973	0.970	75	0.970	0.960	75.4	0.980	0.940	0.990	1.000	0.990	0.993	0.99
80	80	0.970	0.950	80	0.970	0.960	80.4	0.979	0.925	0.970	1.000	0.974	0.981	0.98
85	85	0.966	0.920	85	0.970	0.960	85.4	0.977	0.900	0.940	1.000	0.947	0.962	0.96
90	90	0.961	0.890	90	0.970	0.960	90.4	0.973	0.860	0.910	1.000	0.905	0.938	0.93
95	95	0.954	0.863	95			95.4			0.882				0.90
100	100	0.949	0.847	100						0.865				0.87
105	105	0.941	0.825	105						0.842				0.85
110	110	0.934	0.808	110						0.825				0.83
115	115	0.927	0.793	115						0.810				0.81
120	120	0.917	0.775							0.792				0.79

The average of these three values is given in column 14. The values in column 15, labeled "Adopted," were chosen as giving the best fit for all the data and correspond to the values of x_V in the first column. The articulation values given in Table 61 for an ideal system were determined from these articulation index values.

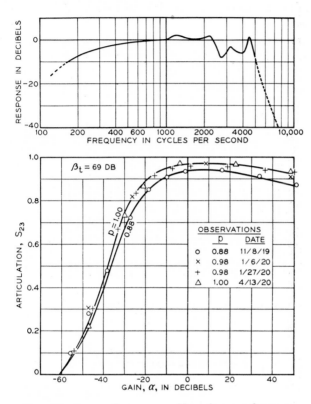

FIG. 186.—SYSTEM I: 1919–1920 HIGH QUALITY SYSTEM.

NOTE.—In Figs. 186–188 and 193–218 the response versus frequency characteristics and the noise, if any, are shown in the upper plots and the articulation versus gain observations (points) and calculations (curves) in the lower plots.

To show how well these values of A fit the observed data, the curves of articulation versus gain were calculated for systems I–III and are given in Figs. 186–188.

The Effects of Noise upon Articulation

In order to take account of the complicated action of an interfering noise in the reception of speech, the effects of the noise must be considered upon each of the factors in equation (17–1). These effects are generally expressed in terms either of the spectrum level B of the noise, or the masking M (threshold shift) which the noise causes in an ear of specified acuity. In the present section of this paper the relation of noise levels to masking will be considered. In the three following sections the effects of noise will be evaluated for the factors V, E, F, and H.

In our calculations here we require the value of M for an ear having the pure tone acuity level β_0 defined in Section 4, which corresponds to the typical articulation crew listener having the hearing loss $\beta_H = -4$ db.

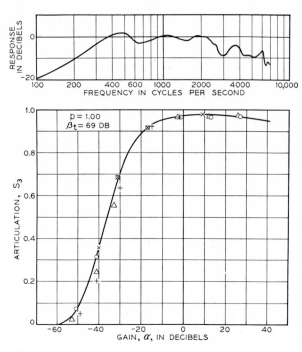

FIG. 187.—SYSTEM II: 1928-1929 HIGH QUALITY SYSTEM.

Under the conditions of listening to speech in the presence of distributed noise, the expression for the level Z in db above threshold for each critical band of noise is no longer the same as equation (17–19). Instead, as stated in Section 10, the threshold $\beta_0' + \beta_H + 4$ must replace β_0 so that

$$Z = B + \kappa - (\beta_0' + \beta_H + 4) \qquad (17\text{–}36)$$

where B is the spectrum level of the noise, κ the critical band width in db, and β_0' the threshold level for the critical bands of noise under the conditions of listening also to speech and for a listener with a hearing loss $\beta_H = -4$ db. It was seen that

$$\beta_0' = \beta_0 + \Delta\beta_0 \qquad (17\text{–}37)$$

where $\Delta\beta_0$ becomes as large as 8 db for low frequencies and is zero for the higher frequencies. It will be remembered that β_0 is the field intensity level of pure tones at the threshold of hearing for typical listeners in all the crews making articulation tests.

Experiments on masking have shown that M can be calculated from Z through the relationship

$$10^{M/10} = 10^{Z/10} + 1. \qquad (17\text{--}38)$$

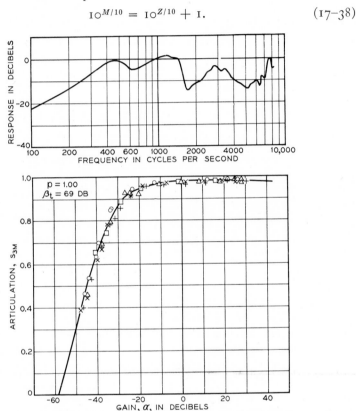

FIG. 188.—SYSTEM III: 1935–1936 HIGH QUALITY SYSTEM.

This satisfies the condition that when $B = -\infty$ (that is, no external noise present) then $M = 0$, and also that Z and M are equal for levels of Z greater than about 20 db. This is subject to the limitation that the slope of the curve representing Z must not be greater than the critical slope σ (equation (17–20)) and it very seldom reaches such steep slopes. If it is greater, however, the same procedure as outlined for speech masking must be followed to get the real masking curve due to the noise.

Let B_R be the spectrum level at each frequency of the room noise at the listener's end and let h be the corresponding attenuation in decibels produced by holding the receiver cap to the ear. Then the spectrum level in the ear due to room noise leaking under the receiver cap is $B_R - h$. Let R_s be the response at each frequency of the sidetone circuit of the telephone set. It gives the amplification or attenuation for the noise going through the microphone of the listener's subset to the ear of the listener and is measured for unity reproduction. For example, if R_s were zero db at all frequencies the noise would go through the microphone, the sidetone circuit and the receiver and arrive at the ear of the listener at the same level as that which would go directly into the ear of the listener with the receiver removed. Let B_L be the spectrum level of the line noise measured at the ear of the listener. If B is the spectrum level of the combined noises, then

$$10^{B/10} = 10^{(B_R-h)/10} + 10^{(B_R+R_s)/10} + 10^{B_L/10}. \qquad (17\text{--}39)$$

Having the spectrum level B at each frequency, then the value of Z at each frequency is given by equation (17–36) and M is obtained from equation (17–38). This holds for all levels except for critical slopes where M is greater than Z by an amount ΔZ. This ΔZ can be obtained in the same way as outlined for the masking of one speech sound by another but using Z_T for noise in equation (17–20) to obtain σ.

To obtain the masking M which speech suffers due to the presence of a pure tone or a combination of pure tones, when the components are separated by more than about 200 cps, the method described above cannot be used. This masking has been obtained from two sets of data: (1) On the masking of one pure tone by another pure tone, and (2) on the masking of a narrow band of thermal noise by a pure tone. Since these data cover only a few levels and frequencies it was necessary to interpolate to obtain data corresponding to those tones used in articulation tests. This was done for both sets of data and the average taken for determining the masking. The two quantities thus averaged differ typically by about 0 to 12 db in the frequency regions of greater masking when the maskings are large, and by about 0 to 6 db when the maskings are small. The resulting $R - M$ curves are plotted in the upper plots of Figs. 207–209, which figures in the lower plots give the data showing the articulation results for various types of pure tone interference.

Calculation of the E and V Factors—Noise Present

In Section 8 it was mentioned that when noise is present the factor E in equation (17–1) is regarded as the same as in the quiet—that is, equal to $E(\alpha - \alpha_0)$ where α_0 is the threshold gain when no noise is present.

The factor V is a known function of the effective gain x_V. To calculate the gain α which corresponds to a chosen value of x_V when noise with masking M is present, one proceeds in the same manner as when noise is absent except that the response at each frequency is taken as $R - M$ instead of R. The quantities $(\langle R - M \rangle)_1$ and $(\langle R - M \rangle)_4$ replace $\bar{R}^1$ and $\bar{R}_4$.[10] Therefore, the gain α_0 to reach the threshold level when noise is present is given by the following equation instead of equation (17–4):

$$\alpha_0 = \beta_H + 12 - \beta_t - (\langle R - M \rangle)_1. \qquad (17\text{–}40)$$

Comparison of this equation with equation (17–4) shows that the threshold gain α_0 has been increased by $\bar{R}_1 - (\langle R - M \rangle)_1$ due to the presence of the noise. If the noise masking is constant with frequency (that is, equal to M db), then the threshold level is shifted M db due to the presence of noise.

It was seen that for $M > 20$ db the value of M is equal to Z, hence by equation (17–36)

$$M = Z = B + \kappa - (\beta_0' + \beta_H + 4).$$

For a noise having masking M constant with frequency, the value $(\langle R - M \rangle)_1 = R_1 - M$. Therefore, for such a noise

$$\alpha_0 = (B + \kappa - \beta_0') - (\beta_t - 8 + \bar{R}_1)$$

and the gain to reach threshold is independent of the acuity β_H of the listener. The first term is the level above threshold of the critical bands of noise and is the same as the constant masking for a typical listener in the articulation crews. The second term is the level of the received speech above the unshifted threshold for the same listener. So in general for high levels of noise the threshold gain α_0 is determined by the talking level and the noise level and is approximately independent of the hearing acuity of the listeners unless the hearing loss is relatively great.

The value of x_V (see equation (17–11)) becomes

$$x_V = \alpha - \alpha_0 - \phi\gamma[(\langle R - M \rangle)_1 - (\langle R - M \rangle)_4] \qquad (17\text{–}41)$$

This is the effective gain x_V that determines $V(x_V)$.

The value of ϕ is the same as for the no-noise case. The value of γ is given by the same formula, namely, equation (17–35), but the values of x_γ and $\sum\Delta$ are different and are dependent upon the values of F_{NO} and F_{NM} now to be described.

Calculation of F Factor—Noise Present

There have been two points of view advanced as to how an observer interprets the speech sounds in the presence of a noise. The first point

---

[10] The angular bracket enclosing $R - M$ replaces the bar over R to indicate a weighted average as before. This is done throughout the text and the charts to facilitate the setting of type.

of view assumes that the relative position of the speech components with respect to the threshold in the noise determines the factor F in equation (17–1). According to this point of view the effective response has been lowered by the threshold shift M due to the noise, so that the quantity $R - M$ takes the place of R in determining the factor F. The second point of view, which was taken by one of the present authors in an earlier formulation of this theory, assumes that the level of the speech components with respect to each other is the principal influence in determining F. Then F is the same in the noise as in the quiet, except in so far as there is an increased masking of one speech component by another because of the higher received speech levels required in order to over-ride the noise.

The articulation tests indicate that some of the sounds of speech act in accordance with the first assumption, while the other sounds follow the second assumption. The sounds of the first class are those having components essentially in a single frequency region, constituting about one-third of the total number of fundamental speech sounds as previously noted in Section 10. For these sounds the quantity $R - M$ is used as though it were the actual response of a system without noise. Otherwise the calculation of the factor F proceeds as in the no-noise case except that for this first class of speech sounds there is no masking of one speech component by another, so that the quantity ΔZ due to speech masking described in Section 10 is considered to be equal to zero. Let the value of F calculated in this manner be designated as F_{NO}, the subscript N referring to the noise condition and the subscript O referring to the fact that there is no masking by speech components.

The second class of speech sounds consists of those sounds having components in more than one frequency region, which compose about two-thirds of the total number. For these sounds the calculation of the factor F uses the response R (not the difference $R - M$) and proceeds as in the case of no noise. However, the noise may have an effect upon this value of F because the slope σ of the speech masking tangent lines on the high frequency side will be greater than in the case of no noise, and may be greater than the critical slope. This is a consequence of the greater amplification α_F which must be used to reach the condition for which $V = 1$. The quantity $R - M$ takes the place of R in determining α_F so that instead of equation (17–31), we have

$$\alpha_F = \alpha_0 + 68 + \gamma[(\langle R - M\rangle)_1 - (\langle R - M\rangle)_4]. \qquad (17\text{--}42)$$

The increase in α_F is due chiefly to the increase in α_0, which was seen in Section 15 to be equal to M when M is constant with frequency.

The value of the critical slope σ_N when noise is present is given by the following equation instead of by equation (17–26):

$$\sigma_N = 75 - \tfrac{1}{2}\{Z_F + R_T - (\langle R - M\rangle)_1 \\ + \gamma[(\langle R - M\rangle)_1 - (\langle R - M\rangle)_4]\}. \quad (17\text{--}43)$$

The decrease in the slope as compared with σ for no noise is due principally to the term $(\langle R - M\rangle)_1$ being smaller than $\bar{R}_1$. The factor F_{NM} for this second class of speech sounds is then given by

$$F_{NM} = \int_0^\infty D \cdot W \left[\frac{68}{Z_F + 5 - \Delta Z} (\bar{R} - R) \right] df. \quad (17\text{--}44)$$

The factor F_{NO} for the other speech sounds is given by

$$F_{NO} = \int_0^\infty D \cdot W \left[\frac{68}{Z_F + 5} [(\langle R - M\rangle) - (R - M)] \right] df \quad (17\text{--}45)$$

where $\langle R - M\rangle$ is given by

$$\langle R - M\rangle = \tfrac{1}{2}(\langle R - M\rangle)_1 + \tfrac{1}{2}(\langle R - M\rangle)_4. \quad (17\text{--}46)$$

Then the final factor F_N to be used in equation (17–1) for the case when noise is present is given by

$$F_N = \tfrac{2}{3}F_{NM} + \tfrac{1}{3}F_{NO}. \quad (17\text{--}47)$$

The value of x_γ then becomes

$$x_\gamma = \tfrac{1}{2}[n_{NO}/F_{NO} + n_{NM}/F_{NM}] \quad (17\text{--}48)$$

where

$$n_{NO} = 10 \int_{f_1}^{f_2} \left\{ D \cdot W \left[\frac{68[(\langle R - M\rangle) - (R - M)]}{Z_F + 5} \right] - 0.9 \right\} df \quad (17\text{--}49)$$

$$n_{NM} = 10 \int_{0f}^{f_2} \left\{ D \cdot W \left[\frac{68(\bar{R} - R)}{Z_F + 5 + \Delta Z'} \right] - 0.9 \right\} df \quad (17\text{--}50)$$

where $\Delta Z'$ refers to the effect of the masking tangent used when noise is present. The frequency limits used correspond to values of $W = 0.9$.

The above may look like difficult calculations to make but it will be seen that when the chart method is used these calculations are very simple.

Similarly there will be two values of $\Sigma\Delta$, one obtained from the R versus f curve, called $\displaystyle\sum_M$ and one obtained from the $R - M$ versus f curve called $\displaystyle\sum_0$. The value to be used in equation (17–35) for γ is

$$\sum\Delta = \tfrac{1}{2}\sum_M + \tfrac{1}{2}\sum_0. \quad (17\text{--}51)$$

Calculation of H Factor Due to Noise and Determination of K_m, α_m, a and J

When the level of an interfering tone or noise becomes high there is an intermodulation between the speech sounds and the noise sounds so the factor H in equation (17–1) becomes less than unity. This is particularly apparent with pure tones of high level. For example, in Fig. 189 are shown the data for a 2000-cycle interfering tone at a level 78.2 db above threshold. The masking caused by this tone shifts the threshold for speech only a few decibels. The lowering of the articulation is caused chiefly by the intermodulation effect.

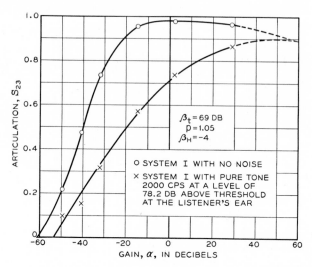

FIG. 189.—ARTICULATION OF 1919–1920 HIGH QUALITY SYSTEM WITHOUT AND WITH LOUD INTERFERENCE BY A PURE TONE AT FREQUENCY 2000 CPS: THE CURVES HAVE BEEN DRAWN TO REPRESENT THE POINTS (OBSERVATIONS).

The deteriorating effect of the modulation would be expected to depend upon the intensity level β and the frequency f of the tone, and the average received total intensity level β_s of the speech. The latter is given by

$$10^{\bar{\beta}_s/10} = \int_0^\infty 10^{(B_s+R+\alpha)/10} df. \qquad (17\text{–}52)$$

For a flat response system where R and α are constant with frequency this reduces to

$$\beta_s = \beta_t + R + \alpha. \qquad (17\text{–}52a)$$

For a system of variable response R it was considered that the approximate equation

$$\beta_s = \beta_t + \bar{R}_1 + \alpha \qquad (17\text{–}52b)$$

would apply adequately instead of the more general form of equation (17–52). The articulation data were not sufficiently accurate to show any difference between these two equations for β_s and the latter is much more simple to apply.

It would be expected that the maximum deteriorating effect of the modulation would occur when the intensity level β of the tone is approximately equal to some aspect of the speech closely related to the average received total intensity level β_s. Let the difference between β and β_s when this maximum deteriorating effect occurs be K_m. Then the amplification α_m when this occurs is given by

$$\alpha_m = \beta - \beta_t - \bar{R}_1 - K_m. \qquad (17\text{–}53)$$

The examination of the data for pure tones indicated that K_m at the various frequencies has the values shown in Table 69. The values of the

TABLE 69

ΔB_s AND K_m VERSUS f

f	100	200	400	800	1000	2000	3000	4000
ΔB_s	7.5	7.8	9.3	10.9	11.5	13.7	15.1	15.5
K_m	9	11	14	13	12	7	−2	−11

peak factor in db ΔB_s for speech (see Appendix 1) are given in Table 69 for comparison. The values are approximately equal in the range of frequencies below 1500 cps. In this range K_m seems to be closely identified with the peak factor. For the higher range of frequencies some other effect is operating to make K much less than the peak factor.

The factor H was chosen of the form

$$H = 1 - aJ(\alpha_m - \alpha) \qquad (17\text{–}54)$$

where the function J varies between zero and unity, a is constant dependent only upon the noise, and α_m has the same meaning as in equation (17–53). When $\alpha_m - \alpha = 0$, then J is unity. When $\alpha_m - \alpha$ becomes large either positively or negatively, the value of J becomes zero. It was taken as symmetrical about α_m and approximately equal to zero when $\alpha_m - \alpha = 40$ db so that $J(x) = J(-x)$. The values between zero and 40 were inferred from the articulation data. The values chosen are shown in Table 70.

The value of α_m determines the amplification which gives the maximum deterioration but the amount of this deterioration is determined by the quantity designed a in equation (17–54). For a pure tone noise this quantity depends upon the intensity level β of the tone and also its frequency f, or

$$a = \varphi(\beta, f).$$

In the middle range of frequencies it was found that a was approximately proportional to $\beta - 40$ but this relation did not hold at the high and low

TABLE 70

VALUES OF $\mathcal{J}(x)$ VERSUS x

x	0	1	2	3	4	5	6	7	8	9
0	1.0	1.0	1.0	0.99	0.99	0.98	0.98	0.97	0.96	0.95
10	0.94	0.92	0.90	0.88	0.85	0.82	0.79	0.76	0.72	0.68
20	0.63	0.58	0.53	0.48	0.44	0.40	0.36	0.33	0.30	0.27
30	0.24	0.21	0.18	0.15	0.12	0.10	0.08	0.06	0.04	0.02

frequencies. So the function represented by the set of values given in Table 71 was adopted as best representing the data.

When more than one pure tone or a continuous noise is producing interference, the same procedure outlined above is used but we must now define the β and f for such noises. For these cases there are two compensating effects. The additional components produce more summation and difference tones but also they mask some of the regions which would otherwise let these tones be audible. This is also true of noises in general.

TABLE 71

VALUES OF a VERSUS β AND f

β	$f=100$	500	600	700	800	900	1000	1200	1400	1600	1800	2000	2500	3000	3500	4000
100	0.20	0.20	0.31	0.42	0.47	0.52	0.57	0.54	0.52	0.54	0.56	0.58	0.48	0.38	0.28	0.18
90	0.14	0.14	0.23	0.32	0.37	0.42	0.47	0.43	0.40	0.42	0.45	0.48	0.40	0.33	0.23	0.13
80	0.08	0.08	0.15	0.22	0.27	0.32	0.37	0.32	0.28	0.31	0.35	0.38	0.32	0.28	0.18	0.08
70	0.02	0.02	0.07	0.12	0.17	0.22	0.26	0.21	0.16	0.20	0.25	0.26	0.24	0.23	0.13	0.03
60	0	0	0.00	0.02	0.07	0.12	0.15	0.10	0.04	0.10	0.15	0.14	0.16	0.18	0.08	0.00
50	0	0	0	0	0.00	0.03	0.04	0.00	0	0.00	0.04	0.02	0.08	0.13	0.03	0.00
40	0	0	0	0	0	0	0	0	0	0	0	0	0	0.08	0	0

The data seem to indicate that as the number of interfering tones of equal level increases, more of the interfering effect is taken over by the masking action and less by the H factor. It is rather complicated and difficult to formulate any simple rule for following the effect. Therefore, it was considered that the best approximation for a combination of tones was to take a value of the quantity a corresponding to the component which alone would give the greatest value of a and this was found to agree with the data as well as they are now known. The intensity level β corresponding to this component having frequency f is used in equation (17–53) to determine α_m and then a is found in Table 71 corresponding to this β and f.   For distributed noises the critical bands are considered as component tones.   So the value of β is equal to $B + \kappa$ where B is the spectrum level of the noise, the particular value of $B + \kappa$ and f being that which gives the greatest value of a.   This can be obtained from inspection of Table 71 and a plot of $B + \kappa$.   This value of a is used in equation (17-54) to find the factor H.

Using these relations for H fits all the available articulation data on systems with noise to within the accuracy of the data.

Special Types of Distortion

Most of the systems for which calculations are shown involve no special types of distortion but only non-uniform frequency response and noise.   For other types of distortion it is difficult to make generalizations, for each problem has to be considered by itself.   However, a method which gives results that are approximately correct is outlined here for common types of special distortion.   The method uses the factor H for this purpose.   If the distortion is in the transmitting or receiving mechanism and is independent of the amplification in the line, then the factor H can be determined from articulation tests using a known type of line. The value of H determined this way can then be used for any other type of line and the calculation can proceed as outlined above except that the factor F is replaced by $H \cdot F$.   Four types of distortion which can be handled in this manner are now considered.

Reproducing Speed Different from Recording Speed.—The first one is the distortion caused by multiplying all frequencies by a common factor such as is produced by a phonograph record of speech.   The speed when reproducing is different from that while recording.   A test of such a transmitting device indicates the factor H to be that given in Table 72.

TABLE 72

VALUES OF H VERSUS SPEED

Speed	0.5	0.6	0.7	0.8	0.9	1.0	1.1	1.2	1.3	1.4	1.5	1.6
$H =$	0.17	0.42	0.60	0.79	0.96	1.0	0.97	0.865	0.76	0.68	0.61	0.54

For example, a system having a factor $pF = 0.72$ and with amplification such that the speech is received at a level so that V and E are unity gave the results shown in Fig. 190.   The curve was calculated for the various speeds.   For any of these speeds an articulation versus gain curve can be made.   For example, for speed equal to 0.8 normal $pF \cdot H = 0.57$, which can be used as the factor F and calculations proceed as outlined above for no special type of distortion.

Frequency Shift.—The second kind of distortion of this type is that due to shifting the frequency components such as may happen in carrier systems. Tests have shown that the factor H for such distortions is the

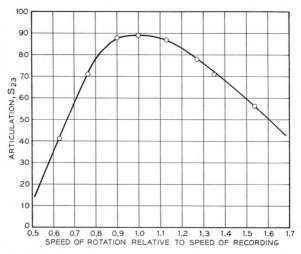

FIG. 190.—ARTICULATION VERSUS SPEED OF ROTATION OF A DISK PHONOGRAPH RECORD OF SPEECH: OBSERVATIONS (POINTS) AND CALCULATIONS (CURVE).

value given in Table 73. Although changes as much as 10 cycles are detectable, shifts as much as 200 produce only moderate distortions not greater than those due to a very resonant system.

TABLE 73

VALUES OF H VERSUS FREQUENCY SHIFT

TABLE XXII. Values of H vs. frequency shift.

Frequency shift	−300	−200	−100	−50	−25	0	25	50	100	200	300	400	500
$H =$	0.56	0.66	0.77	0.85	0.94	1.00	0.98	0.96	0.89	0.78	0.69	0.58	0.49

Reverberation in Rooms at Sending End and at Receiving End.—The third type of distortion considered here is that produced by reverberation in a room at either the transmitting end or the receiving end of the line or both. There are many variables in this problem and one can expect to get only an approximately correct answer by the method to be described, but this answer frequently is very useful in guiding engineering of systems for transmitting speech.

Even if one measured the response of such systems between each speaker and each listener, the procedure so far described still would not be valid because the prolonging of the speech in the room is not taken into account. So it seems better to take the response of the system as that obtained in a room with no reverberation—that is, with perfectly absorbing walls—and then use a factor H_R for rooms of various reverberations.

Since we are dealing with speech, this reverberation should be the average of that obtained with frequencies corresponding to the articulation importance function discussed above if the prolonging of the sound were not involved. Taking both effects into account, it is estimated that the average reverberation time taken at 500, 1000, and 2000 cps will yield the best time to take for a single value. In his book [11] Knudsen gives some results from which the values of H_R were calculated as given in Table 74. These values were obtained by the speaker

TABLE 74

VALUES OF H_R VERSUS REVERBERATION TIME

Reverberation time—seconds	0	1	2	3	4	5	6	7	8
$H_R =$	1.0	0.82	0.70	0.61	0.55	0.50	0.46	0.42	0.37

talking directly to the listeners, who were at various positions in a room having a volume of 2096 cubic feet. The experimental articulation values were considered to be of the type S_{23} with proficiency factor $p = 0.875$. In any telephone system there are two rooms to consider. Let H_L be the factor corresponding to the room in which the listener is placed, and H_S that corresponding to the room in which the speaker is placed. Although there are no data to guide one, it is roughly estimated that H_S approaches values H_R given in Table 74 when the speaker's lips are about five feet away from the usual type of microphone. This value estimated to be five feet depends upon many factors but this figure is given for illustrative purposes. For smaller distances the value H_S to be used for microphones is increased. If one interpolates linearly from H_S to unity as the distance goes from five feet to very close talking, then the value H_S for the speaking end of the lines is given approximately by

$$H_S = 1 - (1 - H_R)d/5 \qquad (17\text{-}55)$$

where d is the distance in feet between the lips of the speaker to the position of the lips for close talking. Similarly for loudspeakers of the usual type one can go to about 20 feet (an estimate given for illustrative purposes) before reaching the value H_R so that for the listening end H_L is given by

$$H_L = 1 - (1 - H_R)d/20. \qquad (17\text{-}56)$$

It must be emphasized that these relations for reverberant rooms are only very approximate since there are many factors not taken into account

---

[11] V. O. Knudsen, *Architectural Acoustics*, John Wiley and Sons, Inc., 1942.

such as shape of the room, speed of talking, size of microphone and loud-speaker, etc., but this method will yield calculated results which show the general relation between reverberation in the speaking and listening rooms, the response, the volume of received speech, the noise conditions and the articulation obtained. Having obtained H_S and H_L, then the factor F is replaced by $F \cdot H_S \cdot H_L$ and the procedure is the same as for non-reverberant rooms or close talking and listening. Research work to obtain more accurate relationships of this kind is greatly needed.

Overloading.—The next type of special distortion considered here is that due to overloading. It is common knowledge that overloading is very frequent in vacuum tube amplifiers. Let α_i be the input level to the vacuum tube amplifier, and α_x be the output. Then in Table 75 is shown a typical set of articulation data when such an amplifier is in the system.

TABLE 75

DATA FOR OVERLOADED VACUUM TUBE

$\alpha_1 =$	-40	-30	-20	-10	0	10	20	30
$\alpha_x =$	-17	-7	2	6	7.7	8.5	9	9
$\Delta\alpha =$	0	0	1	7	15.3	24.5	34	44
$S_{23} =$	0.79	0.79	0.79	0.78	0.745	0.65	0.45	

For input levels below $-$ 20 db the difference between α_x and α_i is constant and equal to 23 db, which is the gain of the amplifier before overloading starts. After overloading starts, this difference becomes progressively smaller and then negative as the input level increases. The quantity

$$\Delta\alpha = 23 - (\alpha_x - \alpha_i)$$

is a measure of the overloading and is given in the third row.

The response characteristics of the system from which the data in Table 75 were obtained was not accurately known but from Table 54 it is evident that corresponding to $S_{23} = 0.79$, $Ap = 0.58$. Therefore, if the value of Ap corresponding to each value of S_{23} is divided by 0.58, one finds the value of H. Such a set of values of H versus $\Delta\alpha$ is given in Table 76.

TABLE 76

VALUES OF H VERSUS $\Delta\alpha$

$\Delta\alpha$	2	4	6	8	10	12	14	16	18	20	22	24	26	28	30	35	40
H	0.997	0.994	0.998	0.976	0.963	0.950	0.93	0.91	0.89	0.85	0.81	0.76	0.72	0.68	0.63	0.52	0.40

In dealing with such systems one must remember it is the output level which governs the received speech level and thus determines the effective gain. For illustration the calculation for system II–RN–1060,

TABLE 77

CALCULATION OF ARTICULATION FOR 3 CASES OF OVERLOADING. FROM RESPONSE, $F = 0.535$ (SEE FIGS. 182 AND 191). LET PROFICIENCY FACTOR $p = 1.0$

Case (1): No overloading $H = 1.0$.

$\alpha_i =$	0	5	10	15	20	25	30	40	50	60
$\Delta\alpha =$	0	0	0	0	0	0	0	0	0	0
$x_V =$	27.8	32.2	36.8	41.7	46.7	51.7	56.7	66.7	76.7	86.7
$x_E =$					69.5	74.5	79.5	89.5	99.5	109.5
$V =$	0.486	0.595	0.693	0.785	0.85	0.908	0.956	1.0	1.0	1.0
$E =$	1.000	1.0	1.0	1.0	1.0	0.992	0.980	0.935	0.87	0.83
$A =$	0.260	0.318	0.371	0.42	0.455	0.482	0.501	0.50	0.465	0.443
$S_3 =$	0.312	0.413	0.500	0.578	0.625	0.658	0.682	0.680	0.639	0.610

Case (2): Overloading starts at $\alpha_i = 6$ db

$\Delta\alpha =$	0	0	1	3.3	7	10.9	15.3	24.5	34	44
$x_V =$	27.8	32.2	35.8	38.4	39.7	40.8	41.4	42.2	42.7	42.7
$x_E =$					62.5	63.6	64.2	65	65.5	65.5
$V =$	0.486	0.595	0.673	0.721	0.747	0.756	0.772	0.785	0.793	0.793
$E =$	1.000	1.0	1.0	1.0	1.0	1.0	1.0	1.0	1.0	1.0
$H =$	1.000	1.0	0.998	0.995	0.982	0.957	0.917	0.744	0.542	0.350
$A =$	0.260	0.318	0.358	0.384	0.394	0.391	0.378	0.313	0.228	0.149
$S_3 =$	0.312	0.413	0.480	0.521	0.537	0.532	0.512	0.404	0.260	0.142

Case (3): Overloading starts at $\alpha_i = 26$ db

$\Delta\alpha =$	0	0	0	0	0	0	1	7	15.3	24.5
$x_V =$	27.8	32.2	36.8	41.7	46.7	51.7	55.7	59.7	61.4	62.4
$x_E =$					69.5	74.5	78.5	82.5	84.2	85.0
$V =$	0.486	0.595	0.693	0.785	0.85	0.908	0.95	0.978	0.983	0.99
$E =$	1.000	1.0	1.0	1.0	1.0	0.992	0.98	0.97	0.964	0.96
$H =$	1.000	1.0	1.0	1.0	1.0	1.0	0.998	0.982	0.917	0.744
$A =$	0.269	0.318	0.371	0.420	0.455	0.482	0.492	0.487	0.475	0.391
$S_3 =$	0.312	0.413	0.500	0.578	0.625	0.658	0.671	0.677	0.650	0.574

whose response curve is given in Fig. 182, will be made here. Three cases will be considered: (1) No overloading, (2) overloading starts at $\alpha_i = 6$ db, and (3) overloading starts at $\alpha_i = 26$ db. The values of $\bar{R}^1$, $\bar{R}_4$, α_0 and γ which are obtained from the response are given in Fig. 182. From these values one obtains for case (1)

$$x_V = \alpha_i + 49.5 - 22.8\phi$$
$$x_E = \alpha_i + 49.5.$$

For cases (2) and (3)

$$x_V = \alpha_i - \Delta\alpha + 49.5 - 22.8\phi$$
$$x_E = \alpha_i - \Delta\alpha + 49.5$$

but the values of $\Delta\alpha$ corresponding to α_i are different in cases (2) and (3). The calculations for the three cases are given in Table 77. The results are plotted in Fig. 191. An examination of this calculation shows that

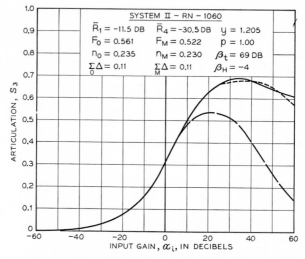

FIG. 191.—CALCULATED ARTICULATION VERSUS GAIN FOR THREE CONDITIONS IN REGARD TO OVERLOAD.

when overloading occurs, E becomes greater but both V and H become smaller. For case (2) the V and H factors are controlling and produce the lowering in articulation shown. But for case (3) these two effects approximately balance for the first 15-db overloading and then the H factor decreases faster than E increases.

Carbon Microphone Distortion

In carbon microphones there are distortions not accounted for by the F factor as calculated. There are two effects which enter into the calculation in a different way. The first is due to the output versus input characteristics of the carbon microphones not being linear and thus the speech sounds are compressed or expanded on the intensity level scale.[12] The second is due to harmonic, summation, and difference tones being generated which affect the interpretation of the sounds.

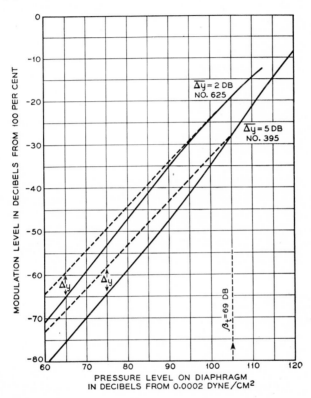

Fig. 192.—Output versus Input Characteristics of No. 395 and No. 625 Carbon Type Microphones Tested in a Constant Sound Field at Frequency 1000 cps.

In Fig. 192 are shown the output versus input characteristics for the No. 625 and No. 395 microphones. As indicated, these results were obtained for a single frequency of 1000 cps. Very similar results will be obtained for any other frequency except those near a resonant peak. Since the loud sounds are 4 or 5 db above the average and also since for close talking the level is about 30 db above that at one meter which has been termed the "talking level," it follows that the level at the diaphragm of the microphone for the more intense sounds, due to a caller having a

[12] A method of handling this effect in a computational manner was first suggested by P. V. Dimock and is given in the paper by French and Steinberg already cited in reference 3.

talking level of 69 db, is about 105 db as indicated in Fig. 192.   This pressure level at the diaphragm varies with the type of mouthpiece, method of holding the microphone, etc.   For purposes of this calculation the 105-db pressure level is sufficiently accurate to correspond to a talking level of 69 db.

Let (x_0, y_0) be the coordinates of the point on the output versus input curve corresponding to the talking level β_t of the caller.   Then

$$x_0 = 105 + (\beta_t - 69). \tag{17-57}$$

When a weak sound is impressed upon the microphone, the input is dropped to a value x—that is, by an amount $x_0 - x$.   If the characteristics were linear the output would also drop by an amount $x_0 - x$ db.   In general, however, the output drops by an amount $x_0 - x + \Delta y$, as shown in Fig. 192.   Consequently the low intensity sounds in the input are dropped to an even lower level in the output with respect to the loud sounds, so more of them will be masked and therefore F will be reduced. It is evident that this additional lowering has the same effect as reducing the response for these sounds.   Since the speech sounds are distributed in level approximately uniformly over a 40-db range, an average value of Δy, designated $\langle \Delta y \rangle$, taken over the 40-db range below x_0, will be used. This $\langle \Delta y \rangle$ is subtracted from Z_F, the db above threshold of the speech sounds, in the formula for r in Section 11.

Calling this new value of r equal to r', then

$$r' = \frac{68}{Z_F + 5 - (\Delta Z + \langle \Delta y \rangle)} = r \frac{68}{68 - r\langle \Delta y \rangle} = r \left(1 + r \frac{\langle \Delta y \rangle}{68} \right). \tag{17-58}$$

In other words, this type of distortion has the effect of increasing the value of r by the factor $68/68 - r\langle \Delta y \rangle$.   For the No. 625 microphone the value of $\langle \Delta y \rangle$ is seen from Fig. 192 to be 2 db, and for the No. 395 microphone to be 5 db.   No reliable data are available for the No. 323 microphone but it is estimated that $\langle \Delta y \rangle$ is equal to 3 db for this microphone.

If the output versus input current in Fig. 192 were above the broken line, then the speech sounds would be compressed and the value of r reduced instead of being increased.   Such compression would help the interpretation if it could be accomplished without producing other deteriorating effects.   Microphones have been made which approach the condition for $\langle \Delta y \rangle = 0$ but none has been made which compresses the range of speech sound levels.

In designing a microphone for commercial use many factors must be taken into consideration besides articulation under ideal conditions. For example, compressing the range of speech sound levels would raise the level of room noise going into the microphone through the sidetone circuit and into the receiver and thus interfere with the perception of the sounds being received.   Expanding the level has the opposite effect.

The effect of producing harmonic, summation and difference tones is handled by making H less than unity.   The value of H should be closely related to the level of the difference tones compared to the fundamental. Let two tones of frequency f_1 and $f_1 + 200$ cps and each at a pressure level of β be impressed upon the microphone diaphragm.   Let the output

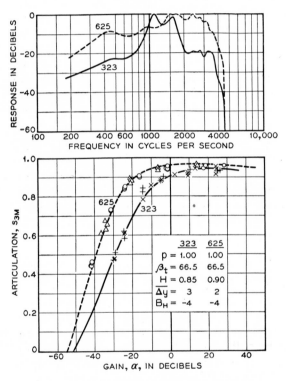

FIG. 193.—SYSTEMS III–C–323, −625, CONTAINING CARBON MICROPHONES: RESPONSE VERSUS FREQUENCY AND ARTICULATION VERSUS GAIN.

level of the two fundamentals be β_1 db and β_1' db, respectively, and let the output level of the difference tone be β_d.   Now let f_1 be changed progressively from 400 to 4000 cps and all of the output levels mentioned above measured.   Call the average level of the two fundamentals $\bar{\beta}_1$, and of the difference tone $\bar{\beta}_d$.   Then H should be related to $\bar{\beta}_1 - \bar{\beta}_d$.   Since the effect upon H is small, it was considered that the relation could be made entirely dependent upon the level of the difference tone rather than considering the summation tones and the harmonics.   Consequently the simple formula (17–59) was chosen:

$$H = 1 - 0.009[25 - (\bar{\beta}_1 - \bar{\beta}_d)].$$ (17–59)

The constant 25 signifies that when the average level of the difference tone is down 25 db, H is unity. For larger values of $\bar{\beta}_1 - \bar{\beta}_d$ there is no effect upon articulation produced by such distortions and this equation must be so interpreted. The constant 0.009 was chosen to fit the data on the No. 395 and No. 625 microphones.

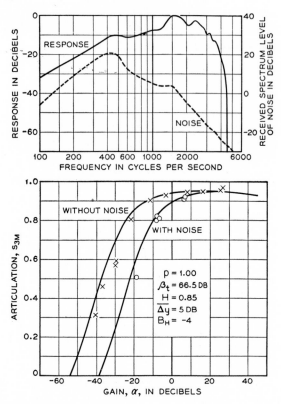

FIG. 194.—SYSTEM III–C–395 CONTAINING CARBON MICROPHONE, WITHOUT AND WITH A NOISE INTRODUCED ELECTRICALLY FROM A PHONOGRAPHIC RECORD OF ROOM NOISE.

Consequently, for engineering purposes the value of H for the No. 395 and for the No. 625 microphones may be considered 0.85 and 0.9 respectively. No reliable data were available for the No. 323 microphone so the value of H was estimated to be the same as for the No. 395, namely, 0.85.

Using these values calculations were made upon systems having such microphones. In Fig. 193 are shown the results for the No. 625 and No.

323 microphone systems.   The response curves are given at the top of the figure and observed and calculated data on articulation are given in the bottom part.   It is seen that the calculated curves fit the observed points very well.

In Fig. 194 the results are given for a No. 395 carbon transmitter system for the cases when the listener is (1) in a quiet place, and (2) in a noisy place.   The spectrum level of the noise at the listener's ear and the response curve for the system are given in the top part of the figure.

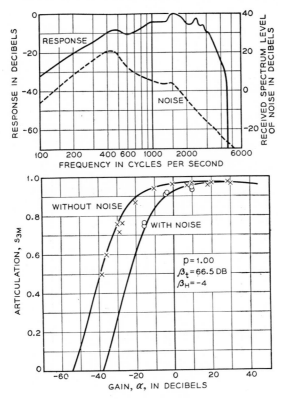

FIG. 195.—SYSTEM III–HY-395 CONTAINING LINEAR MICROPHONE (RESEMBLING NO. 395 CARBON MICROPHONE IN CERTAIN PROPERTIES), WITHOUT AND WITH NOISE.

The two articulation versus gain curves are given in the bottom part of the figure.   A shift of 3 db in the calculated curves would give a better fit. It is considered that there is this much uncertainty in the combination of talking levels and response for these systems.   Results were also taken on a system which had approximately the same response as for the No. 395 carbon microphone system but used a condenser transmitter. The results for this system are given in Fig. 195.

CHART I

SYSTEMS WITH NO NOISE

f	R	$10^{R/10}$	$\beta_t=$ f	R	$10^{R/40}$	f	r	R	$p=$ $\bar{R}-R$	$(\bar{R}-R)_r$	W	Δ
510			320			310	1.33					−0.03
640			500			470	1.06					−0.01
730			630			610	1.02					+0.01
820			750			740	1					+0.03
900			870			880	1					+0.04
980			990			1020	1					+0.04
1070			1120			1170	1					+0.03
1160			1260			1330	1					+0.02
1250			1410			1520	1					+0.00
1360			1570			1720	1					−0.02
1470			1760			1950	1					−0.04
1590			1960			2200	1					−0.05
1710			2190			2470	1					−0.06
1860			2440			2770	1					−0.06
2020			2740			3090	1					−0.05

2210	3090		3480	1.03	−0.04
2430	3520		3920	1.06	−0.02
2700	4080		4480	1.10	0.00
3100	4890		5210	1.17	+0.01
3930	6600		6370	1.39	+0.03

$SUM =$
$1/20(SUM) =$
$\overline{R}_l =$
$\overline{R} = \frac{1}{2}(\overline{R}_l + \overline{R}_t) =$

$SUM =$
$1/20(SUM) =$
$\overline{R}_t =$

$n_0/F_0 =$
$pF =$

$SUM =$
$F_0 = 1/20(SUM) =$
$F_M =$
$F = \frac{2}{3}F_M + \frac{1}{3}F_0 =$

x_V	0	5	10	15	20	25	30	35	40	45	50	60	70	80	90	100	110	120
x_E																		
E																		
V	0.00	0.05	0.11	0.20	0.30	0.41	0.54	0.66	0.75	0.83	0.89	0.98	1.0	1.0	1.0	1.0	1.0	1.0
$A \cdot p$																		
S																		
α																		

$x_E = \alpha + \overline{R}_l + \beta_l - 8 - (\beta_H + 4) = \alpha - \alpha_0$
$\Sigma\Delta =$ summation of all values of Δ where $W \geq 0.99 =$
$W = 1.0$
$n_0 = \frac{1}{3} \sum\limits_{W=0.9}^{W=1.0} (W - 0.9) =$

CHART 2

SYSTEMS WITH NO NOISE

f	Z_F	y	R	ΔR	r	$\bar{R}-R$	$(\bar{R}-R)r$	W
310	46							
470	59							
610	62							
740	63							
880	63							
1020	63							
1170	63							
1330	63							
1520	63							
1720	63							
1950	63							
2200	63							
2470	63							
2770	63							
3090	63							
3480	61							
3920	59							

$\bar{R}_1 =$

$\bar{R}_t$ $\Sigma\Delta =$

Construction of Speech Masking Curves

High frequency side $f_T =$

$R_T =$

$Z_T =$

$y_{T} = R_T - 63 + Z_F =$

y at $2f_T = y_T - \sigma =$

Low frequency side $f_T =$

$R_T =$

$y_{p_i} = R_T - 63 + Z_F =$

y at $0.7f_T = y_T - 40 =$

y at $\frac{1}{2}f_T = y_T - 60 =$

y at $0.35f_T = y_T - 70 =$

y at $\frac{1}{4}f_T = y_T - 75 =$

4480	57
5220	53
6370	44

$$\sigma = 75 - \tfrac{1}{2}[Z_F + R_T - \bar{R}_1 + \gamma(\bar{R}_1 - \bar{R}_4)] =$$

$$\Delta R = y - R$$

$$r = \frac{Z_F + 5 - (63 - Z_F + \Delta R)}{68}$$

$$n_M/F_M =$$

$$x_\gamma = \tfrac{1}{3}(n_0/F_0 + n_M/F_M) =$$

$$\psi =$$

$$\gamma = \psi + x_\gamma \Sigma \Delta =$$

$$SUM =$$

$$F_M = 1/20(SUM) =$$

$x_V =$	0	5	10	15	20	25	30	35	40	45	50
$\phi =$	0.00	0.22	0.45	0.65	0.85	0.93	0.97	0.99	1.0	1.0	1.0
$\phi \cdot \gamma \cdot (\bar{R}_1 - \bar{R}_4) =$											
$\alpha_0 + x_V =$											
$\alpha =$											

$$\alpha_0 = -\bar{R}_4 - \beta_4 + 8 + (\beta_H + 4) =$$

$$\alpha = \alpha_0 + x_V + \gamma\phi(\bar{R}_1 - \bar{R}_4)$$

$$W = 1.0$$

$$n_M = \tfrac{1}{2} \sum_{W=0.9} (W - 0.9) =$$

NOTE.—Use successive approximations, in drawing the speech-masking tangent lines on the high frequency side, as follows:

1. First assume that $x_\gamma = n_0/F_0$. Take the value of n_0/F_0 from Chart 1 and proceed to find a tentative value of ψ from Chart 6 (3). Compute tentative values of γ and σ by the formulas on Chart 2 and use this value of σ to draw a tentative tangent line. This tangent gives tentative values of y.

2. Using these values of ΔR, fill in the blank tabulation in the upper part of Chart 2 and thus derive n_M/F_m. Then obtain a revised value of x_γ from the formula on Chart 2 and proceed to find a revised value of σ, etc.

3. It will be found that the labor involved in these successive approximations can be greatly reduced as one becomes experienced in judging the shapes of response characteristic curves.

CHART 3

SYSTEMS WITH NOISE

f	β_0'	$\kappa-\beta_0'$	B	Z	M	R	$R-M$	$B+\kappa$
200	34	−16.8						
300	26	− 9.0						
400	20.2	− 3.2						
500	15.2	+ 1.8						
600	12.2	5.0						
700	9.9	7.4						
800	8.1	9.5						
900	6.8	11.0						
1000	5.6	12.4						
1250	3.7	14.8						
1500	2.4	16.6						
1750	1.7	17.7						
2000	0.6	19.3						
2500	−0.6	21.4						
3000	−1.2	22.7						
4000	−0.1	23.1						
5000	2.8	21.6						

$a_m =$

$(B+\kappa)m =$

$f_m =$

6000	7.1	18.6
7000	12.1	14.7
8000	15.1	12.6

β_0' = threshold levels of critical band widths of speech.

κ = critical band widths in db for one ear listening.

B = spectrum level of noise,

$Z = B + (\kappa - \beta_0') - (\beta_H + 4)$.

$$10^{M/10} = 10^{Z/10} + 1$$

Calculation of H for noise.

$\beta = \kappa + B = \qquad f_m = \qquad a = \qquad \alpha_m =$

α							
α_m							
$\alpha - \alpha_m$							
$J(\alpha - \alpha_m)$							
$a \cdot J$							
$H = 1 - aJ$							

$\alpha_m = \beta - \beta_t - \bar{R}_t - K_m.$

CHART 4

Systems with Noise

f	$R-M$	$10^{(R-M)/10}$	$B_1 = $ $\dfrac{R-M \ 10^{(R-M)/10}}{f}$	f	r	$R-M$	$(R-M)^*$	$p=$ $-(R-M)$ $[(R-M)-(R-M)]r$	W	Δ
510			320	310	1.33					−0.03
640			500	470	1.06					−0.01
730			630	610	1.02					+0.01
820			750	740	1					+0.03
900			870	880	1					+0.04
980			990	1020	1					+0.04
1070			1120	1170	1					+0.04
1160			1260	1330	1					+0.03
1250			1410	1520	1					+0.02
1360			1570	1720	1					0.00
1470			1760	1950	1					−0.02
1590			1960	2200	1					−0.04
1710			2190	2470	1					−0.05
1860			2440	2770	1					−0.06
2020			2740	3090	1					−0.06
2210			3090	3480	1.03					−0.05
										−0.04

2430	3520	3920	1.06		−0.02
2700	4080	4480	1.10		0.00
3100	4890	5220	1.17		+0.01
3930	6600	6370	1.39		+0.03

$SUM =$
$1/20(SUM)_1 =$
$\langle (R-M) \rangle_1 =$
$(R-M) = \frac{1}{2}\langle (R-M) \rangle_1 + \frac{1}{2}\langle (R-M) \rangle_4 =$

$SUM =$
$1/20(SUM) =$
$\langle (R-M) \rangle_4 =$

$SUM =$
$1/20(SUM) =$
$F_{NO} = 1/20(SUM) =$
$F_{NM} =$
$F = \frac{1}{2}F_{NM} + \frac{1}{2}F_{NO} =$

$n_{NO}/F_{NO} =$

$pF =$

x_V	0	5	10	15	20	25	30	35	40	45	50	60	70	80	90	100	110	120
x_E																		
E																		
V	0	0.05	0.11	0.20	0.30	0.41	0.54	0.66	0.75	0.83	0.89	0.98	1.0	1.0	1.0	1.0	1.0	1.0
H																		
$A \cdot p$																		
S																		
α																		

$x_E = \alpha + \bar{K}_1 + \beta_l - 8 - (\beta_H + 4)$
$\Sigma_0\Delta$ = summation of all values of Δ where $W \geq 0.99$ =

$n_{NO} = \frac{1}{4} \sum_{W=0.9}^{W=1.0} (W - 0.9) =$

CHART 5
Systems with Noise

f	R	$10^{R/10}$	f	R	$10^{R/10}$	f	ΔR	Z_F	r	R	$\bar{R}-R$	$(\bar{R}-R)r$	W	Δ
510			320			310		46						−0.03
640			500			470		59						−0.01
730			630			610		62						+0.01
820			750			740		63						+0.03
900			870			880		63						+0.04
980			990			1020		63						+0.04
1070			1120			1170		63						+0.03
1160			1260			1330		63						+0.02
1250			1410			1520		63						0.00
1360			1570			1720		63						−0.02
1470			1760			1950		63						−0.04
1590			1960			2200		63						−0.05
1710			2190			2470		63						−0.06
1860			2440			2770		63						−0.06
2020			2740			3090		63						−0.05

2210		3090		3480	61					−0.04
2430		3520		3920	59					−0.02
2700		4080		4480	57					0.00
3100		4890		5220	53					+0.01
3930		6600		6370	44					+0.03

SUM =

1/20 SUM =

$\bar{R}_1 =$

$\bar{R} = \frac{1}{2}(\bar{R}_1 + \bar{R}_t) =$

$r = Z_F + 5 - \dfrac{(63 - Z_F + \Delta R)}{68}$

$n_{NM}/F_{NM} =$

$SUM =$

$1/20\,SUM =$

$F_{NM} = 1/20(SUM) =$

$SUM =$

$x_\gamma = \frac{1}{2}(n_{NO}/F_{NO} + n_{NM}/F_{NM}) =$

$\psi =$

$\gamma = \psi + \frac{1}{2}x_\gamma(\Sigma_0\Delta + \Sigma_M\Delta) =$

$\gamma = \psi + \frac{1}{2}x_\gamma[((R-M))_1 - ((R-M))_\lambda] =$

$\sigma_M = 75 - \frac{1}{4}[Z_F + R_T - ((R-M)) - ((R-M))_\lambda] =$

	0	5	10	15	20	25	30	35	40	45	50
$xv =$											
$\phi =$	0	0.22	0.45	0.65	0.85	0.93	0.97	0.99	1	1	1
$\phi \cdot \gamma[((R-M))_1 - ((R-M))_4] =$											
$\alpha_0 + xv =$											
$\alpha =$											

$\alpha_0 = -((R-M))_1 + 8 - \beta_t + (\beta_H + 4) =$

$\alpha = \alpha_0 + xv + \gamma\phi[((R-M))_1 - ((R-M))_\lambda] =$

$\Sigma_M\Delta$ = summation of all values of Δ where $W \geq 0.99$ =

$W = 1.0$

$n_{NM} = \frac{1}{2} \sum_{W=0}^{W=1.0} (W - 0.9) =$

CHART 6

(1) Values of W vs. x_V

x_V	0	1	2	3	4	5	6	7	8	9	Difference
0	1.0	0.997	0.994	0.990	0.985	0.980	0.973	0.966	0.958	0.950	0.007
10	0.940	0.930	0.920	0.910	0.899	0.887	0.874	0.860	0.846	0.832	0.012
20	0.818	0.804	0.789	0.774	0.759	0.744	0.728	0.712	0.695	0.678	0.017
30	0.660	0.642	0.623	0.603	0.582	0.561	0.539	0.516	0.492	0.467	0.022
40	0.441	0.415	0.390	0.365	0.340	0.315	0.291	0.267	0.244	0.222	0.022
50	0.202	0.183	0.165	0.148	0.132	0.118	0.104	0.091	0.080	0.070	0.013
60	0.060	0.050	0.040	0.030	0.022	0.015	0.010	0.005	0.000		0.010

(2) Values of E vs. x_E

x_E	0	1	2	3	4	5	6	7	8	9
60	1.00	1.0	1.0	1.0	1.0	1.0	1.0	1.0	1.0	1.0
70	0.980	0.998	0.996	0.994	0.992	0.990	0.988	0.986	0.984	0.982
80	0.931	0.977	0.973	0.969	0.965	0.960	0.955	0.949	0.943	0.937
90	0.870	0.925	0.919	0.913	0.907	0.900	0.894	0.888	0.882	0.876
100	0.830	0.866	0.862	0.858	0.854	0.850	0.845	0.841	0.838	0.834
110	0.790	0.826	0.822	0.818	0.814	0.810	0.806	0.802	0.798	0.794
120		0.786	0.782	0.778	0.774	0.77	0.766	0.762	0.758	0.754

(3) Values of ψ vs. x_γ

x_γ	.00	.01	.02	.03	.04	.05	.06	.07	.08	.09
0.3	1.20	1.20	1.20	1.20	1.20	1.20	1.198	1.196	1.194	1.192
0.4	1.185	1.176	1.167	1.158	1.149	1.140	1.128	1.114	1.097	1.083
0.5	1.070	1.060	1.045	1.030	1.010	0.990	0.970	0.940	0.905	0.870
0.6	0.840	0.805	0.770	0.740	0.710	0.685	0.655	0.625	0.595	0.560
0.7	0.530	0.500	0.475	0.445	0.415	0.390	0.360	0.335	0.310	0.285
0.8	0.265	0.240	0.215	0.185	0.155	0.130	0.110	0.090	0.070	0.055
0.9	0.045	0.035	0.025	0.015	0.008	0.003	0	0	0	0

(4) Values of $J(x) = J(-x)$

x	0	1	2	3	4	5	6	7	8	9
0	1.0	1.0	1.0	0.99	0.99	0.98	0.98	0.97	0.96	0.95
10	0.94	0.92	0.90	0.88	0.85	0.82	0.79	0.76	0.72	0.68
20	0.63	0.58	0.53	0.48	0.44	0.40	0.36	0.33	0.30	0.27
30	0.24	0.21	0.18	0.15	0.12	0.10	0.08	0.06	0.04	0.02

(5) Values of a in terms of β and f

β	f=100	500	600	700	800	900	1000	1200	1400	1600	1800	2000	2500	3000	3500	4000
100	0.20	0.20	0.31	0.42	0.47	0.52	0.57	0.54	0.52	0.54	0.56	0.58	0.48	0.38	0.28	0.18
90	0.14	0.14	0.23	0.32	0.37	0.42	0.47	0.43	0.40	0.42	0.45	0.48	0.40	0.33	0.23	0.13
80	0.08	0.08	0.15	0.22	0.27	0.32	0.37	0.32	0.28	0.31	0.35	0.38	0.32	0.28	0.18	0.08
70	0.02	0.02	0.07	0.12	0.17	0.22	0.26	0.21	0.16	0.20	0.25	0.26	0.24	0.23	0.13	0.03
60	0.00	0.00	0.00	0.02	0.07	0.12	0.15	0.10	0.04	0.10	0.15	0.14	0.16	0.18	0.08	0.00
50	0.00	0.00	0.00	0.00	0.00	0.03	0.04	0.00	0.00	0.00	0.04	0.02	0.08	0.13	0.03	0.00
40	0.00	0.00	0.00	0.00	0.00	0.00	0.00	0.00	0.00	0.00	0.00	0.00	0.00	0.08	0.00	0.00

(6) Values of K_m in terms of f_m

f_m =	100	200	300	400	500	700	1000	1400	2000	3000	4000
K_m =	9	11	13	14	15	14	12	10	7	-2	-11

CHART 7

Articulation versus Articulation Index

Ap	s3M	S3	S23	S2	Ap	s3M	S3	S23	S2
0.01	0.041	0.004	0.014	0.010	0.51	0.882	0.693	0.721	0.794
0.02	0.080	0.008	0.028	0.023	0.52	0.887	0.704	0.732	0.802
0.03	0.118	0.013	0.043	0.040	0.53	0.891	0.714	0.742	0.810
0.04	0.154	0.018	0.058	0.058	0.54	0.896	0.725	0.752	0.818
0.05	0.189	0.024	0.073	0.075	0.55	0.900	0.736	0.761	0.825
0.06	0.222	0.031	0.088	0.093	0.56	0.904	0.746	0.771	0.832
0.07	0.254	0.040	0.103	0.111	0.57	0.908	0.757	0.780	0.839
0.08	0.285	0.049	0.118	0.129	0.58	0.912	0.767	0.790	0.846
0.09	0.314	0.060	0.133	0.146	0.59	0.916	0.777	0.799	0.852
0.10	0.342	0.071	0.148	0.164	0.60	0.919	0.787	0.807	0.858
0.11	0.369	0.084	0.163	0.182	0.61	0.922	0.797	0.815	0.864
0.12	0.395	0.098	0.177	0.199	0.62	0.925	0.806	0.822	0.869
0.13	0.421	0.112	0.191	0.217	0.63	0.928	0.815	0.829	0.874
0.14	0.444	0.127	0.205	0.234	0.64	0.931	0.824	0.836	0.879
0.15	0.466	0.144	0.219	0.252	0.65	0.934	0.832	0.843	0.884
0.16	0.488	0.156	0.233	0.269	0.66	0.937	0.839	0.850	0.889
0.17	0.509	0.173	0.247	0.286	0.67	0.939	0.846	0.857	0.894
0.18	0.529	0.186	0.261	0.304	0.68	0.942	0.854	0.864	0.898
0.19	0.548	0.201	0.275	0.323	0.69	0.944	0.861	0.870	0.902
0.20	0.567	0.216	0.289	0.342	0.70	0.947	0.868	0.877	0.906
0.21	0.585	0.231	0.303	0.362	0.71	0.949	0.875	0.884	0.910
0.22	0.602	0.247	0.318	0.382	0.72	0.951	0.882	0.890	0.914
0.23	0.618	0.263	0.333	0.402	0.73	0.953	0.888	0.895	0.917
0.24	0.634	0.279	0.348	0.422	0.74	0.955	0.894	0.900	0.920
0.25	0.649	0.295	0.363	0.441	0.75	0.957	0.900	0.905	0.923

0.76	0.958	0.906	0.910	0.926
0.77	0.960	0.911	0.915	0.929
0.78	0.962	0.916	0.921	0.932
0.79	0.963	0.921	0.926	0.934
0.80	0.965	0.926	0.931	0.937
0.81	0.967	0.930	0.935	0.939
0.82	0.968	0.935	0.939	0.941
0.83	0.969	0.939	0.943	0.943
0.84	0.970	0.943	0.947	0.945
0.85	0.972	0.946	0.950	0.947
0.86	0.973	0.950	0.953	0.949
0.87	0.974	0.953	0.956	0.951
0.88	0.975	0.956	0.959	0.952
0.89	0.976	0.959	0.961	0.954
0.90	0.977	0.961	0.963	0.955
0.91	0.978	0.963	0.965	0.956
0.92	0.979	0.964	0.966	0.958
0.93	0.980	0.965	0.967	0.960
0.94	0.980	0.967	0.969	0.961
0.95	0.981	0.968	0.970	0.963
0.96	0.982	0.970	0.972	0.964
0.97	0.983	0.971	0.973	0.966
0.98	0.983	0.973	0.975	0.967
0.99	0.984	0.974	0.976	0.968
1.00	0.985	0.976	0.978	0.970

0.26	0.663	0.312	0.378	0.460
0.27	0.677	0.329	0.393	0.478
0.28	0.690	0.347	0.407	0.496
0.29	0.703	0.365	0.422	0.514
0.30	0.715	0.382	0.437	0.531
0.31	0.727	0.399	0.452	0.548
0.32	0.738	0.416	0.467	0.564
0.33	0.749	0.433	0.482	0.580
0.34	0.759	0.450	0.497	0.596
0.35	0.769	0.467	0.512	0.611
0.36	0.778	0.483	0.527	0.625
0.37	0.787	0.499	0.542	0.639
0.38	0.796	0.515	0.558	0.653
0.39	0.805	0.531	0.574	0.666
0.40	0.813	0.547	0.589	0.679
0.41	0.821	0.563	0.604	0.692
0.42	0.828	0.578	0.617	0.704
0.43	0.835	0.592	0.630	0.715
0.44	0.842	0.606	0.642	0.726
0.45	0.848	0.619	0.654	0.737
0.46	0.854	0.632	0.665	0.747
0.47	0.860	0.644	0.677	0.757
0.48	0.866	0.657	0.689	0.767
0.49	0.871	0.669	0.700	0.776
0.50	0.877	0.681	0.711	0.785

Detailed Instructions for Using the Chart Method of Calculation

The objective is to calculate a curve showing the relation between the gain α in the system and the articulation obtained by any speaker-listener pair. For this purpose charts have been prepared to make such calculations easier to follow. Charts 1 and 2 are used when no noise is present. Charts 3–5 are used when noise is present. Chart 6 contains all the tables used in the calculations except the one giving the relationship between articulation index and articulation. This is given in Chart 7.

CASE I—NO NOISE AND NO SPECIAL TYPES OF DISTORTION

1. Calculation of $\bar{R}_1$. (Use Chart 1.)

   1a. From the response curve of R versus f read the values of R corresponding to each of the frequencies in column 1 of Chart 1 and record in column 2.

   1b. From the proper tables read the values of the exponential $10^{R/10}$ and record in column 3.

   1c. Add the numbers in column 3 and take 1/20th of this sum. Then $\bar{R}_1 = 10 \log(1/20 \text{ sum})$.

2. Calculation of $\bar{R}_4$. (Use Chart 1.)

   2a. From the curve of R versus f read the values of R corresponding to each frequency in column 4 and record in column 5.

   2b. Take the exponential indicated and record in column 6.

   2c. Then $\bar{R}_4 = 40 \log(1/20 \text{ sum})$.

3. Calculation of $\bar{R}$. (Use Chart 1.)

   3a. The value of $\bar{R}$ is the average of $\bar{R}_1$ and $\bar{R}_4$ and is recorded in the place indicated.

4. Determination of F_0.

   4a. From the response curve read the values of R corresponding to each frequency in column 7 and record in column 9.

   4b. Subtract each value of R from $\bar{R}$ and record in column 10.

   4c. Multiply $\bar{R} - R$ by values of r found in column 8 and record the result in column 11.

   4d. From these values find the corresponding values of W from Table I on Chart 6.

   4e. The average of these twenty values of W is the desired value of F_0.

5. Determination of the value of n_0 and n_M. (Use Charts 1 and 2.)

   5a. Subtract 0.9 from each value of W which is greater than 0.9.

   5b. Add the resulting differences.

   5c. One-half of the sum is the desired value of n_0.

   5d. Perform a similar operation of the values of W on Chart 2 to find n_M.

6. Determination of $\sum\Delta$. (Use Chart 1.)

    The value of Δ are given in the last column.

Those values opposite values of W equal to unity or greater than 0.99 are added together to obtain $\sum\Delta$. The summation is recorded at the bottom of the chart at the place indicated.

7. Determination of F_M. (Use Chart 2.)

    The procedure for calculating F_M is the same as for calculating F_0 except different values of r are used. The values of $\bar{R}_1$, $\bar{R}_4$, and $\sum\Delta$ are transferred from Chart 1 to Chart 2 to the places indicated.

    7a. Determination of ΔR. (Use Chart 2.)

        Construct the speech masking line on the high frequency side as follows. Determine the frequency f_T where the slope of the response curve exceeds the critical slope and record in the space indicated. This can usually be done with sufficient accuracy by inspection. From this frequency determine the corresponding response R_T from the curve and Z_T from values in column 2 of Chart 2. From this calculate y_T at f_T. The value of σ is obtained from the equation in the middle of the chart and so y at $2f_T$ can be calculated. A straight line is drawn between these points. Similarly on the low frequency side one follows the steps indicated on the chart to construct the speech masking curve on this side. The ordinates of these curves or series of straight lines corresponding to the frequencies in column 1 are recorded in column 3 under y. The values of R in column 4 are the same as on Chart 1. The values of ΔR are differences between y and R and are recorded in column 5.

    7b. Calculation of r. (Use Chart 2.)

        Determine the values of r from these values of ΔR by means of the formula in the middle of Chart 2 and record them in column 6. Whenever $63 - Z_F + \Delta R$ calculates to be zero or negative it is taken as zero. Also for large values of ΔR which make r negative, the value of r is taken as infinity.

    7c. Transfer values of $\bar{R} - R$ from Chart 1 to Chart 2.

    7d. Multiply these values by r to obtain $(\bar{R} - R)r$ and record in column 11.

    7e. Find corresponding values of W and record in column 12.

    7f. The value of F_M is the average of these values of W.

8. Calculation of γ. (Use Chart 2.)

    From the values of n_0/F_0 and n_M/F_M one calculates the value of x_γ by the equation indicated in the middle of the chart. The value of ψ is read from Table (3), Chart 6. The value of γ is calculated by the equation indicated and recorded.

9. Calculation of α.   (Use Chart 2.)

The table at the bottom of Chart 2 is used for this purpose.

9a. First calculate values of $\phi_\gamma(\bar{R}_1 - \bar{R}_4)$ and record in the third row.   The values of ϕ corresponding to each value of x_V are given in the second row.

9b. Calculate α_0 from the equation at the bottom of the chart using β_H derived as in appendix 2, and add α_0 to each value of x_V and record in the fourth row.

9c. Add values in the third and fourth row and record in the last row.   These are the desired values of α.   They are transferred to the last row of Chart 1.

10. Calculation of F and pF.   (Use Chart 1.)

The value of p is determined from experimental data and given at the top of Chart 1.   The value of F is obtained from F_0 and F_M by the formula in the middle of the chart.   Its value is recorded.   The value pF is then calculated and recorded in the place indicated.

11. Calculation of E.   (Use Chart 1.)

The value of x_E is the db above threshold level for the listener in a quiet place or $\alpha - \alpha_0$.   The values are recorded in the second row of the table at the bottom of the chart.   Remember, no values below 70 db need by tabulated since E is unity for these values of x_E.   The corresponding values of E are read from Table (2) of Chart 6.

12. Calculation of A and S.   (Use Chart 1.)

The values in Chart 1 of pF, E and V are multiplied together to get Ap.   These values of Ap are recorded in the fifth row opposite Ap in the chart.   Corresponding articulation values are obtained from tables of Chart 7.   These articulation values of S correspond to the α below them and consequently the desired curve of S versus α can be plotted and compared with experimental results.

CASE II—NOISE—NO SPECIAL TYPES OF DISTORTION

1. Calculation of the $R - M$ versus f curve.   (Use Chart 3.)

1a. On Chart 3 write in column 4 the values of B, the spectrum level of noise.

1b. Add columns 3 and 4 and subtract $\beta_H + 4$ to find values of Z and record in column 5.

1c. Calculate values of M from Z by the formula in the middle of Chart 3.   It should be noticed that for Z greater than 20 db, $Z = M$ and consequently for such values no calculation is needed.

1d. Read the values of the response R for each frequency in column 1 from the graph showing R versus f for the system being calculated and record in column 7.

1e. Subtract the numbers in column 6 from those in column 7 and record in column 8.

1f. Plot the curve of $R - M$ versus f from the numbers in columns 8 and 1.

The last column is used later for determining a.

2. Calculation of $(\langle R - M \rangle)_1$.   (Use Chart 4.)

   2a. From the curve of $R - M$ versus f found in step 1 read the values of $R - M$ corresponding to each of the frequencies in column 1 of Chart 4 and record in column 2.

   2b. From the proper tables read the values of the exponential $10^{(R-M)/10}$ and record in column 3.

   2c. Add the numbers in column 3 and take 1/20th of this sum. The value of $(\langle R - M \rangle)_1 = 10 \log(1/20 \text{ sum})$.

3. Calculation of $(\langle R - M \rangle)_4$.   (Use Chart 4.)

   3a. Write down values of $R - M$ found from the curve of $R - M$ versus f determined in step 1 corresponding to each of the frequencies in column 4 and record in column 5.

   3b. Take the exponential indicated and record in column 6.

   3c. The value of $(\langle R - M \rangle)_4$ is $(\langle R - M \rangle)_4 = 40 \log(1/20 \text{ sum})$.

4. Determination of $\langle R - M \rangle$.   (Use Chart 4.)

   This value is the average of $(\langle R - M \rangle)_1$ and $(\langle R - M \rangle)_4$ and is recorded in the place indicated.

5. Determination of F_{NO}.   (Use Chart 4.)

   5a. Again using the curve of $R - M$ versus f, write down in column 9 the values of $R - M$ corresponding to the frequencies in column 7.

   5b. From the value of $\langle R - M \rangle$ obtained in step 4 subtract each of the values of $R - M$ in column 9 and record the resulting values in column 10. Opposite each negative value found in column 10 enter a value of W equal to 1 in column 12.

   5c. Multiply each value in column 10 by r found in column 8 and record the resulting values in column 11.

   5d. From each value found in column 11 find from Table (1) of Chart 6 the corresponding value of W and enter in the last column. Add the twenty values of W thus obtained and divide by 20 to find the desired value of F_{NO}.

6. Determination of F_{NM}.   (Use Chart 5.)

   6a. In column 2 record the values of R from the graph of R versus f.

   6b. Take the exponential indicated and record in column 3.

   6c. Add the twenty values together and divide by 20. The value of $\bar{R}_1$ is given by $\bar{R}_1 = 10 \log(1/20 \text{ sum})$.

6d. Find the values of R corresponding to the frequencies in column 4 and record in column 5.

6e. Take the exponential indicated and record in column 6.

6f. Add the twenty values in column 6 together and divide by 20. The value of $\bar{R}_4 = 40 \log(1/20 \text{ sum})$.

6g. The value of $\bar{R}$ is the average of $\bar{R}_1$ and $\bar{R}_4$.

6h. Determination of ΔR.   (Use Chart 5.)

   The speech masking curve is constructed the same as for the no-noise case except a different value of the critical slope is used. Its value σ_M is calculated by the formula at the top of the lower table in Chart 5.   If y_M is the ordinate of the speech masking curve constructed as above, then $\Delta R = y_M - R$ and these values are recorded in column 9.

6i. Determination of r.   (Use Chart 5.)

   Determine r from the values of ΔR found in step 6h by the formula in the middle of Chart 5 and record in column 10.   For values of $\Delta R + (63 - Z_F)$ which are zero or negative, the value of $r = 68/(Z_F + 5)$.   Also for large values of ΔR which make r negative, the value of r is taken as infinity.   In other words, for such a high value of ΔR, the corresponding value of W is always zero.

6j. Subtract the values of R given in column 11 from the value $\bar{R}$ determined in 6g and record the values thus obtained in column 12.

6k. Multiply these values of $\bar{R} - R$ by r given in column 10 and record the resulting values in column 13.

6l. Look up the values of W corresponding to the values in column 13 from Table (1) of Chart 6 and record the results in column 14.

6m. The average of these twenty values of W is the value F_{NM} sought.

7. Determination of n_{NO}, n_{NM}, Σ_{NO}, and Σ_{NM}.

   These values are determined respectively from Charts 4 and 5 in the manner described for the no-noise case.

8. Determination of γ.   (Use Chart 5.)

   From the values F_{NO}, F_{NM}, n_{NO}, and n_{NM} the value of x_γ is calculated by the equation indicated.   From this value of x_γ the value of ψ is determined from Table (3) of Chart 6.   The value of γ is then calculated by the formula indicated.

9. Calculation of the values of α.   (Use Chart 5.)

   The table at the bottom of Chart 5 is used for this purpose and the procedure is the same as outlined for the no-noise case.   These values of α are now transferred to the last row of Chart 4.

10. Calculation of E.   (Use Chart 4.)

This is the same as for the no-noise case and is given by the formula at the bottom of Chart 4.

11. Determination of F.   (Use Chart 4.)

The value of F is given by

$$2F_{NM} + F_{NO}/3 = F.$$

This is multiplied by the proficiency factor p and entered on Chart 4 at the place indicated.

12. Calculation of the values of H.   (Use Chart 3.)

12a. Find from Chart 3 the value of $\beta = \kappa + B$ which yields the highest value of a when the pair of values of β and f are introduced into the table showing the values of a on Chart 6.   For pure tones β is the intensity level and f the frequency.   This maximum value of a is the value to use in the calculation and is entered at the top of Chart 3 in the place indicated.   The values of β and f corresponding to this maximum value of a are the values β_m and f_m, which are also entered at the top of Chart 3 in the place indicated.

12b. From these values of β_m and f_m using the formula shown at the bottom of Chart 3 the value of α_m is obtained.   The values of K_m are found from Table (6) of Chart 6.

12c. Enter in the first row of the table at the bottom of Chart 3 the values of α found on the last row of Chart 4.

12d. Enter the values of α_m in the second row.

12e. Enter the values of $\alpha - \alpha_m$ in the third row.

12f. Find the values of J corresponding to each of the values of $\alpha - \alpha_m$ from Table (4) of Chart 6.

12g. Multiply J by a and enter the result in the fourth row.

12h. The value of $1 - J \cdot a$ is the value H sought and is entered in the sixth row.   These values of H are now transferred to Chart 4 in the fifth row, opposite H.

13. Calculation of A and S.   (Use Chart 4.)

The values in Chart of pF, E, V, and H are multiplied together to get Ap.   These values of Ap are recorded in the sixth row opposite Ap in Chart 4.   The corresponding values of articulation are obtained from the Table in Chart 7.   These values of articulation correspond to the α below them and consequently the desired curve of S versus α can be plotted and compared with experimental results.

*Comparison of Observed and Calculated Articulation versus Gain Curves
for a Large Variety of Telephone Systems*

Using the chart method described in Section 20, calculations of articulation were made upon a large variety of systems for which articulation data and response characteristics were known. Figs. 186–188, and 193 to 218 inclusive show the results of such calculations. In general,

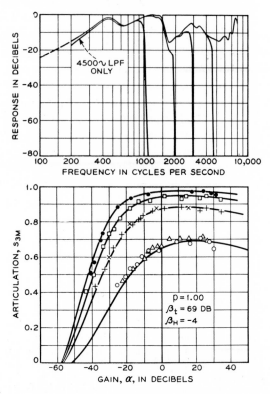

FIG. 196.—FILTER SYSTEMS III–LP–1000, −1850, −2850, −4500.

one figure does not repeat the conditions considered in another, so that the total number of different telephone systems or of different sets of conditions computed is almost eighty. However, for purposes of comparison, one of the systems included in Fig. 200 is shown also in Fig. 201, and one system in Fig. 205 occurs also in Fig. 206.

The data necessary for the calculation are given on each figure. The reader is referred to Table 52 of this paper for an explanation of the designations of these telephone systems and of the symbols used to represent the articulation, and to Section 3 for a description of the type of response. The quantities p, β_t and β_H have been explained in Sections 2, 5, and 7,

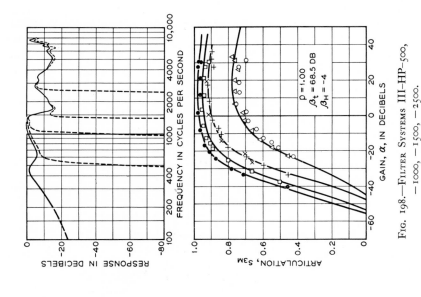

FIG. 198.—FILTER SYSTEMS III–HP-500,
−1000, −1500, −2500.

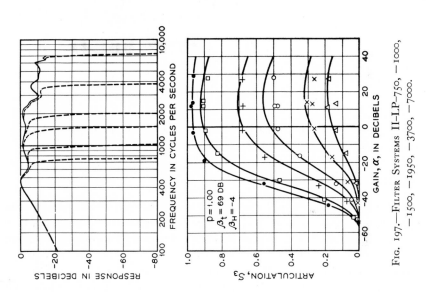

FIG. 197.—FILTER SYSTEMS II–LP-750, −1000,
−1500, −1950, −3700, −7000.

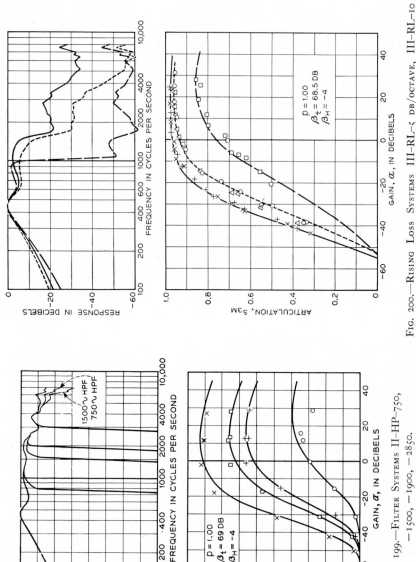

FIG. 200.—RISING LOSS SYSTEMS III-RL-5 DB/OCTAVE, III-RL-10 DB/OCTAVE, AND PARTIAL SUPPRESSION FILTER SYSTEM III-LP-1000-P.

FIG. 199.—FILTER SYSTEMS II-HP-750, -1500, -1900, -2850.

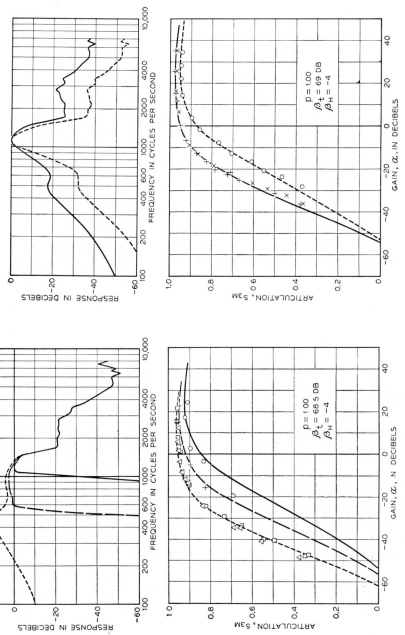

Fig. 202.—Resonant Systems: III-RN-1100-3.9, -8.9.

Fig. 201.—Rising Loss System III-RL-10 db/octave without Filter and with HPF-500, -1000.

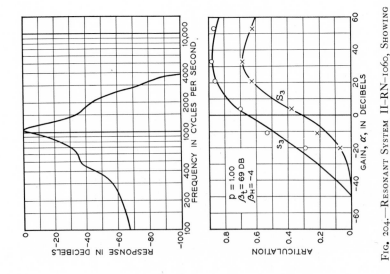

Fig. 204.—Resonant System II–RN–1060, Showing Average Speech Sound Articulation s_3 and Also CVC Syllable Articulation S_3.

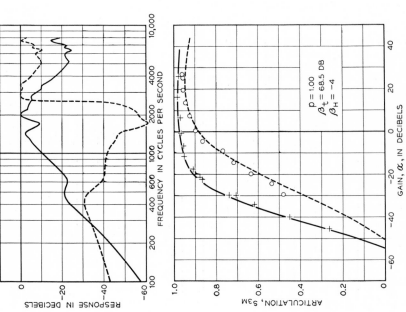

Fig. 203.—Resonant System III–RN–2000 and Partial Suppression Filter System III–HP–2500–P.

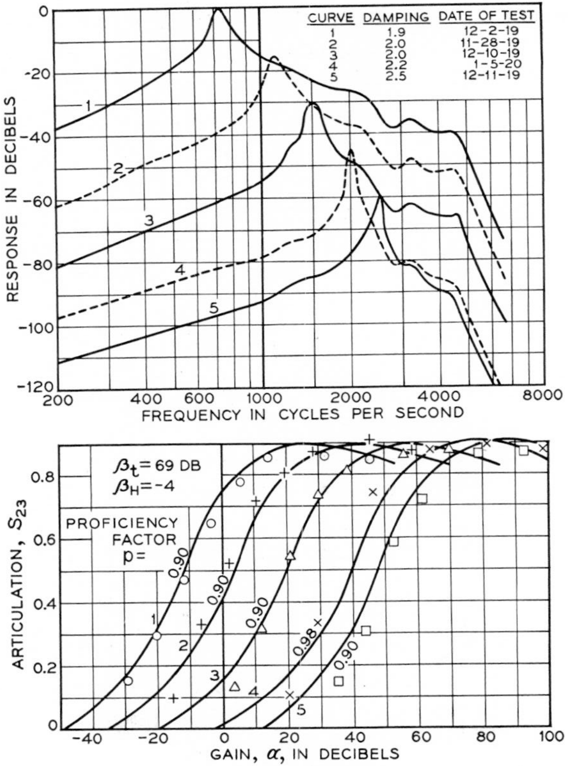

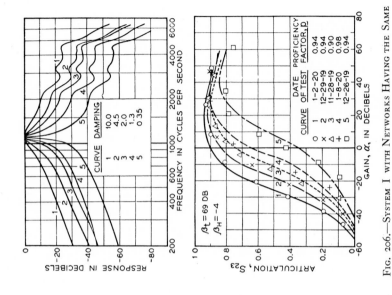

Fig. 206.—System I with Networks Having the Same Resonant Frequency but Different Values of Damping (db per millisecond).

Fig. 205.—System I with Networks Having Different Resonant Frequencies but Almost Uniform Damping.

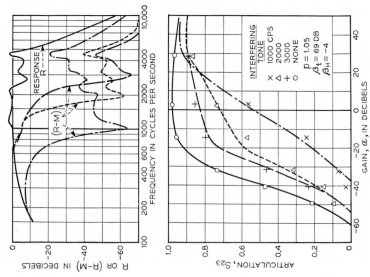

FIG. 208.—SYSTEM I WITH INTERFERING TONE AT 78.2 DB ABOVE THRESHOLD, FOR THREE DIFFERENT TONE FREQUENCIES.

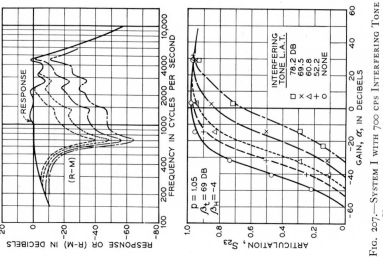

FIG. 207.—SYSTEM I WITH 700 CPS INTERFERING TONE AT VARIOUS LEVELS ABOVE THRESHOLD. THE UPPER PLOT SHOWS R AND ALSO $R - M$ WHERE M IS THE MASKING CAUSED BY THE PURE TONE.

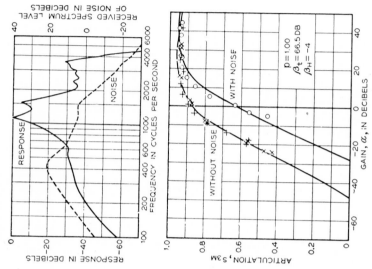

FIG. 210.—SYSTEM III–HY–323 CONTAINING LINEAR MICROPHONE (RESEMBLING No. 323 CARBON MICROPHONE IN CERTAIN PROPERTIES), WITHOUT AND WITH A NOISE INTRODUCED ELECTRICALLY FROM ROOM NOISE RECORD.

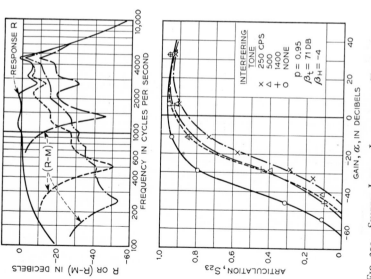

FIG. 209.—SYSTEM I WITH INTERFERING TONE AT 60.8 DB ABOVE THRESHOLD, FOR THREE DIFFERENT TONE FREQUENCIES.

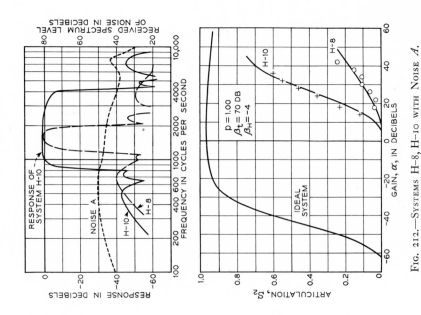

Fig. 212.—Systems H-8, H-10 with Noise A.

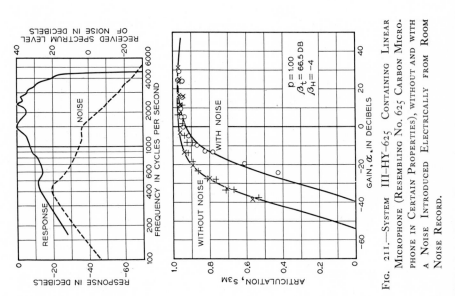

Fig. 211.—System III-HY-625 Containing Linear Microphone (Resembling No. 625 Carbon Microphone in Certain Properties), without and with a Noise Introduced Electrically from Room Noise Record.

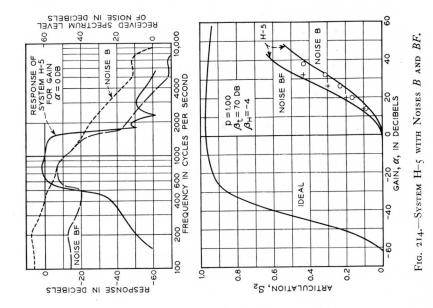

Fig. 214.—System H-5 with Noises B and BF.

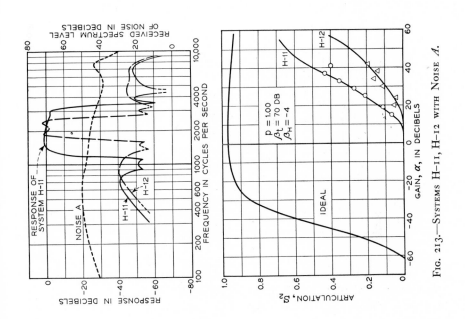

Fig. 213.—Systems H-11, H-12 with Noise A.

respectively.   Unless interference is indicated by notations on the plots, the tests were made under quiet conditions.   For interfering pure tones the frequency and the level above threshold (L.A.T.) are indicated, and the difference $(R - M)$ is plotted versus frequency—where $R =$ response and $M =$ shift of threshold for speech sounds, caused by the tone.

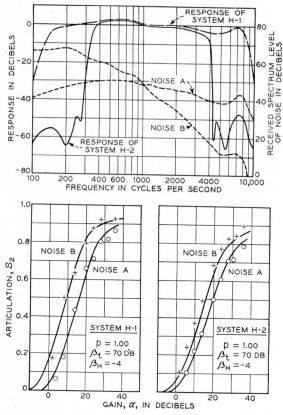

Fig. 215.—Systems H-1, H-2, with Noises *A* and *B*.

When there was a noise having energy distributed through a frequency interval, the upper plot in the figure shows at each frequency the spectrum level of the noise—that is, the level of the intensity per cycle, in decibels from 10^{-16} watt/cm².

The remarkable agreement between observed articulations (shown by points) and calculated articulations (shown by curves) gives one considerable confidence that this method of calculation is valid for almost any kind of system that need be considered.   The attention of the reader is directed to the instance of poorest agreement, which is shown

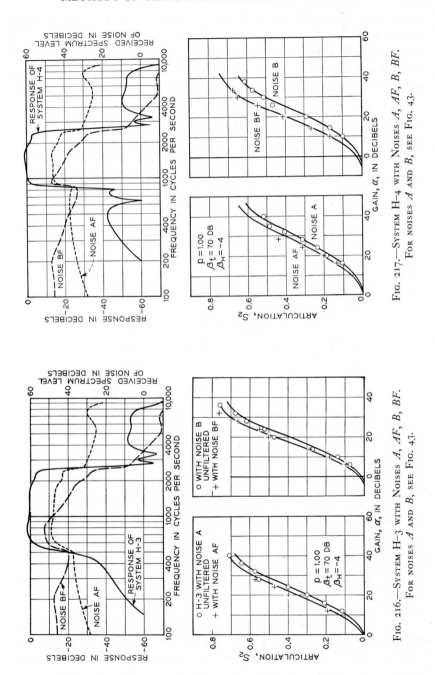

Fig. 217.—System H-4 with Noises *A*, *AF*, *B*, *BF*.
For noises *A* and *B*, see Fig. 43.

Fig. 216.—System H-3 with Noises *A*, *AF*, *B*, *BF*.
For noises *A* and *B*, see Fig. 43.

in Fig. 201 by one of the observations (a circle point) displaced almost 8 db from the corresponding calculated curve. In this instance one cannot suppress the wish that more observations had been made at the lowest level. On the other hand, the reader should note the variety of noiseless systems which show a close agreement; also the systems with

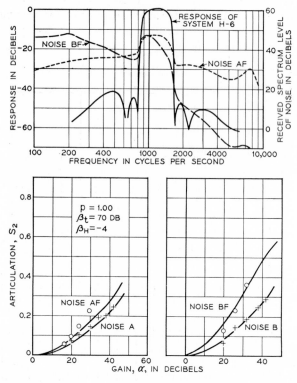

FIG. 218.—SYSTEM H–6 WITH NOISES A, AF, B, BF. FOR NOISES A AND B, SEE FIG. 43.

noise which are computed well, especially Fig. 208 where the effects are very different for the three different interfering tones, and Figs. 212 to 214 and 218 where each combination of restricted frequency band and intense noise causes a heavy but not uniform penalty.

Applications

In this section calculations will be made for a variety of systems which are of general interest.

There is first considered a commercial telephone system consisting of one-mile No. 24 gauge cable with 9-db trunk into which is connected a filter cutting off all frequencies above 4000 cps. The articulation obtained using such a system has been calculated in Fig. 219 for certain conditions involving no noise, and in Fig. 220 for a variety of conditions involving noise. The response of the system is shown in Fig. 220 by the curve R. It was obtained by W. Koenig of the Bell Telephone Laboratories. A proficiency factor of 0.9 was taken for a typical talker-listener pair. The heavy curve in Fig. 219 is for a talking level of $\beta_t = 68$, which is considered an average conversational level, and for a listener having zero hearing loss $\beta_H = 0$ db at all frequencies on a standard audiometer and for no room or line noise at the listener's ear.

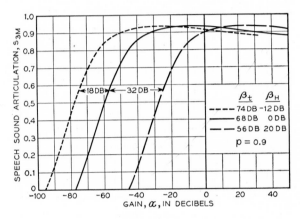

FIG. 219.—CALCULATED ARTICULATION VERSUS GAIN FOR COMMERCIAL SYSTEM IN QUIET WITH RANGE OF TALKING LEVEL β_t AND HEARING LOSS β_H

Measurements upon a large number of speakers who were talking in a conversational manner over an experimental telephone system indicated that the average talking level of the different speakers varied from 56 to 74 db, or a range of 18 db, when the softest 5 percent and loudest 5 percent were excluded. Similarly, excluding the extreme 5 percent having poorest hearing and 5 percent having most acute hearing, the acuity level of a typical set of listeners varies over a range of 32 db from cases having a hearing loss of 20 db to cases having an acuity 12 db better than the average zero on the audiometer. Consequently, for the poorest listener (hearing loss = 20 db) and softest caller ($\beta_t = 56$ db) the curve must be shifted 32 db to the right of the solid curve in Fig. 219, while for the best listener (hearing loss = $-$ 12 db) and the loudest talker ($\beta_t = 74$ db) the curve must be shifted 18 db to the left, as shown by the two dashed curves. For other talker-listener pairs the curve will lie between these extreme limits representing a range of 50 db. If we assume that a grade of transmission for which $A = \frac{1}{2}$ (which corresponds to $s_{3M} = 0.88$, $S_3 = 0.68$, $S_{23} = 0.71$, $S_2 = 0.79$ and

$I = 98$) is a tolerable one, then it is seen that this system will always give a better grade than this for this wide range of talker-listener pairs for $\alpha = 0$—that is, with no additional attenuation or amplification. If one considered only the average talker-listener pair, an attenuation of 30 db could be introduced before the articulation s_{3M} drops to 0.88. The manner in which the talker and listener hold the transmitter and receiver modifies these general conclusions but in general when two persons fail

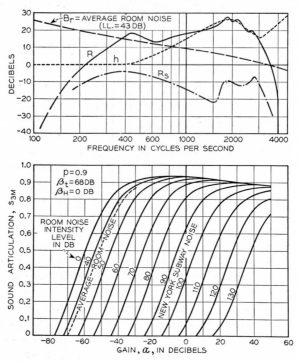

FIG. 220.—CALCULATED ARTICULATION VERSUS GAIN FOR COMMERCIAL SYSTEM WITH ROOM NOISE AT LISTENER'S LOCATION. R = RESPONSE OF SYSTEM. B_r = ACOUSTIC NOISE SPECTRUM LEVEL. h = ATTENUATION OF NOISE GOING UNDER EARPHONE CAP TO THE EAR. R_s = SIDETONE RESPONSE. $I.L.$ = TOTAL INTENSITY LEVEL.

to understand each other the speaker raises his voice and the listener holds the receiver more snugly. Both of these effects tend to push the right limiting curve to the left. One never has the ideal listening conditions considered in this case except in the laboratory because noise is always present.

Calculations will now be made for this system when room noise is present. D. F. Hoth [13] found that the relative spectrum level of room

[13] D. F. Hoth, *Room Noise Spectra at Subscribers' Telephone Locations*, Journal Acoustical Society America, 12, 499, 1941.

noise was the same for a very wide range of noise levels.   D. F. Seacord [14] made measurements at a large number of telephone locations and found that the average room noise in residences corresponded to 43-db intensity level.   The spectrum level corresponding to this average room noise is shown in Fig. 220 by the dashed line.   The values of h, the attentuation of the noise going under the receiver cap to the ear, and the values of sidetone response R_s are given in this figure.   The data were obtained by E. E. Mott and W. D. Goodale, Jr. of the Bell Telephone Laboratories. This, then, gives sufficient data to calculate A for any talker-listener pair for any intensity level of room noise since the relative spectrum level remains constant.   At the bottom of Fig. 215 are shown such calculations for $\beta_t = 68$ db and a listener of zero hearing loss, $\beta_H = 0$.   The intensity level of room noise as measured by a sound level meter is shown on each curve covering a range from 0 to 130-db intensity level.   The first curve marked 0 is the same as the solid curve in Fig. 219.   It is seen that average room noise causes only about an 8-db shift from the curve for the no-noise case.   All the listeners having a hearing loss of 8 db or less will have their threshold levels limited by the room noise.   So when average room noise is present at the listener's end, then the effective acuity levels range from a hearing loss of 8 to a hearing loss of 20, or only 12 db instead of 32 db.   But the talking levels cover the same range from 56 to 74 db. Therefore, when average room noise is present the range of curves is from one 2 db to the right of the one marked 0 to one which is 32 db to the right, or a range of 30 db.   Then for a room noise of 55-db intensity level or greater, the threshold level of the listeners is determined entirely by the noise so variations above this are due only to the variations of the talking level or through a range of only 18 db.   It is seen from the curves of Fig. 220 that the room noise can reach about 70-db intensity level before the transmission over this system reaches the tolerable limit of $s_{3M} = 0.88$ for a 68-db talker and zero loss listener and when no amplification or attenuation is introduced into the system.   It will be noticed that for noises of more than 100-db intensity level the tolerable limit of articulation chosen above is never reached even with amplifications as high as the ear can tolerate.

These calculations are for room noise at the listener's end of the line. If the noise is present at the talker's end, then the speech and noise are attenuated together as they go through the line to the receiver.   The level difference at the receiving end is approximately the same as at the transmitting end.   In a noise the talking level at a microphone close to the lips is approximately 100 db.   As will be seen in the next calcuation, unless the room noise level is greater than 60 db (that is, less than 40 db

[14] D. F. Seacord, *Room Noise at Subscribers' Telephone Locations*, Journal Acoustical Society America, 12, 183, 1940.

below the talking level) no reduction in articulation will occur. For greater levels of room noise at the transmitting end, one must find the spectrum level of the transmitted noise when it arrives at the listener's ear and then combine this with the noise at the receiving end to find the resultant noise spectrum.

In the next calculation is considered the effect of a noise having spectrum level constant with frequency upon the transmission from an ideal filter system passing frequencies from 125 to 5700 cps. The noise is also limited to this frequency range. Thus one can compare the transmission for various values of the average speech intensity level β_s, and of the noise intensity level β_N, at the listener's ear. The results of the calculation are shown in Fig. 221. The ordinates of each solid line give syllable articulation S_3 for one value of β_N and the abscissas give the received speech intensity level β_s. Each dashed curve represents a condition in which β_s differs from β_N by a constant number of db, namely, -10, 0, 10, 20, 30, and 40 db. Thus each dashed curve shows the effect of increasing and decreasing the gain in a receiving set which amplifies or attenuates both the noise and the speech. These curves show that under the assumed conditions increasing the gain so that the speech at the listener's ear is more than about 70 db above the threshold is harmful in all cases.

A third application will show how to calculate the shift of the articulation versus gain curve due to changing some of the elements in the system. The gain curve shift as used in this paper will now be defined. Consider a system which has a response R versus f. Now introduce a network into this system that changes the response to R' versus f and other distortions that change H to H'. The articulation index A of the unchanged system will be designated

$$A = H \cdot E \cdot F \cdot V(x_V)$$

and that of the changed system,

$$A' = H' \cdot E' \cdot F' \cdot V(x'_V).$$

If a curve of articulation index versus gain is calculated for the two systems, then if $\alpha_{\frac{1}{2}}$ is the gain to reach $A = \frac{1}{2}$ for the first system and $\alpha_{\frac{1}{2}}'$ the gain to reach $A' = \frac{1}{2}$ for the second system, then $\alpha_{\frac{1}{2}}' - \alpha_{\frac{1}{2}}$ is the gain curve shift.

For the unchanged system

$$\alpha = x_V + \alpha_0 + \gamma\phi(\bar{R}_1 - \bar{R}_4).$$

Let the primed quantities represent the values for the changed system or

$$\alpha' = x'_V + \alpha_0' + \gamma'\phi'(\bar{R}_1' - \bar{R}_4').$$

Then $\alpha' - \alpha$ represents the shift of one articulation index versus gain

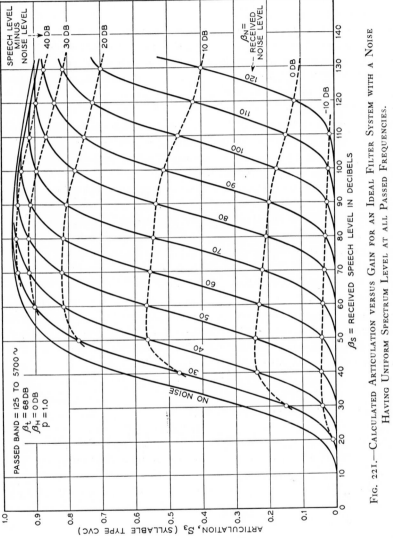

Fig. 221.—Calculated Articulation versus Gain for an Ideal Filter System with a Noise Having Uniform Spectrum Level at all Passed Frequencies.

curve from the other and its value at the ordinate $A = \frac{1}{2}$ is the value of the gain curve shift or $(\alpha' - \alpha)_{\frac{1}{2}}$, which is given by

$$(\alpha' - \alpha)_{\frac{1}{2}} = (x'_V - x_V)_{\frac{1}{2}} + (\bar{R}_1 - \bar{R}_1')$$
$$+ [\gamma'\phi(\bar{R}_1' - \bar{R}_4') - \gamma\phi(\bar{R}_1 - \bar{R}_4)] \quad (17\text{--}60)$$

since $\alpha_0' - \alpha_0 = \bar{R}_1 - \bar{R}_1'$.

To illustrate, consider the gain curve shift due to introducing singly resonant elements into an ideal system (flat response $R = 0$). The response R' is given by

$$R' = 10 \log\{1 + 745(f_0/\Delta)^2[(f/f_0) - (f_0/f)]^2\}, \quad (17\text{--}61)$$

where the resonant frequency f_0 is expressed in kilocycles and the damping constant Δ is expressed in db per millisecond. Consider systems where $f_0/\Delta = 0.4$. For such resonant systems $R = 0$ at $f = f_0$. For the ideal system $\bar{R}_1 = \bar{R}_4 = R = 0$ at all frequencies. For this ideal system the effective gain x_V for $A = \frac{1}{2}$ is 28.4. Therefore, the gain curve shift $(\alpha' - \alpha)_{\frac{1}{2}}$ is given by

$$(\alpha' - \alpha)_{\frac{1}{2}} = x'_V - 28.4 - \bar{R}_1' + \gamma'\phi'(\bar{R}_1' - \bar{R}_4'). \quad (17\text{--}62)$$

For the resonant system x'_V is determined by the relation

$$F' \cdot V(x'_V) = \frac{1}{2} \quad \text{or} \quad V(x'_V) = 1/2F. \quad (17\text{--}63)$$

The values F', $\bar{R}_1'$, $\bar{R}_4'$, γ' and ϕ' were calculated from such response curves and are given in Table 78 (omitting the primes used in the text). The values of gain curve shift given in the last column were calculated from equation (17–62).

It is seen that the value of F is approximately the same for all five resonant systems, from which it follows that the maximum value of articulation for each of these systems is about the same. Thus the resonant frequency can be placed anywhere between 250 to 4000 cps without reducing the factor F below 0.90. However, the values of gain curve shift are quite different, varying from 18.7 to 34.7 db. If the diaphragm of the transmitter or receiver is considered as the resonant element, then the gain curve shift is equal in magnitude to the gain that would be achieved if the instrument had the same efficiency at all frequencies as for that corresponding to the resonant frequency.

Similar calculations are shown in Table 79 for the case of two independent resonant elements in the system, each having the same resonant frequency. In other words, the response R in db is double that for the singly resonant system. The resonant elements may be considered as diaphragms in the microphone and the receiver.

If one resonant peak is placed at 1000 cps and the other at 2000 cps, the value of $F = 0.84$ and the gain curve shift is only 14.7 db.

If four resonant elements of this type are arranged so that the resonant peaks are at 500, 1000, 2000, and 4000 cps, then $F = 0.978$ and the gain curve shift is only 4.7 db.   In this case one has essentially a high quality system.   In the modern design of telephone microphones and receivers the diaphragms are made essentially multiresonant so that they pass efficiently a wide band of frequencies.

A fourth application of the present method will show how to calculate articulation for deafened persons.   This application will be described in chapter 19 with a comparison between calculations and observations.

Acknowledgments

In the text of these two chapters, and in the references, the names of various persons have been indicated who have taken an active part in planning, performing, and interpreting the articulation tests.   It may be found that some names have been omitted which should equally have been included.   The author desires to acknowledge the achievements of all of the individuals who have contributed to the material used in this study.

The author wishes particularly to thank Miss Priscilla A. Pecon for her able work in the many computations here reported, and to thank Miss Jane A. Otto for invaluable assistance in editing.

Appendix 1: The Loudness Functions G_1 and G_4

In this appendix the two loudness functions G_1 and G_4 used in the calculation of the articulation are derived.   The equations defining G_1 and G_4 are, from equations (17–5) and (17–8) in the text,

$$10^{\bar{R}_1/10} = \int_0^\infty G_1 10^{R/10} df \qquad (17\text{–}5)$$

and

$$10^{\bar{R}_4/40} = \int_0^\infty G_4 10^{R/40} df. \qquad (17\text{–}8)$$

For an ideal system, R is independent of frequency and equal to $\bar{R}_1$ or $\bar{R}_4$ so

$$\int_0^\infty G_1 df = \int_0^\infty G_4 df = 1. \qquad (17\text{–}10)$$

The value of G_1 will be determined first.   Consider an ideal high quality system, having the same response R at every frequency.   Consider also several ideal filter systems with various cut-off frequencies, having the same response R at every transmitted frequency and the response $-\infty$ at all other frequencies.   The gain of each of these systems, having these values of response, is designated as gain $\alpha = o$ db.   Any other gain may be specified by assigning a value to α.

Heretofore in this paper the symbol α_0 has been used to designate for any system the value of gain at which the received speech is at the threshold of audibility.   In this appendix, however, α_0 will be used to designate the threshold adjustment for the unfiltered system only.   The gain corresponding to received speech at threshold for any of the filtered systems will be designated as $\alpha_0 + \Delta\alpha$.   Thus let the ideal unfiltered system have the gain α_0, so that speech is at threshold.   Then if an ideal filter is inserted, the gain must be increased by the amount $\Delta\alpha$ in order that the filtered speech may be at threshold.

Then for low pass filter systems

$$10^{(\bar{R}_1 + \alpha_0)/10} = \int_0^{f_c} 10^{(R + \alpha_0 + \Delta\alpha)/10} G_1 df.$$

But in the passed region $\bar{R}_1 = R$ so

$$10^{-\Delta\alpha/10} = \int_0^{f_c} G_1 df. \qquad (17\text{--}6)$$

Similarly for high pass filter systems

$$10^{-\Delta\alpha/10} = \int_{f_c}^{\infty} G_1 df = 1 - \int_0^{f_c} G_1 df. \qquad (17\text{--}7)$$

These values $\Delta\alpha$ are the number of decibels the filter system must be raised from α_0 to make the received speech audible.

Experimental values of $\Delta\alpha$ were obtained from threshold observations upon twenty-six filter systems which had been used in articulaton tests. Eighteen of these systems were in the 1928–1929 group, ten of these having the responses shown in Figs. 197 and 199.   The remaining eight systems were in the 1935–1936 group and had the responses shown in Figs. 196 and 198.   It will be seen that these were not ideal filter systems, hence corrections were necessary in order to convert the observed attenuation for threshold for each actual filter into the gain change $\Delta\alpha$ corresponding to the cut-off frequency f_c of an ideal filter.

For each actual filter system, and for the corresponding actual high quality (i.e., unfiltered) system, the average response in the transmitted region was found for the gain adjustment at which the received speech was at the threshold of audibility.   The difference between these two average responses was taken to be the desired gain change $\Delta\alpha$.   It was necessary to adopt some form of frequency weighting in finding the average response, which was done in the manner about to be described.   It was necessary also to select some value of frequency to be regarded as the cut-off frequency for any particular filter.   The frequencies so selected were the same as those adopted in the study of maximum values of articulation observed for the filters, as recorded in Tables 53 and 55. Although somewhat different frequencies might more properly have been chosen for the threshold data, the effects of such differences are regarded as small in comparison with the uncertainties involved in threshold observations.

If the function G_1 were known, the average response R_{AV} for the entire passed frequency region would be given by the equation

$$10^{R_{AV}/10} = \frac{\displaystyle\int_0^{f_c} G_1 10^{R/10} df}{\displaystyle\int_0^{f_c} G_1 df}. \tag{17-64}$$

Thus the frequency weighting which should be employed in determining R_{AV} depends upon the same function G_1 which we are seeking. Here we have recourse to successive approximations.

TABLE 78

CALCULATION OF GAIN CURVE SHIFT FOR SINGLY RESONANT SYSTEM

f_0	F	$\bar{R}_1$	$1/2F$	x_V	ϕ	$\gamma\phi(\bar{R}_1-\bar{R}_4)$	Gain curve shift in db
250	0.909	−31.7	0.550	30.3	0.97	1.1	34.7
500	0.908	−16.2	0.551	30.4	0.97	9.8	28.0
1000	0.911	−10.7	0.548	30.2	0.97	10.1	22.6
2000	0.926	−10.3	0.540	30	0.97	6.8	18.7
4000	0.933	−16.6	0.536	29.8	0.97	3.1	21.1

TABLE 79

CALCULATION OF GAIN CURVE SHIFT FOR DOUBLY RESONANT SYSTEM

f_0	F	$\bar{R}_1$	$1/2F$	x_V	ϕ	$\gamma\phi(\bar{R}_1-\bar{R}_4)$	Gain curve shift in db
250	0.795	−57.9	0.63	32.8	0.98	1.9	64.2
500	0.590	−19.2	0.847	46.6	1	30.3	67.7
1000	0.599	−14.2	0.835	45.5	1	26.4	57.6
2000	0.655	−13.8	0.752	40.2	1	21.8	47.2
4000	0.678	−20.2	0.737	39.0	1	20.6	51.4

As a first approximation, the average response R_{AV} was estimated by inspecting the response versus frequency characteristic of each system. Using these tentative values of R_{AV}, preliminary values of G_1 were obtained which were then used to determine R_{AV} more accurately. This procedure can be repeated as often as may be needed. Such values of R_{AV} are given in column 3 of Table 77. Each of these values corresponds

TABLE 80

Derivation of the Function $\int_0^{f_c} G_1 df$ from Threshold Observations upon Filtered Speech*

(1) System designation	(2) f_c c.p.s.	(3) R_{AV} for $\alpha=0$ db	(4) A_0 db to threshold	(5) R_{AV}' for threshold db	(6) $\Delta\alpha$ db	(7) $\int_0^{f_c} G_1 df$
II	6750	−2.8	58.2	−61.0	0.0	1.000
II–LP–7000	6750	−2.8	58.2	−61.0	0.0	1.000
II–LP–5500	5440	−2.8	58.2	−61.0	0.0	1.000
II–LP–4500	4300	−2.8	58.2	.−61.0	0.0	1.000
II–LP–3750	3625	−2.8	57.9	−60.7	0.3	0.933
II–LP–3250	3185	−2.7	58.2	−60.9	0.1	0.977
II–LP–2850	2800	−2.7	57.8	−60.5	0.5	0.891
II–LP–2450	2400	−3.1	57.7	−60.8	0.2	0.955
II–LP–1950	1950	−3.1	58.2	−61.3	−0.3	1.072
II–LP–1500	1460	−3.3	55.0	−58.3	2.7	0.537
II–LP–1000	990	−4.0	52.0	−56.0	5.0	0.316
II–LP–750	755	−4.0	48.9	−52.9	8.1	0.155
II	260	−2.8	58.2	−61.0	0.0	0.000
II–HP–250	320	−2.8	58.2	−61.0	0.0	0.000
II–HP–500	530	−3.0	58.0	−61.0	0.0	0.000
II–HP–750	810	−3.3	56.2	−59.5	1.5	0.292
II–HP–1000	1030	−3.8	54.8	−58.6	2.4	0.425
II–HP–1500	1525	−5.6	51.3	−56.9	4.1	0.611
II–HP–1900	1915	−5.7	49.2	−54.9	6.1	0.754
II–HP–2900	2865	−8.2	44.2	−52.4	8.6	0.862
III	6500	−3.8	56.3	−60.1	0.0	1.000
III–LP–4500	4400	−4.0	55.1	−59.1	1.0	0.794
III–LP–2850	2885	−3.5	55.6	−59.1	1.0	0.794
III–LP–1850	1905	−3.1	55.2	−58.3	1.8	0.661
III–LP–1850	1905	−3.1	53.3	−56.4	3.7	0.427
III–LP–1000	1040	−3.5	46.2	−49.7	10.4	0.091

For the above tests $\beta_t = 69.0$ db; below, $\beta_t = 68.5$ db.

III	285	−3.8	55.8	−59.6	0.0	0.000
III–HP–500	565	−4.7	52.6	−57.3	2.3	0.411
III–HP–1000	1025	−5.4	52.4	−57.8	1.8	0.339
III–HP–1500	1425	−9.9	46.1	−56.0	3.6	0.563
III–HP–1500	1425	−9.9	44.2	−54.1	5.5	0.718
III–HP–2500	2520	−8.2	40.8	−49.0	10.6	0.913

* The entries in columns 6 and 7 for II–LP–1950 are interpreted in Figs. 50 and 51 as though $\Delta\alpha = 0.0$ db.

to an over-all gain adjustment which has been designated as $\alpha = 0$ db in the figure showing the response R versus f.

For each system, column 4 of Table 77 gives the experimental value of the attenuation required to bring the received speech to the threshold level. Subtracting the attenuation in column 4 from R_{AV} in column 3 we obtain in column 5 the value R_{AV}', which is the average response when speech is at threshold. If we let R_0 be the value of R_{AV}' for the unfiltered system, then for any filter system $R_{AV}' = R_0 + \Delta\alpha$.

In column 6 of Table 80 the value of $\Delta\alpha$ is the difference between two values in column 5, namely between $R_{AV}' = R_0 + \Delta\alpha$ for each filter system and $R_{AV}' = R_0$ for the unfiltered system. Finally, the values of $\Delta\alpha$ are substituted in equations (17–6) and (17–7) to obtain column 7, which gives the values of $\int_0^{fc} G_1 df$.

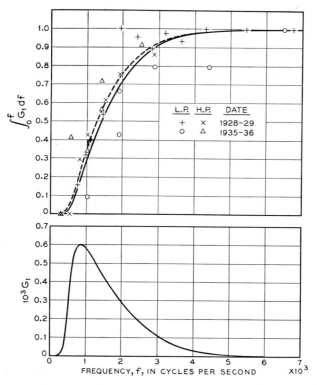

FIG. 222.—DERIVATION OF $\int_0^f G_1 df$ AND G_1 FROM FILTERED SPEECH THRESHOLDS. (See also Fig. 181 and Table 59.) THE DISCRETE POINTS IN THE UPPER PLOT SHOW VALUES OF $\int_0^{fc} G_1 df$ VERSUS f_c DERIVED IN TABLE 80 FROM OBSERVED THRESHOLDS.

The determination of $\Delta\alpha$ in the manner just described is based upon the assumption that the same talking level β_t was used in the threshold test of a filtered system as in the companion test of the unfiltered system. All of the 1928–1929 (i.e., System II) data have been entered in Table 80 on this basis, with $\beta_t = 69$ db. The 1935–1936 (i.e., System III) low pass filter data in Table 80 column 4 have been referred to the talking level $\beta_t = 69$ db as in Fig. 196, whereas the corresponding high pass filter data have been referred to $\beta_t = 68.5$ db as in Fig. 196.

The values of $\int_0^{fc} G_1 df$ versus f_c from Table 80 are plotted as discrete points in Fig. 222. The solid curve drawn through the array of points shows the function $\int_0^{fc} G_1 df$ used in this paper, the slope of which is the function G_1 also shown in Fig. 222 and given in Table 81 column 3. The same pair of functions are shown in Fig. 9. As a check these functions were used with equations (17–6) and (17–7) to calculate values of $\Delta\alpha$, which are shown in Fig. 223 by the pair of curves together with the observed values of $\Delta\alpha$ from Table 80 plotted as points. Although the curves fit the points only fairly well, the fit was accepted as adequate in view of the success attained by the functions of this paper (including the G_1 function) in the calculation of articulation.

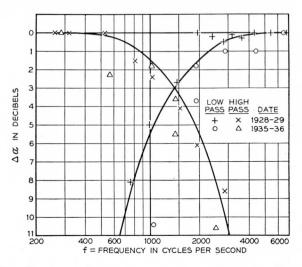

FIG. 223.—GAIN CHANGE $\Delta\alpha$ REQUIRED FOR SPEECH TO REMAIN AT THRESHOLD WHEN CUT-OFF FREQUENCY IS CHANGED FROM 0 OR ∞ TO f. POINTS OBSERVED, CURVES CALCULATED. VALUES OF $\Delta\alpha$ ARE ZERO OR POSITIVE BUT ARE PLOTTED INCREASING DOWNWARD.

Except for the time involved in continuing the revision of the functions, it would have been better as the next approximation to represent the observed points by a revised graph of $\int_0^{fc} G_1 df$ versus f about as that shown by the broken line in Fig. 222. The slope of this revised integral curve at each frequency would then constitute a revised G_1 function which would more accurately represent the observations of speech thresholds than does the G_1 function used in this paper.

In the 1928–1929 threshold tests the procedure was to find a gain adjustment such that at this gain the speech was heard by the listener but that with the attenuation increased by 5 db the speech was inaudible. The gain halfway between these two points was taken as the threshold adjustment. The average of these adjustments was found for the entire articulation test crew, so that all voices both male and female and all ears entered into the average, although it is not certain whether or not every voice-ear combination was used. For each system, filtered or unfiltered, the result was expressed as an integral number of db of attenuation required to bring the received speech to threshold. This adoption of integral numbers implies a smoothing operation to the extent of a fraction of one db, which results in a less scattered set of points in Fig. 227 representing the earlier observations as compared with the later observations which received no smoothing.

In the 1935–1936 tests the procedure was to change the attenuation by steps of 2 db in determining the threshold. The attenuation A_0 was found at which speech was audible in about three-fourths of the trials, but such that with $(A_0 + 2)$ db the speech was heard in much less than one-half of the trials. The attenuation A_0 was adopted as the adjustment for threshold. Care was taken to obtain this adjustment for each talker-listener combination of the articulation test crew. For any given filter, also for the unfiltered system, the average was found of the values of A_0 obtained by a listener for the various voices. Thus there was a group of seven or eight (for one crew, six) listener's averages of which the mean or grand average was adopted in Table 80 as the observed attenuation A_0 for threshold for the entire crew. The r.m.s. deviation of one listener's average from the grand average for the crew was typically about 4 db.

The accuracy of repetition of the 1935–1936 threshold tests can be judged from three different systems. As column 4 of Table 80 indicates, in two instances a repetition of the test upon a filter system resulted in a second grand average A_0 which differed from the first value by 1.9 db. In the tests of the unfiltered system, three values of the grand average A_0 showed a total spread of 2.6 db; only the mean of these results is given in Table 80. Each of these repetitions involves a change of only one or two crew members. Where it was possible, each value of $\Delta \alpha$ comes from a pair of tests (of the filter system, and of the unfiltered system) made by the same crew.

The function G_1 can be calculated from loudness relations as follows.

It was shown in chapter 11 that the loudness N of thermal noise could be calculated from the formula

$$N = \int_0^{100} Q(Z)dx, \qquad (17-65)$$

where Z, Q, and x are functions of the frequency.

The value x is the percent of the total nerve endings in the inner ear which has been passed over by the maximum stimulation as the impressed frequency of a tone goes from zero to f. The quantity Z is defined in terms of the sum of three other quantities, namely

$$Z = B + \kappa - \beta_0. \qquad (17\text{--}19)$$

All of these quantities vary as the frequency varies. The quantity B is the spectrum intensity level at each frequency.

It has been found for systems having an approximately flat response such as systems I, II, or III that the loudness of speech at the receiving end of the system varies with the db above threshold $\alpha - \alpha_0$ as shown in Fig. 224. The points $\times$ give unpublished data obtained by W. A.

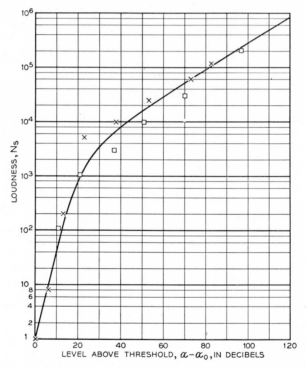

FIG. 224.—LOUDNESS OF UNDISTORTED SPEECH VERSUS LEVEL ABOVE THRESHOLD.   POINTS OBSERVED, CURVE DRAWN TO REPRESENT BOTH SETS OF DATA.

Munson and the points $\square$ give data from the book, *Speech and Hearing*, (see reference 9, p. 232, Fig. 111). The curve was taken as the best fit of the combined sets of data. From this curve values of Q_s were determined such that for speech

$$N_s = \int_0^{100} Q_s(Z_s)dx, \qquad (17\text{--}66)$$

where for a flat response system

$$Z_s = Z_F + \alpha - \alpha_0 - 68. \qquad (17\text{--}67)$$

Here, as explained in Section 10, Z_F is the level above threshold of a critical band of speech when the speech is received at the optimum level for interpretation. The values of Q_s satisfying the loudness data for speech are shown in Fig. 225. When used in equation (17–66) the

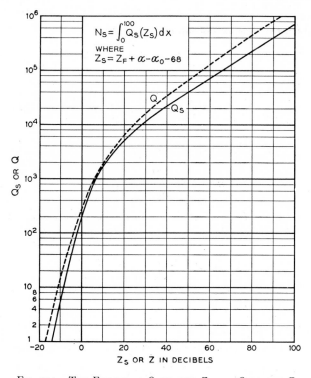

FIG. 225.—THE FUNCTIONS Q_s VERSUS Z_s AND Q VERSUS Z.

observed data shown in Fig. 224 will be calculated correctly. For comparison, Fig. 225 shows also the values of Q for thermal noise as given in chapter 11. It will be seen that at levels of Z_s near zero the value of Q_s can be represented approximately by

$$Q_s(Z_s) = K_1 10^{Z_s/10} \qquad (17\text{--}68)$$

and at levels above $Z_s = 35$, Q_s can be represented by

$$Q_s(Z_s) = K_4 10^{Z_s/40}. \qquad (17\text{--}69)$$

If these values of Q_s and the value of Z_s from equation (17–67) are substituted in equation (17–66) the required formula for calculating the loudness of speech from a transmission system is obtained. However, the loudness N_s is given in terms of the variable x instead of f.

It is known that κ is related to the critical band width $(\Delta f)_c$ by the equation

$$(\Delta f)_c = 10^{\kappa/10}. \tag{17–70}$$

Also, if $(\Delta x)_c$ is the critical band of x—that is, the critical width of the nerve patch in the inner ear corresponding to the critical frequency band width $(\Delta f)_c$, then the slope

$$\frac{\Delta x}{\Delta f} = \frac{(\Delta x)_c}{(\Delta f)_c} = (\Delta x)_c 10^{-\kappa/10}. \tag{17–71}$$

From the theory of hearing $(\Delta x)_c$ is interpreted as a constant for all frequency regions and has been found to be equal to 1.56 percent, which is equivalent to about $\frac{1}{2}$ mm along the basilar membrane. So the values of the slope $\Delta x/\Delta f$ can be obtained from equation (17–71) and the values of x can be obtained from the equation

$$x = 1.56 \int_0^f 10^{-\kappa/10}\, df. \tag{17–72}$$

From equations (17–66) and (17–68), the equation for calculating loudness for the low levels of received speech then becomes

$$N_s = 1.56 K_1 \int_0^\infty 10^{(Z_s-\kappa)/10}\, df.$$

For a flat response system it was seen that Z_s is given by equation (17–67). In general, for a system having a non-uniform response R the value of Z_s is given by

$$Z_s = Z_0 + R + \alpha + (\beta_t - 68)$$

where Z_0 is the db above threshold when α and R are zero and $\beta_t = 68$. The value of Z_0 is given by

$$Z_0 = B_s + \Delta B_s + \kappa - \beta_0'$$

where the values of B_s, ΔB_s, κ and β_0' are those given in Table 81.

Then

$$N_s = 1.56 K_1 \int_0^\infty 10^{(Z_0+R+\alpha+\beta_t-68-\kappa)/10}\, df. \tag{17–73}$$

Consider two telephone systems 1 and 2. System 1 has a response R which is different at each frequency but known from the response curve for the system. System 2 is an ideal flat response system with $R = 0$ at all frequencies. Let the amplification α_2 in system 2 be set so that

TABLE 81

VALUES OF THE G FUNCTIONS AND OF B_s, β_0, β_0', $\kappa - \beta_0'$, AND Z_F

(1) f	(2) $\int_0^f G_1 df$	(3) $G_1 \times 10^3$	(4) $G_4 \times 10^3$	(5) $\int_0^f G_4 df$	(6) Average speech B_s	(7) Peaks ΔB_s	(8) $B_s + \Delta B_s - 10\log G_1 - 70$	(9) Pure tone β_0	(10) For listening to speech β_0'	(11) Critical bands of speech in db κ	(12) $\kappa - \beta_0'$	(13) $B_s + \Delta B_s + 8 + \kappa - \beta_0'$ Z_F
100	0.0000	0.00001	0.019	0.000	34.7	7.5		41.4	(48)	19.4	-28.6	21.6
200	0.0000	0.001	0.090	0.009	38.3	7.8		26.9	(34)	17.2	-16.8	37.3
300	0.0009	0.016	0.186	0.019	39.5	8.6		18.6	(26)	17.0	-9.0	48.1
400	0.0056	0.078	0.266	0.041	39.8	9.3	20.2	13.4	20.2	17.0	-3.2	53.9
500	0.0221	0.252	0.371	0.075	39.4	9.8	15.2	9.9	15.2	17.0	1.8	59.0
600	0.057	0.448	0.414	0.112	38.5	10.2	12.2	7.4	12.2	17.2	5.0	61.7
700	0.107	0.557	0.430	0.153	36.8	10.6	9.9	5.7	9.9	17.3	7.4	62.8
800	0.165	0.593	0.414	0.195	34.9	10.9	8.1	4.6	8.1	17.6	9.5	63.3
900	0.224	0.599	0.401	0.233	33.3	11.3	6.8	4.2	6.8	17.8	11.0	63.6
1000	0.284	0.587	0.386	0.279	31.8	11.5	5.6	4.0	5.6	18.0	12.4	63.7
1250	0.421	0.512	0.345	0.372	28.7	12.1	3.7	3.7	3.7	18.5	14.8	63.6
1500	0.539	0.436	0.301	0.453	26.1	12.7	2.4	2.7	2.4	19.0	16.6	63.4
1750	0.639	0.358	0.263	0.522	24.0	13.2	1.7	1.6	1.7	19.5	17.8	63.0
2000	0.720	0.290	0.233	0.582	22.1	13.7	1.2	0.1	0.6	19.9	19.3	63.1
2500	0.839	0.187	0.179	0.685	19.0	14.6	0.9	-2.1	-0.6	20.8	21.4	63.0
3000	0.914	0.113	0.140	0.764	16.4	15.1	1.0	-3.4	-1.2	21.5	22.7	62.2
3500	0.957	0.060	0.104	0.823	14.2	15.4	1.8	-3.7	-1.0	22.3	23.3	60.9
4000	0.976	0.030	0.077	0.870	12.3	15.5	3.0	-3.2	-0.1	23.1	23.0	58.9
4500	0.987	0.016	0.059	0.904	10.6	15.5	4.1	-2.0	1.0	23.7	22.7	56.3
5000	0.993	0.008	0.044	0.931	9.1	15.5	5.6	0.1	2.8	24.4	21.6	53.7
6000	0.998	0.0014	0.023	0.963	6.5			7.1	7.1	25.7	18.6	47.1
7000	0.999	0.0003	0.012	0.980	4.3			12.1	12.1	26.8	14.7	42.0
8000	1.000	0.0001	0.008	0.988	2.4			15.1	15.1	27.7	12.6	38.0
9000	1.000	0.0000	0.006	0.994	0.7			17.5	17.5	28.5	11.0	34.3
10000	1.000	0.0000	0.004	1.000	-0.7			19.5	19.5	29.2	9.7	32.0

the speech received from this system sounds equally loud to that received from system 1 with $\alpha = 0$.   Under these conditions the loudness values N_s from equation (17–73) are equal or

$$\int_0^\infty 10^{(Z_0+\alpha_2-\kappa)/10}\, df = \int_0^\infty 10^{(Z_0+R-\kappa)/10}\, df. \qquad (17\text{–}74)$$

Then the value of α_2 is the desired value of $\bar{R}_1$ so that

$$10^{\bar{R}_1/10} \quad \frac{\displaystyle\int_0^\infty 10^{(Z_0-\kappa)/10} \cdot 10^{R/10}\, df}{\displaystyle\int_0^\infty 10^{(Z_0-\kappa)/10}\, df}. \qquad (17\text{–}75)$$

Comparing equations (17–75) and (17–5) it is seen that the value of G_1 is given by

$$G_1 = \frac{10^{(Z_0-\kappa)/10}}{\displaystyle\int_0^\infty 10^{(Z_0-\kappa)/10}\, df}. \qquad (17\text{–}76)$$

In a similar way at the high levels the condtion for equality of loudness is

$$\int_0^\infty 10^{[(Z_0+\alpha_2)/40]-[\kappa/10]}\, df = \int_0^\infty 10^{[(Z_0+R)/40]-[\kappa/10]}\, df \qquad (17\text{–}77)$$

and in this case α_2 becomes $\bar{R}_4$ so that

$$G_4 = \frac{10^{(Z_0-4\kappa)/40}}{\displaystyle\int_0^\infty 10^{(Z_0-4\kappa)/40}\, df}. \qquad (17\text{–}78)$$

Comparing equations (17–76) and (17–78) it is seen that

$$G_4 = G_1^{\frac14}10^{-3\kappa/40} \quad \text{(constant)}. \qquad (17\text{–}79)$$

The constant can be determined by the requirement that

$$\int_0^\infty G_4 df = 1.$$

Thus it is seen that the values of G_4 can be derived from the values of G_1 which were determined experimentally.   Such values of G_4 and the corresponding values of $\int_0^\infty G_4 df$ are given in Table 81 and the integral is given in a more extended manner in Table 60.

The values of β_0', the threshold values while listening to speech with no noise present, can also be obtained from the values of G_1 by equation (17–76).   Since $Z_0 = B_s + \Delta B_s + \kappa - \beta_0'$, the values are given by the equation

$$\beta_0' = B_s + \Delta B_s - 10 \log G_1 - \text{constant}. \qquad (17\text{–}80)$$

The spectrum level for speech B_s and peak levels ΔB_s[17] and G_1 are given in Table 81. This spectrum level is for a speaker having a talking level 68 db and whose spectrum level curve has the shape adopted as typical by French and Steinberg.[3] The constant was taken equal to 70 db so that values of β_0' and β_0 would agree in the frequency range from 1250 to 1750 cps. The values thus calculated are given in column 8 of Table 81. It will be seen from Fig. 220 that values of G_1 above 2000 cannot be considered very accurate so for the frequencies above this an average between β_0 for pure tone and the quantity $(B_s + \Delta B_s - 10 \log G_1 - 70)$ was taken for final values of β_0'. These values are tabulated in column 10. The values of κ, the critical band widths in db for monaural listening, are given in column 11. The values of $\kappa - \beta_0'$ which are used in noise calculations are given in column 12, and values of Z_F from equation (17–23) or

$$Z_F = B_s + \Delta B_s + 8 + \kappa - \beta_0' \qquad (17\text{–}23)$$

are given in the last column.

Appendix 2: Hearing Loss for Speech

In this appendix the relationship between the hearing loss for speech [15] and the hearing loss audiogram will be considered. Let β_f be the hearing loss at the frequency f for a pure tone. It is the ordinate in the audiogram. If we consider β_f has the same effect upon the threshold level as an attenuation $-R$ from the flat response system, then by analogy to equation (17–5) the hearing loss for speech β_s is given by

$$10^{-\beta_s/10} = \int_0^{\infty} G_1 10^{-\beta_f/10}\, df. \qquad (17\text{–}81)$$

If we consider only the octave frequencies 125, 250, 500, 1000, 2000, 4000, and 8000, then the following equation is approximately correct.

$$\beta_s = -10 \log\{\textstyle\sum W_k 10^{-\beta_k/10}\} \qquad (17\text{–}82)$$

where k takes the successive values of 125, 250, 500, 1000, 2000, 4000, and 8000. The weights are given by

$$W_k = \int_{0.7k}^{1.4k} G_1\, df.$$

[17] H. K. Dunn and S. D. White, *Statistical Measurements on Conversational Speech*, Journal Acoustical Society America, 11, 278, 1940.

[15] H. Fletcher, *A Method of Calculating Hearing Loss for Speech from an Audiogram*, Journal Acoustical Society America, volume 22, page 1, 1950.

For 125 cps W = 0.000, 250 cps W = 0.003, 500 cps W = 0.104, 1000 cps W = 0.388, 2000 cps W = 0.395, 4000 cps W = 0.106, 8000 cps W = 0.004. So for most purposes one needs to consider only the four frequencies 500, 1000, 2000, and 4000 and use weights 0.1, 0.4, 0.4 and 0.1.

For a fairly flat audiogram it is approximately correct to take an average of the hearing loss at 500, 1000, and 2000 cps.

CHAPTER 18

EFFECTS OF DISTORTION ON THE INDIVIDUAL SPEECH SOUNDS

The data for determining the gain articulation curve shown in Fig. 186 of Chapter 17 were analyzed to find the articulation scores for each individual speech sound. The curves shown in Figs. 226, 227, 228, 229, 230, and 231 give the results for each of the fundamental sounds. The abscis-

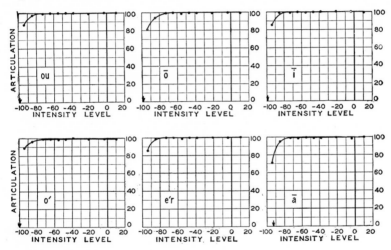

FIG. 226.—ARTICULATION VERSUS INTENSITY LEVEL.

sas are given in terms of the intensity level for average speech rather than for the speech sound itself. The threshold intensity level for each of the speech sounds is indicated by the small arrow. It was from these articulation data that the figures given in the last column of Table 7 were calculated. The sounds in each of the groups have similar characteristics from a recognition standpoint.

In Table 82 are shown the results of the articulation tests for the range of intensities usually used in conversation. As a check against these results obtained with the high-quality telephone circuit, tests were made with the observers stationed at 3 feet away from the speaker, thus permitting the speech sounds to be transmitted through the air. These tests checked the results given in Table 82 within the observational error.

Instead of the articulation, 100 minus the articulation or the articulation error is given.   The speech sounds are arranged according to the magnitude of the articulation error and, consequently, according to the relative difficulty of recognizing them.   It will be noticed that the consonants are

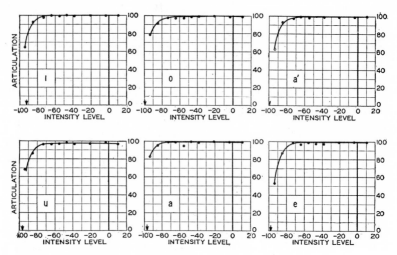

FIG. 227.—ARTICULATION VERSUS INTENSITY LEVEL.

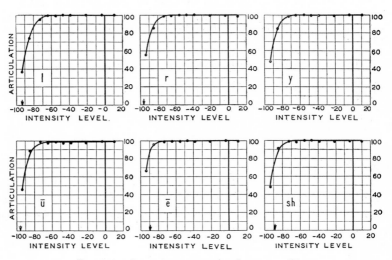

FIG. 228.—ARTICULATION VERSUS INTENSITY LEVEL.

usually harder to recognize correctly than the vowels.   However, the speech sounds e and l, r, ng form notable exceptions to this rule since the former is among the most difficult, while the latter are among the very easiest speech sounds to recognize at normal intensities.   At all inten-

sities, the sounds th, f, and v are the most difficult to recognize. The
sound z, which is readily recognized at normal intensities, becomes very
difficult at weak intensities. The sounds i, ou, er, and ó are missed less
than 10 percent of the time even when very near the threshold value for

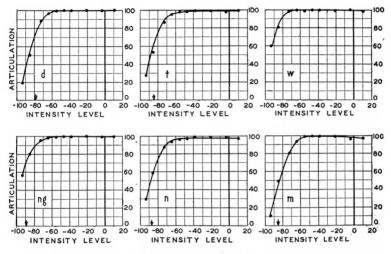

FIG. 229.—ARTICULATION VERSUS INTENSITY LEVEL.

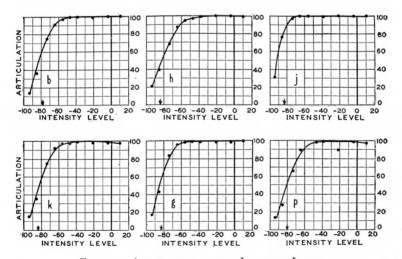

FIG. 230.—ARTICULATION VERSUS INTENSITY LEVEL.

average speech. It is seen from Table 82 that for intensities commonly
used in conversation the sounds v, f and th count for more than half of
the mistakes in the recognition of the fundamental speech sounds.

There is a characteristic difference between the shape of the curves for the vowels and for the consonants. For the former the curves run along horizontally and then drop off very abruptly. For the latter the drop is more gradual. The threshold points marked on the axis of abscissas do not correspond in general to zero articulation. A consonant sound may sometimes be identified by the modification produced on the following or preceding vowel even though it is below the threshold as determined by an isolated sound. It might seem logical to consider this modification of the vowel as part of the consonant. If it is so considered,

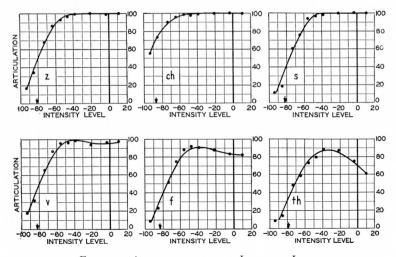

Fig. 231.—Articulation versus Intensity Level.

then it is evident that as long as the vowel is heard there is always a chance of identifying the consonant preceding or succeeding it, and consequently the threshold of a consonant so considered will be the same as that for the vowel. It is for this reason that all of the curves seem to go through the same zero articulation point.

The articulation data were analyzed to find the effect of filter distortion on each of the speech sounds. The results of this analysis are shown in Figs. 232, 233, 234, 235, 236, and 237. These curves indicate that some of the sounds are farily well localized in a limited frequency range while others seem to have characteristics extending throughout the entire range. For example, the sound ē could be recognized correctly 98 percent of the time when either the range of frequencies above 1700 cycles or the range of those below 1700 cycles was used. On the other hand, the sound "s" was only slightly affected by eliminating frequencies below 1500 cycles, but its characteristics were practically destroyed by eliminating frequencies above 4000 cycles. The short vowels, u, o, á, and e, are seen to have important characteristics carried by frequencies below 1000.

More than a 20 percent error is made in recognizing these three sounds when the frequency components below 1000 are eliminated. On the other hand, the elimination of frequencies above 2000 cycles for these sounds produces only slight effects. The long vowels and the diphthong sounds seem to have sufficient distinguishing characteristics in either half of the frequency range to be identified. The intersection point of the curve for these sounds is always above 90 percent, showing that by using a frequency range on either side of the intersection point, the sounds

TABLE 82

ARTICULATION ERROR OR THE PERCENT OF TIMES THE SOUND IS MISINTERPRETED

Speech Sound	Key Word	Average	Speech Sound	Key Word	Average
l	look	0.2	g	gold	1.0
ī	time	0.2	a	top	1.1
ou	town	0.3	b	ball	1.1
ng	sing	0.3	n	no	1.1
r	red	0.3	ē	team	1.2
z	zest	0.3	h	hat	1.2
ér	term	0.4	sh	ship	1.5
y	you	0.4	á	tap	1.5
ō	tone	0.5	ch	cheap	1.8
d	day	0.5	s	say	1.8
i	tip	0.6	k	keep	1.8
t	ten	0.6	ū	tool	2.2
m	man	0.7	u	took	2.5
j	jump	0.8	p	pay	2.5
o	ton	0.8	e	ten	2.8
ó	talk	0.8	v	view	3.9
w	we	0.9	f	fall	12.7
ā	take	1.0	th	then	17.3

can be readily identified. The fricative sounds are seriously affected by the elimination of the high frequencies. The elimination of frequencies above 3000 reduces the articulation of the sound "s" to 40 percent, the sound "th" to 66 percent, the sound "z" to 80 percent, the sound "t" to 81 percent, and the sound "f" to 85 percent. All other sounds are reduced less than 10 percent by the elimination of this frequency range. The pure vowels, the diphthongs, and the semi-vowels are affected only a negligible amount by the elimination of this region. The curves indicate that for the unvoiced stop consonants the frequencies in the region of 1000 and 3000 cycles are the important ones for carrying the recognition properties.

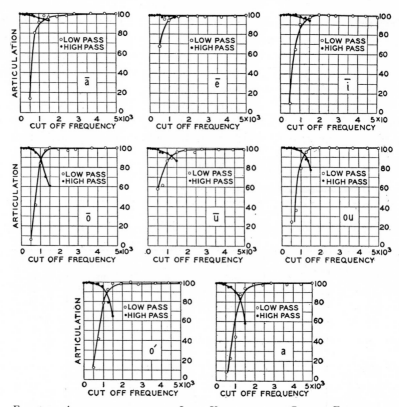

FIG. 232.—ARTICULATION FOR THE LONG VOWELS VERSUS CUT-OFF FREQUENCY.

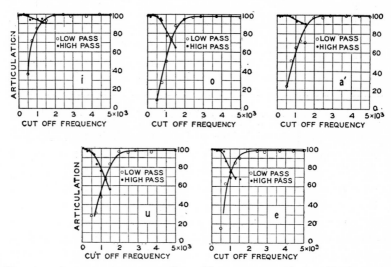

FIG. 233.—ARTICULATION FOR THE SHORT VOWELS VERSUS CUT-OFF FREQUENCY.

The sound "t" has a noticeable characteristic, namely, that the elimination of all sounds below 1500 cycles produces no noticeable effect upon its recognition.   It is also the first one of this group to be affected by the

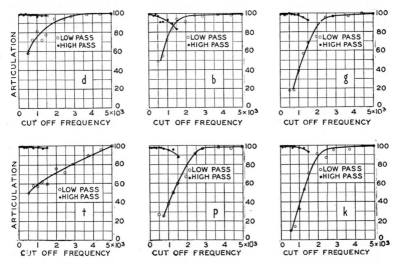

Fig. 234.—Articulation for the Stop Consonants versus Cut-off Frequency.

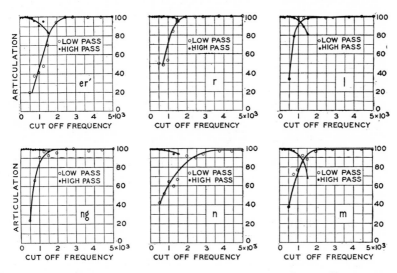

Fig. 235.—Articulation for the Semi-Vowels versus Cut-off Frequency.

elimination of the high frequencies.   The transitional sound w has important characteristics in the frequency region between 700 and 1500 cycles.   The sound y has characteristics similar to the sounds ī and ē.

When all frequencies below 1500 cycles are eliminated, it still has an articulation of 99 percent.

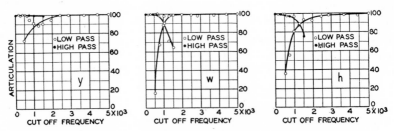

FIG. 236.—ARTICULATION FOR THE TRANSITIONALS VERSUS CUT-OFF FREQUENCY.

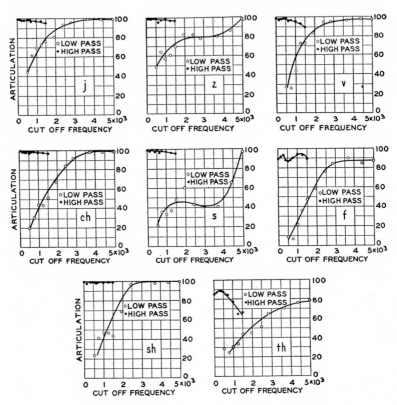

FIG. 237.—ARTICULATION FOR THE FRICATIVES VERSUS CUT-OFF FREQUENCY.

It must be remembered that in spite of the fact that high articulation values are obtained for these sounds under the distorting conditions mentioned, the quality of the sound is materially altered, that is, the naturalness is considerably reduced. However, there are some characteristics of the sound which seem to be sufficient to identify it in spite of its greatly altered quality.   For example, ē sounds very much like ū when frequencies above 1000 cycles are eliminated, but from the fact that the percent articulation at this point is over 90 percent it is evident that some features are still preserved in the low-frequency region for the sound ē that distinguish it from the the sound ū.

CHAPTER 19

THE PERCEPTION OF SPEECH SOUNDS BY DEAFENED PERSONS

In the previous chapters a method was described for measuring experimentally and also for calculating the interpretation aspect of the perception of speech. The listeners were considered to have normal hearing. In the present chapter the same principles are applied to persons having abnormal hearing. In this chaper a simplified method of calculating articulation is presented which applies not only to deafened listeners but also to listeners having normal hearing.

It is well known that there are three types of hearing loss that must be distinguished, namely: (1) conductive deafness, (2) nerve deafness, and (3) mixed deafness. The first type is due to some trouble that blocks the acoustical transmission path between the air sound waves and the nerves on the end organ of hearing. The second type is due to trouble with the nerve endings of the auditory nerve. The third type occurs when both these causes are present.

As discussed in the previous chapters, the hearing loss is represented by an audiogram whose ordinates are expressed in db from a reference level. This reference level is supposed to correspond to the average pressure level at which pure tones are just perceived by normal ears. The value of the hearing loss at the frequency f will be designated β_c for conductive deafness, β_N for nerve deafness, and β_M for mixed deafness.

When a person has a conductive deafness of β_C and at the same time a nerve deafness β_N, then

$$\beta_M = \beta_C + \beta_N. \qquad (19\text{--}1)$$

The air conduction audiogram gives directly the values of β_M, and the bone conduction audiogram gives the values of β_N. If the conductive deafness is made artificially by putting an object in the external ear canal (such as a finger, cotton or wax), then it is obvious that the hearing loss β_C can be treated as though there were interposed between the talker and the listener a transmission system having a response R where $R = -\beta_C$. Thus for this case the value β_C can be subtracted from the response of the system being used by the talker-listener pair. In other words, β_C may be considered as an additional attenuation in the transmission system and then the procedure for calculation is the same as for the normal ear.

If this same philosophy is applied to all conductive deafness, then it would follow that a person having a hearing loss β_c would obtain the highest articulation score by using a system having a *response R with the inverse frequency characteristic* of β_c or such that $\beta_c + R$ would be the same for different frequencies.

On the other hand, a person with a small amount of deafness and an audiogram which is not flat uses this hearing characteristic daily to hear speech which is transmitted by an essentially flat response system, the air path between the speaker and the listener. So when a transmission system departs from a flat response the received speech, to such a listener, appears somewhat distorted and therefore one might expect that, under such conditions, a lower articulation score would result.

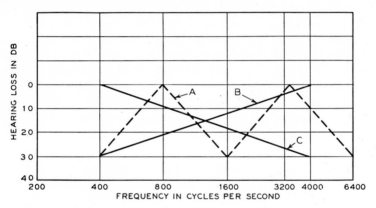

FIG. 238.—THREE HYPOTHETICAL AUDIOGRAMS.

Since these two points of view lead to different calculated results, one asks the question, "Which one agrees with the observed facts?" Unfortunately, there are not data [1] that are sufficiently accurate to distinguish between these two points of view when the hearing losses are moderate. One would expect such a result because the difference in the calculated results using these two points of view is very small indeed, as will now be illustrated.

Consider the three audiograms A, B and C in Fig. 238, when the hearing losses are all less than 30 db. Under the first point of view if such a person uses a flat response system the calculated articulation index values are 0.95, 0.96 and 0.95, respectively. The corresponding syllable

[1] The book entitled *Hearing Aids: An Experimental Study of Design Objectives* by Hallowell Davis and his associates contains the most comprehensive set of data yet obtained and frequent reference will be made to it as *Hearing Aids*.

articulation values are 0.968, 0.97, and 0.968, respectively. Using the second point of view, the articulation index is unity, which corresponds to 0.976 for the three types. The difference between 0.97 and 0.976 is less than the experimental error even when a very elaborate technique is used in making the articulation tests. If the PB lists are used the difference between the two points of view is even smaller, so there seems to be no hope of determining for such moderate hearing losses which point of view is correct. Either point of view shows the foolishness of trying to correct the response of a hearing aid so it will be the inverse of the audiogram when the latter does not depart from flat by more than 30 db. However, for large departures from a flat audiogram it is my opinion based upon a limited experience that the first point of view is more nearly correct.

It is for these reasons that the procedure outlined in the previous chapter for normal ears is used when the departures of the hearing loss from the average is small; namely, to use a single number β_H for the hearing loss for speech to represent the acuity of the listener. In general, however, the conductive hearing loss β_C can be treated as an attenuation to be subtracted from the response of the transmission system being used by the deafened person.

The nerve deafness β_N is considered to have the same effect upon articulation scores as though the ear were normal but a listening end noise were present which produces a masking M which is equal to β_N.

When no external noise is present then the procedure for calculating the articulation index A is as follows: The response $R - \beta_C$ is used to calculate F_{NM} and the response $R - \beta_M$ is used to calculate F_{NO}. The response $R - \beta_M$ is also used to calculate α_0, the threshold gain setting, and the procedure is the same as outlined in Chapter 17 when noise is present, causing a masking M equal to β_N and the additional attenuation equal to β_C.

When an external noise is present in the ear canal then if its level is high enough it will cause additional masking to that produced by β_N which may be calculated as follows: Let the noise be specified in terms of the pressure level β, in the ear canal, of pure tones which can just be perceived by a normal ear in the presence of the noise. This is called the masking pressure level of the noise. It was shown in the chapter on masking that when white noise is used this is equivalent to specifying the pressure level of the noise in critical frequency band widths. The pressure level in a critical frequency band width of a fictitious noise in the ear canal which will account for the nerve deafness then must be

$$\beta_N + \beta_C + \beta_O = \beta_M + \beta_O$$

where β_O is the pressure level under the ear cap of the audiometer receiver, which is used to determine β_C and β_N, when the dial of the audiometer is set at zero hearing loss. Therefore, if $\beta_M{}'$ is the effective nerve deafness due both to the actual nerve deafness and also that caused by the presence of the noise, then

$$\beta_M{}' + \beta_0 = 10 \log \left[10^{\beta/10} + 10^{\frac{(\beta_M + \beta_0)}{10}} \right]. \qquad (19\text{-}2)$$

This value of $\beta_M{}'$ can be used in place of β_M and the procedure then is as outlined above for the no noise condition.

When the masking level β due to the noise is 10 db less than $\beta_M + \beta_0$ it produces no change in the effective nerve deafness, that is, $\beta'_N = \beta_N$. When the usual type of audiometer is used (Bureau of Standards calibration by means of a coupler), then the values of β_0 are as follows for the six frequencies used in audiometry:

TABLE 83

f =	250	500	1000	2000	4000	8000
β_0 =	40	25	17	17	15	21

Recent measurements at the Bureau of Standards [2] show that measurements of the pressure level under an ear cap give values which are approximately the same as those obtained on the coupler except for frequency 250 cps. The level for this frequency was about 4 db less than for the coupler, but depended upon the pressure used in holding the receiver to the ear.

The factor E is dependent upon x_E which is the db difference between the maximum gain α_t which can be tolerated and the actual gain α in the system or

$$x_E = \alpha_t - \alpha \qquad (19\text{-}3)$$

It was found that the maximum level of speech that could be tolerated by a group of listeners, whose average hearing loss was -4 db, was 110 db above their threshold level. Since their threshold intensity level for speech was found to be 8 db, the tolerable intensity level for speech is 118 db. Tests by Davis indicated this level was about the same for deafened ears varying only $\pm$ 10 db from the tenderest to the toughest ear. Therefore

$$\alpha_t + \beta_t + \bar{R}_2 = 118 \pm 10 \qquad (19\text{-}4)$$

where β_t is the speech level at the listners ear and $\bar{R}_2$, the average of the two highest response values of the system at the three frequencies 500, 1000, and 2000 cps.

[2] American Standards Association.   Spec Z 245–1951.

The value of x_E then becomes

$$x_E = 118 \pm 10 - \beta_t - \bar{R}_2 - \alpha \qquad (19\text{--}5)$$

The relation between x_E and E is given in table 84.

TABLE 84

RELATION BETWEEN x_E AND E

x_E =	0	10	20	30	40	50
E =	.83	.87	.93	.98	1.0	1.0

When x_E exceeds 40 db the value of E is always unity. Since no tolerable levels were determined for each individual case, the value of 118 was taken for all cases.

Calculations by the above method are long, particularly when sending end noise is present. Even so, one would be justified in making exact calculation if any experimental data were available comparable in accuracy to those given in Chapter 17 for normal ears. A comparison of calculated and observed results then would show whether or not the assumptions on which the method depends are justified for deafened listeners. Because of the great difficulty in obtaining such data for deafened ears there is necessarily a very large experimental error.

For these reasons the method of calculating the articulation index has been very much simplified by making approximations which will now be described. This simplified method is not only useful for deafened listeners but can be applied to all cases where great accuracy is not required.

The first simplification is to use only the six frequencies used in audiometry; namely, 250, 500, 1000, 2000, 4000 and 8000 cps. The responses of the hearing aid or the telephone system, and the hearing losses β_C and β_N, are given for these six frequencies. Then the following other approximations are made concerning various of the quantities defined in earlier chapters.

The factor γ is considered to be always unity. The factor H will be taken as unity. This is a bad approximation when pure tones produce noise interference but this is rarely encountered in practice. The masking of speech upon itself will be neglected. For most systems used this is a very good approximation. The calculation of $\bar{R}_1$ and $\bar{R}_4$ is long and it has been found that a good approximation to these values is obtained as follows: Consider the three values of R at the frequencies 500, 1000 and 2000; namely, R_{500}, R_{1000} and R_{2000}. Then R_1 is taken as the average of the two highest of these three values, and $\bar{R}_4$ is taken as the average of the three values. This looks like a very rough approximation but it works fairly well except when there are large fluctuations in R in the frequency region between 500 and 2000 cps.

The procedure will be first outlined when no noise is present. Then when noise is present the procedure is exactly same except β_M' replaces β_M. To determine α_0, the gain in the system for the speech to be at the threshold level, one proceeds as follows: Let R be the response for any of the six frequencies when the gain $\alpha = 0$. Then the effective response for this zero gain setting due both to the attenuation effect of the conductive deafness and the masking effect of the nerve deafness is given by

$$R - \beta_C - \beta_N = R - \beta_M$$

where β_C and β_M correspond to losses at the same frequency for which R was taken.

The values of $R - \beta_M$ for the three frequencies of 500, 1000 and 2000 cps are examined and the average of the two highest values is taken. This average value is designated $(\overline{R - \beta_M})_2$.

The threshold gain α_O is then given by

$$\alpha_O = -\beta_t - (\overline{R - \beta_M})_2 + 12 \qquad (19\text{--}6)$$

where β_t is the talking level. This value is independent of the type of hearing loss and depends only upon the talking level β_t and the two values of $R - \beta_M$ from which the average $(\overline{R - \beta_M})_2$ is taken.

The value F_{NM} will be designated F_C because it is obtained directly from the response of the system and the conductive hearing loss values or from $R - \beta_C$. Its value is given approximately by

$$F_C = \sum_{k=1}^{k=6} D_k W_k \qquad (19\text{--}7)$$

where D_1, D_2, D_3, D_4, D_5 and D_6 are read from the curve in Fig. 177 of Chapter 17 as follows:

$$D_1 = \int_0^{350} D_{df} = 0.04, \qquad D_2 = \int_{350}^{700} D_{df} = 0.13,$$

$$D_3 = \int_{700}^{1400} D_{df} = 0.23, \qquad D_4 = \int_{1400}^{2800} D_{df} = 0.30,$$

$$D_5 = \int_{2800}^{5600} D_{df} = 0.25, \qquad D_6 = \int_{5600}^{\infty} D_{df} = 0.05.$$

The value of W_k is the value in Chart 6 corresponding to x_W given by

$$x_W = \tfrac{1}{2}(\overline{R - \beta_C})_2 + \tfrac{1}{2}(\overline{R - \beta_C})_3 - (R - \beta_C) \qquad (19\text{--}8)$$

for the six values of $(R - \beta_C)$ corresponding to the six frequencies.

Similarly the value of F_{NO}, which will be designated F_M since it is obtained from the mixed deafness audiogram, is given by (19–5) except in this case the values of x_W are given by

$$x_W = \tfrac{1}{2}\overline{(R - \beta_M)}_2 + \tfrac{1}{2}(R - \beta_M)_3 - (R - \beta_M). \qquad (19\text{-}9)$$

The value of F then is given by

$$F = (2/3)F_C + (1/3)F_M. \qquad (19\text{-}10)$$

The value of x_V from which the factor V is obtained is given by

$$x_V = \alpha - \alpha_0 - \phi\Delta\alpha \qquad (19\text{-}11)$$

where

$$\Delta\alpha = \overline{(R - \beta_M)}_2 - \overline{(R - \beta_M)}_3 \qquad (19\text{-}12)$$

and the values of ϕ are obtained from x_V as in Chapter 17 or

x_V =	0	10	20	30	40	50
ϕ =	0	.45	.85	.97	1.0	1.0

The factor E is determined from x_E given by 15 and table 84.

As already mentioned, most of the available data on articulation with deafened persons is given in *Hearing Aids*. These data will be used to illustrate the method of calculation and for drawing some general conclusions regarding hearing aids.

Six different systems were used in these tests which are designated Flat, HP-6, HP-12, LP-6, LP-12. The orthotelephonic responses for the six frequencies mentioned above are given in Table 85. These were ob-

TABLE 85

System f =	125	250	500	1000	2000	4000	8000	6500
Flat R =	48	58	62	59	53	47	46	56
HP-6 R =		30	40	42	42	41	43	54
HP-12 R =		9	23	32	38	40	43	54
LP-6 R =		52	52	43	30	19	12	23
LP-12 R =	45	51	48	34	16	0	−14	−4

tained from the response curves given in *Hearing Aids* when $\alpha = 0$ which corresponds to an attenuator setting of 10 db. It will be remembered that the orthotelephonic reference for $R = 0$ is a talker at one meter distance from a line joining the two ears of a listener. So corrections to the response curves given in *Hearing Aids* must be made to give orthotelephonic responses which are the ones for which the method applies for calculating articulation scores outlined here. The talking levels β_t were maintained at 66 db at one meter distance which corresponds to 70 db at the distance of 25 inches used in their data.

The observed articulation scores were obtained by these investigators when these six systems were used with listeners having various kinds and amounts of hearing loss. The PB lists were generally used and only those cases using them will be considered here.

Two audiograms were given in this report, one taken at the psycho-acoustic laboratory and one taken at the M. E. E. I. hospital in Boston. The former are considered more accurate and will be used in the calculation. These hearing losses were given in terms of the pressure levels above the Sivian and White pressure levels (see Fig. 92) for threshold which are given in Table 82 for the six frequencies. If this is compared to the standard pressure threshold levels given above it will be seen that the correction given in the third line must be subtracted from the Harvard observed hearing losses to get those corresponding to values obtained by the standard audiometer. When this correction is made the resulting values of hearing loss obtained compare favorably with those obtained by the audiometer in the M. E. E. I. hospital.

This then might indicate that the hearing levels of the listeners with normal hearing were below the pressure levels corresponding to zero of the audiometer by the amounts opposite correction in Table 86.

TABLE 86

f =	250	500	1000	2000	4000	8000
β_0(S & W) =	26	14	7	5	8	19
correction =	10	11	10	12	7	2

Since on the average these listeners obtained the same threshold levels as given by the Sivian and White curve, one concludes this crew had the same acuity of hearing as the crews which made the tests at the Bell Telephone Laboratories which was taken as a uniform loss of -4 db. So for the reasons given before in Chapter 17 the amount greater than this which is shown in Table 86 may be considered as practice effect due to these very experienced observers. In the calculation for normal ears the hearing loss $\beta_M = \beta_C = -4$ db was used for all of the six frequencies.

Calculations of the articulation index A were made for the flat system for each gain α using normal experienced listeners. From the experimental values of articulation score obtained with the PB lists for the same values of α, one can then obtain the relation between A and S_W. This comparison was made for all the systems with no noise present. The values when noise was present for gains as high as 30 db above the threshold were also included. The calculation shows that the articulation scores are not affected for gains smaller than this. For this range, however, in most cases, larger values were obtained when noise was present as seen by Fig. 239. The crosses are for no noise, and the solid dots for noise $S/N = 10$, and the open circles for noise $S/N = 5$. The curves are calculated. There seems to be no explanation why the noise would increase the articulation, unless the talker increased his talking level when the noise was turned on. He was immersed in the noise but he regulated his talking level by watching a volume level meter. Even under these circumstances the noise will tend to make the talker emphasize the consonant sounds. With the various approximations which have been described it is estimated that results can be obtained which are not in error by more than the observational error and the calculations are comparatively simple.

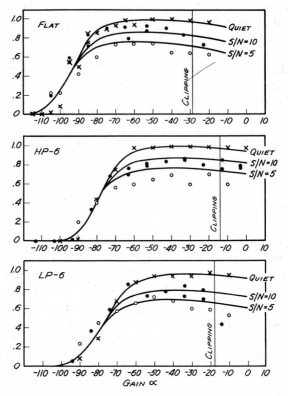

FIG. 239.—ARTICULATION FOR LISTENERS OF NORMAL HEARING VERSUS GAIN FOR SYSTEMS FLAT, HP-6 AND LP-6.

TABLE 87

THE VALUES OF A SERSUS S_W WHICH WERE CHOSEN

$A =$	0	.1	.15	.20	.25	.30	.35	.40	.45	.50	.60	.70	.80	.90	1.00
$S_W =$	0	.08	.15	.24	.32	.42	.51	.58	.67	.74	.84	.90	.95	.98	.995

Chart 8 enables one to follow the simplified calculations when no external noise is present. In lines 1, 2 and 3 the values of k, f_k and D_k are given. They are the same for all systems and listeners and callers. In line 4 the values of β_M are taken directly from the air conduction audiogram. In this illustration the values are taken for the case FB-L, given

CHART 8

SIMPLIFIED METHOD OF CALCULATING ARTICULATION INDEX

	$k=$	1	2	3	4	5	6	
	$f_k=$	250	500	1000	2000	4000	8000	DATE: Feb. 20, 1952
	$D_k=$	.04	.13	.23	.30	.25	.05	LISTENER—FB-L
(1)	$\beta_M=$	42	50	63	58	75	98	CALLER—9EP
	$\beta_N=$	30	35	45	50	65	98	$\beta_t=66;\ p=1.1$
	$\beta_C=$	12	15	18	8	10	0	SYSTEM—Flat
	$R=$	58	62	59	53	47	46	$CL=124$
								NOISE $S/N=10$

		1	2	3	4	5	6	
	$R-\beta_M=$	6	12	−4	−5	−28	−52	$\overline{(R-\beta_M)}_2=4$
(2)	$\overline{R-\beta_M}-(R-\beta_M)=$	—	—	1	2	25	49	$\overline{(R-\beta_M)}_3=1$
	$W=$	1.0	1.0	1.0	.99	.74	.22	$\overline{R-\beta_M}=\frac{1}{2}\overline{(R-\beta_M)}_2+\frac{1}{2}\overline{(R-\beta_M)}_3=3$
	$W\cdot D=$	.04	.13	.23	.30	.18	.01	$\Sigma W\cdot D=F_M=.89$

		1	2	3	4	5	6	
	$R-\beta_C=$	46	47	41	45	37	46	$\overline{(R-\beta_C)}_2=46$
(3)	$\overline{R-\beta_C}-(R-\beta_C)=$	—	—	4	—	8	0	$\overline{(R-\beta_C)}_3=44$
	$W=$	99	1.0	.98	1.0	.96	1.0	$\overline{R-\beta_C}=45$
	$W\cdot D=$	.04	.13	.23	.30	.24	.05	$\Sigma W\cdot D=F_C=.99$

$$F=\tfrac{2}{3}F_C+\tfrac{1}{3}F_M=95$$

(4)
$$\alpha_0=-\beta_t+12-\overline{(R-\beta_M)}_2=-58 \qquad \Delta\alpha=\overline{(R-\beta_M)}_2-\overline{(R-\beta_m)}_3=3$$
$$x_v=\alpha-\alpha_0-\phi\Delta\alpha \qquad \text{and} \qquad x_E=\alpha_t-\alpha=-8-\alpha$$

	$x_v=$	0	10	20	30	40	47	60	70	80	90
	$V=$	0	.11	.30	.54	.75	.86	.98	1.0	1.0	1.0
	$\phi=$	0	.45	.85	.98	1.0	1.0	1.0	1.0	1.0	1.0
	$\phi\Delta\alpha=$	0	2	3	3	3	3				
(5)	$\alpha=$	−58	−46	−35	−25	−15	−8				
	$x_E=$	50	38	27	17	7	0				
	$E=$	1.0	1.0	.97	.91	.86	.83				
	$A=$	0	.11	.30	.51	.67	74				
	$S_w=$	0	.10	.42	.75	.88	.92				

S_w (with noise) =   .42   .78   .81   .81

in *Hearing Aids*. The calculation is for the Flat system. In line 5 the values B_N are taken directly from the bone conduction tests. The values of the conductive deafness β_C is the difference between β_M and β_N and are given in line 6. The values of R are given in line 7 from Table 85. These data, together with a knowledge of the proficiency factor p, which in this case is taken as 1.0, enable one to make the calculation. The proficiency factor p was taken to give the best fit for the flat system in each case. In section (2) of the chart the steps for calculating F_M are shown. Similarly the steps for calculating F_C are shown in section (3). The values of F, α_0, and $\Delta\alpha$ are tabulated in section (4). The fifth section is similar to the previous calculation charts of Chapter 17. The value of A is calculated by

$$A = F.\ V.\ E.$$

and the corresponding S_W is obtained from Table 83.

When noise is present the value of $\beta_M{}'$ calculated from (19–2) is substituted for β_M in the above calculations, and the procedure is the same as shown in Chart 8 provided the noise is independent of the gain α.

In the Harvard tests, however, the signal to noise ratio was constant and so the noise level changes as α changes. The masking noise level β for a normal ear was given for the condition when $\alpha = -37$ and for the noise condition designated $S/N = 10$ db. The values for each of the six frequencies are given in the second line of Table 88. In the third line the values are given for the condition $\alpha = 0$.

TABLE 88 *

f =	250	500	1000	2000	4000	8000
$\beta(-37)$ =	54	62	58	58	56	38
$\beta(0)$ =	91	99	95	95	93	75

* Note: The values for $\beta(-37)$ are greater by 40 db than those published in *Hearing Aids* and called masking. It was learned from those who made the tests that this correction was necessary.

The masking level β due to the noise for a normal ear, then, when any system is used with a gain α is

$$\beta = \beta(0) + \alpha - \Delta R \qquad (19\text{–}13)$$

where ΔR is the difference in response between the FLAT system and that of any of the other five systems. The value of ΔR for each system is obtained from the published response curves. So the values of $\beta - \alpha$ for each system can be calculated and are given in Table 89.

It is thus seen that the received spectrum level curves for the sending end noise were greatly changed as one switched from one system to the other. These values are all for the noise condition indicated by

$S/N = 10$. For the condition $S/N = 5$, then, 5 db must be added to these values; and for the condition indicated by $S/N = 15$, then, 5 db must be subtracted from these values.

TABLE 89

SYSTEM		$f = 250$	500	1000	2000	4000	8000
Flat		$= 91$	99	95	95	93	75
HP-6		$= 63$	77	78	84	87	72
HP-12	$\beta - \alpha$	$= 42$	60	68	80	86	72
LP-6		$= 85$	79	79	82	65	41
LP-12		$= 84$	85	70	58	46	15

So it is seen that β_M' will be different for each gain setting α. So one proceeds as follows. A gain α is chosen and the corresponding values of β_M' computed from (19–2). Using this value in place of β_M, the values of α_0, $\phi\Delta\alpha$ and x_V are calculated as indicated in Chart 8. From this the value of V is obtained. The values of E and F_C are the same as for the no noise condition. The values on the last row of Chart 8 are calculated in this way.

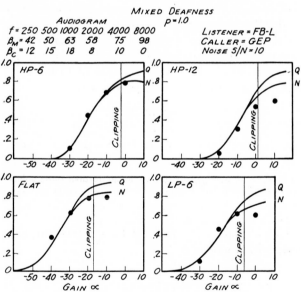

FIG. 240.—ARTICULATION GAIN CURVES FOR LISTENER FB-L AND NOISE CONDITION $S/N = 10$ (MIXED DEAFNESS).

The observed data in *Hearing Aids* are plotted with abscissas as db above the clipping level, which was observed on an oscilloscope as the level where the clipping of the peaks started. This level was set so that the levels of speech received by the listener would not be intolerable.

The relation between this abscissa and the gain α for the system can be deduced as follows: The response curves given above are for $\alpha = 0$ and correspond to a setting on the attenuation box of 10 db.

Then the gain α_C corresponding to the clipping level CL is related to observed reading on the attenuation box CA when clipping occurred by

$$-\alpha_C = CA - 10. \qquad (19\text{--}14)$$

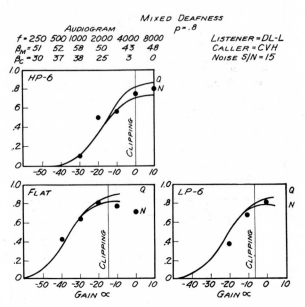

FIG. 241.—ARTICULATION GAIN CURVES FOR LISTENER DL-L AND NOISE CONDITION
$S/N = $ 1t (MIXED DEAFNESS).

From this equation and the observed values of CA the values shown in Table 90 were computed for the various conditions shown when the clipping level CL was at 124 db.

For other clipping levels

$$\alpha_C = \alpha_C \text{ (for } CL = 124) + 124 - CL. \qquad (19\text{--}15)$$

TABLE 90

Values of α_C when $CL = 124$

SYSTEM	$S/N =$	00	15	10	5
Flat		−14	−15	−17	−18
HP-6		3	0	− 2	− 3
HP-12		6	4	1	− 4
LP-6		− 5	− 6	− 6	− 7
LP-12		− 2	− 2	− 3	− 3

The abscissa for the observed data is then $\alpha - \alpha_C$. Since α_C was chosen somewhat arbitrarily it was decided to plot the usual α vs. S_W plots but show the position α_C by a heavy vertical line.

The solid lines in the Figs. 239 to 245 give the calculated articulation scores, the upper ones for the no noise condition, and the lower ones for the noise condition specified on the figure. The calculated points above the gain α_C were calculated as though no clipping were present. The points should agree with the lower solid curve for gains below α_C.

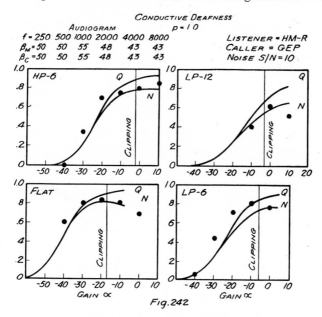

FIG. 242.—ARTICULATION GAIN CURVES FOR LISTENER HM-R AND NOISE CONDITION $S/N = 10$ (CONDUCTIVE DEAFNESS).

For levels above α_C the speech has a distortion (overloading) not taken into account in the calculation so the observed points should be below the curve for values of α in this region.

In Figs. 240 and 241 are shown the results for two cases of mixed deafness. In Figs. 242 and 243 are similar curves for two cases of conductive deafness. In Figs. 244 and 245 are shown the results for two cases of nerve deafness. The audiogram is given in each case at the top of the figure.

Calculations were made for all the cases given in *Heavy Aids* and the above results are typical. The calculated and observed results were within the observational error except for one case; namely listener WW-R. For this case the Harvard observers found the hearing loss for speech

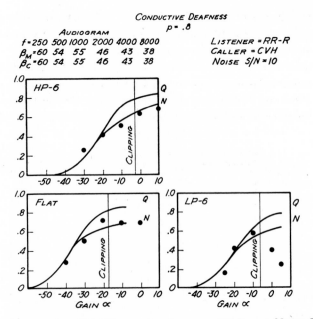

FIG. 243.—ARTICULATION GAIN CURVES FOR LISTENER RR-R AND NOISE CONDITION
$S/N = 10$ (CONDUCTIVE DEAFNESS).

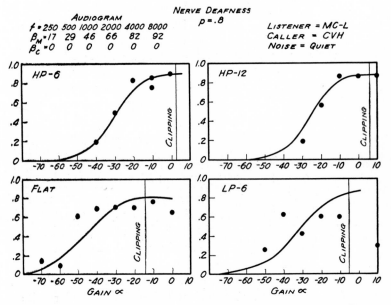

FIG. 244.—ARTICULATION GAIN CURVES FOR LISTENER RW-L AND NOISE CONDITION
$S/N = 15$ (NERVE DEAFNESS).

by using spondee lists to be 56 db and by using PB lists to be 57 db, but the audiogram gave 79 db, a discrepancy of 22 db which seems to indicate that the audiogram showed too great a hearing loss.

The agreement between calculated and observed results is so good one is justified in using the philosophy underlying the method of calculation for obtaining fundamental information for the design of a hearing aid for a listener having any amount and kind of deafness. To do this

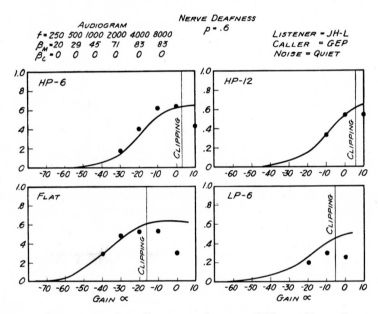

FIG. 245.—ARTICULATION GAIN CURVES FOR LISTENER JH-L AND NOISE CONDITION QUIET (NERVE DEAFNESS).

is not a straight forward or simple procedure. All of the factors of the articulation index A, namely F, V, and E must be considered. For listeners of normal hearing the gain can be such that V and E are unity, so the criterion of the goodness of the response of the system is expressed by the value of F. This is not so with deafened listeners where the gain α_t corresponding to the tolerable level is reached before it is large enough to make the factor V equal to unity. Generally it will be found that the best response R is given by

$$R = \beta_C + r\beta_N \qquad (19-16)$$

where the fraction r lies between .2 and .4. For example for listener

MC-L the following values were computed by the more exact method.

r	R	α_t	F_C	F_M	F	E_C	V_C	A(max)	S_w(max)
0	0	52	1.0	.735	912	.83	99	.747	.83
.2	$.2\beta_N$	40	.99	.833	.938	.83	.97	.756	.85
.3	$.3\beta_N$	33	.981	.871	.944	.83	.93	.73	.82
.5	$.5\beta_N$	19	.977	.920	.958	.83	.88	.70	.80
.7	$.7\beta_N$	4	.911	.976	.933	.83	.72	.56	.67
1.0	β_N	−20	.796	1.0	.864	.83	.64	.46	.54

The above values correspond to the gain α_t which corresponds to the maximum tolerable speech level at the listener's ear. As the level is lowered the factor E becomes higher and the factor V becomes lower, but the latter at a faster rate.

It is seen that any of the systems having values of r from 0 to .3 gives about equally good results. The one with $r = 0$ corresponds approximately to the Harvard HP-6, and the one with $r = .2$ corresponds approximately to HP-12. It will be seen from F 197 that these two systems give about equally good results, and are definitely better than any of the other systems. The system labelled "FLAT" slopes downward about 15 db from 500 cpc to 4000 cps and should give poorer results and the observed values verify this. Similar conclusions are reached concerning listener JH-L and verified by the results of Fig. 248. Consider the two conductive loss cases. For the listener HM-R, the ideal response should drop about 10 db from 500 cpc to 4000 cps. This corresponds approximately to the "FLAT" system, and the tests show that the "FLAT" system gives the best results. The same conclusions are reached for the listener RR-R.

Similar for listener F^{1}B-L the response $R = \beta_c + .3\beta_n$ gives one which is closest to HP-6, the one which gave the best articulation. And finally for listener DL-L the response

	R	=	$\beta_c + .3\beta_n$ gives				
	f	=	250	500	1000	2000	4000	8000
PRESCRIBED	R	=	36	32	44	33	15	15
"FLAT"	R	=	42	46	43	37	31	30
"LP-6"	R	=	52	52	43	30	19	12

It is seen that this prescribed response is between the "FLAT" and the "LP-6" and should give slightly better results than either of these two systems. So as a first trial one uses

$$R = \beta_c + .3\beta_n \qquad (19\text{--}17)$$

and then calculates F, E, and V, at the tolerable limit which is given by a gain

$$\alpha_t = 118 - \beta_t - \bar{R}_2 \qquad (19\text{--}18)$$

where $\bar{R}_2$ is the average of the two highest values of R from equation (19–17) of the three values at 500, 1000, and 2000 cps. It is interesting to compare the tolerable gains α_t as shown in table 91 with those value of α_c the clipping gains used in the tests at Harvard

TABLE 91

System	Flat	HP-6	HP-12	LP-6	LP-12
Calculated α_t =	− 8	10	17	5	11
Values given for α_c in Hearing Aids	−14	3	6	−5	−2

This then gives a method of determining the response characteristics and maximum gain necessary for a hearing aid to be used by a listener having any amount and kind of deafness. It also indicates that a limiter of some sort should be placed in the set, that stops the speech levels from reaching values greater than 118 db plus the following peak values.

f =	250	500	1000	2000	4000	8000
peak value	10	12	8	5	1	1

This means that the pressures levels produced by the receiver on the standard coupler should not be permitted to go higher than 128, 130, 126, 123, 119 and 119 db at the six frequencies respectively. This will be accomplished if a general cut off level of 128 db be used.

CHAPTER 20

A METHOD OF COMPUTING THE PERCENT HEARING LOSS IN COMPENSATION CASES

When one is deafened due to war or industrial processes one is entitled to a certain amount of compensation depending upon the handicap produced. The methods described in this book suggest a rational method of calculating this compensation, which will now be described.

1. *Determination of Audiogram*

Obtain by an audiometer the hearing loss in each ear at the seven frequencies

(1) 125 (2) 250 (3) 500 (4) 1000 (5) 2000 (6) 4000 (7) 8000 cps.

Call the values obtained on the right ear

$$R_1, R_2, R_3, R_4, R_5, R_6, R_7$$

and those on the left ear

$$L_1, L_2, L_3, L_4, L_5, L_6, L_7.$$

2. *Determination at Each of These Frequencies of the Effective Loss Using Both Ears*

The effective loss at each frequency is computed from the values of R and L at that frequency. One could take an arithmetic average but that would obviously be wrong when L and R are far apart in magnitude.

From a loudness standpoint they would be combined as follows: Let E be effective loss using both ears. Then at high loudness levels above 50 db

$$10^{-E/40} = \tfrac{1}{2}(10^{-L/40} + 10^{-R/40}). \qquad (20\text{--}1)$$

This can be written

$$E = L + 12 - 40 \log (1 + 10^{-(R-L)/40}) \qquad (20\text{--}2)$$

if L is the best ear and

$$E = R + 12 - 40 \log (1 + 10^{-(L-R)/40}) \qquad (20\text{--}3)$$

if R is the best ear. This means that if the patient is totally deaf in one ear he loses only 12 db in loudness level. From this standpoint the effective hearing loss then would be between that of the best ear and 12 db below that ear.

However, he has also partially lost his binaural sense. So the effective loss should be somewhat lower than that obtained from a loudness standpoint. It was estimated that the db down of the effective hearing loss for both ears acting was just twice that if loudness were the only criterion. Therefore E is given by

$$E - R = 24 - 80 \log \left(1 + 10^{-(L-R)/40}\right) \qquad (20\text{--}4)$$

or

$$E - L = 24 - 80 \log \left(1 + 10^{-(R-L)/40}\right). \qquad (20\text{--}5)$$

The values of $E - L$ can be readily found from the following Table 92.

TABLE 92

$R - L$ or $L - R =$	5	10	15	20	25	30	35	40	50	60	70	100
$E - L$ or $E - R =$	4	8	12	15	17	19	20	21	22	23	24	24

The value of E then is the hearing loss in the best ear plus one of the values in Table 91 depending upon how far down the bad ear is from the good ear. It is seen that for one ear totally deaf and the other ear normal, it will have an effective loss of 24 db. That is, he will be handicapped the same as if both ears had a hearing loss of 24 db. This corresponds roughly to my limited experience with persons having these two types of hearing loss.

Therefore, at frequency 125 take the difference $L_1 - R_1$ or $R_1 - L_1$ and by use of the table read effective loss E_1. In this way find E_1, E_2, E_3, E_4, E_5, E_6 and E_7.

3. Determine the Percent Hearing Loss at Each Frequency

If one uses the pressure levels for feeling given in Fig. 97 and the pressure levels in Table 83 for the zero setting, then the following settings on the present types of audiometers should give pressure levels in the ear canal at the pain and feeling level.

$f =$	125	250	500	1000	2000	4000	8000
audiometer setting =	75	85	100	105	105	105	100

To obtain these values 6 db at 125 cps and 4 at 250 was subtracted from the standard levels in a coupler for the zero setting. A patient who cannot experience the sensation of hearing when the dials are set at these values is considered to be totally deaf. Sometimes a patient can tolerate higher values than these but any higher values should be discarded and these values used on the calculation. Then, the percent hearing loss at

$$125 \text{ cps is } 100 \ (E_1/ \ 75) = p_1, \qquad (20\text{–}6)$$

$$450 \text{ cps is } 100 \ (E_2/ \ 85) = p_2, \qquad (20\text{–}7)$$

$$500 \text{ cps is } 100 \ (E_3/100) = p_3, \qquad (20\text{–}8)$$

$$1000 \text{ cps is } 100 \ (E_4/105) = p_4, \qquad (20\text{–}9)$$

$$2000 \text{ cps is } 100 \ (E_5/105) = p_5, \qquad (20\text{–}10)$$

$$4000 \text{ cps is } 100 \ (E_6/105) = p_6, \qquad (20\text{–}11)$$

$$8000 \text{ cps is } 100 \ (E_7/100) = p_7. \qquad (20\text{–}12)$$

4. Determination of Weighted Average Percent Loss of Hearing

These percents must now be averaged in some way to find the overall effective percent loss or the weighted average. Percent hearing loss P is given by

$$P = \sum_{R=1}^{R=7} W_R p_R. \qquad (20\text{–}13)$$

From a loudness standpoint for listening to speech at the higher levels these weighting factors are

frequency =	125	250	500	1000	2000	4000	8000
k =	1	2	3	4	5	6	7
W_k =	.005	.025	.125	.27	.31	.22	.045

From the standpoint of understanding speech these weighting factors are

W_k =	0	.04	.13	.23	.30	.25	.05

Since these two are not greatly different it was concluded that one would be justified in taking an average which results in

W_k =	.003	.037	.13	.25	.30	.23	.05

Then

$$P = .003E_1 + .04E_2 + .13E_3 + .25E_4 + .30E_5 + .23E_6 + .05E_7. \quad (20\text{–}14)$$

To get the final percent loss of hearing P one multiplies each value of E obtained in (20–2) by the factors indicated and adds the seven products to find P.

5. *Illustration of the Method of Computing P, the Percent Loss in Hearing*

$k =$	1	2	3	4	5	6	7
$f =$	125	250	500	1000	2000	4000	8000 cps
$L =$	.10	10	15	25	25	50	50
$R =$	20	15	20	30	45	55	40
$E =$	18	14	19	29	40	54	48
$W =$	.04	.04	.13	.24	.29	.22	.05
$EW =$	.1	.6	2.5	7.0	11.6	11.9	2.4

$P = \Sigma EW = 36$ Compensation $C = 37.8$

6. *Relation of Compensation C to the Percent Loss of Hearing P*

Again it is obvious that the compensation C should not be linearly related to the percent hearing loss except as a very rough approximation. Losses up to 10 or 15 db produce an almost negligible handicap and losses about 90% are almost the same as total deafness. The curve in Fig. 244 represents my best judgment as to how P and L should be related. However, the experienced otologist may wish to alter the form somewhat. The straight line in this figure runs from o compensation at 10% hearing loss to 100% compensation for 90% hearing loss. It might be desirable to use this until the form of the curve is better known. It can be expressed accurately by the equation

$$C = (5/4)(P - 10)$$ $(20–15)$

CHART 9

Name..   Date..

$f =$	125	250	500	1000	2000	4000	8000	
$L =$								Hearing Loss in Left Ear
$R =$								Hearing Loss in Right Ear
$E_k =$								Effective Hearing Loss
$W_k =$	.003	.037	.13	.25	.30	.25	.05	
$E_k W_k =$								

PERCENT HEARING LOSS $P = \Sigma E_k W_k =$ COMPENSATION $C = 5/4 (P - 10) =$
For $P < 10$ $C = 0\%$ for $P > 90$ $C = 100\%$

TABLE FOR DETERMINING E FROM L AND R

Difference in hearing loss between the two ears =	5	10	15	20	25	30	35	40	50	60	70	100
Amount to be added to hearing loss in best ear to obtain $E =$	4	8	12	15	17	19	20	21	22	23	24	24

with the qualification that C is taken equal to unity for calculated values greater than this.

So the final step in determining the compensation C is to use the computed value P and find the corresponding C from Fig. 246 or from equation (20-15). For example, if the curve is used a 10% hearing gives $3\frac{1}{2}\%$, and if the straight line is used this gives 0% compensation. Until the shape of this curve is better known it may be better to use the formula shown by equation (20–15) since calculations from it can be made exact.

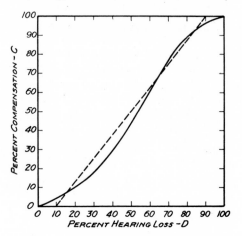

FIG. 246.—RELATION BETWEEN PERCENT HEARING AND PERCENT COMPENSATION.

Using this then for a person having one normal ear and one totally deaf ear, the value of P becomes 24 and the value of C the compensation is 17.5%. If the loss in the bad ear is only 40 db then the compensation is only 13.75%.

The chart form in Chart 9 will be helpful in making this computation.

This method differs from that proposed by Fowler * and indorsed by the American Medical Association. The differences are as follows:

Seven frequencies instead of four are used in the Fletcher method. Fowler uses 100 db for total loss of hearing for all frequencies, rather than for 75, 85, 100, 105, 105, 105, and 100 db, the seven frequencies used above. However it is seen that as a general average 100 db is a good approximation. He finds a weighted average for each ear and then combines the two weighted values to find the effective loss for both ears. In my method the effective loss for both ears is found at each frequency and then a weighted average for the effective loss for both ears is found. He uses a corrective factor for recruitment in nerve deafness cases which results in less compensation for such cases than for conductive deafness

* Journal of the Acoustical Society of America, Vol. 13, page 373, Jan. 1942.

cases having the same hearing loss.   This seems to me to be in the wrong direction if any difference is made.   It is the general experience that nerve deafness cases are more seriously handicapped than conductive deafness cases, but there seems no rational way of expressing this difference in a quantitative way.

Finally the Fowler method rates a person having normal hearing in one ear and 100% loss in his other ear, as having a combined effective loss of only 9%, whereas in my method the combined effective loss is 24%. Presumably in the Fowler method the compensation is proportional the combined effective loss or in the above case 9%.   In my method the compensation will be for this case $17\frac{1}{2}$%.

It is evident from what has been said that I consider the method outlined in this chapter the more rational one and propose it for consideration to the medical profession.

AUTHOR INDEX

449

GENERAL INDEX

451